ATLAS OF DESCRIPTIVE HISTOLOGY

ATLAS OF
Descriptive Histology

EDWARD J. REITH, Ph.D.
Professor of Anatomy, New York Medical College

MICHAEL H. ROSS, Ph.D.
Associate Professor of Anatomy, New York University School of Medicine

WITH 281 ILLUSTRATIONS

HOEBER MEDICAL DIVISION

Harper & Row, Publishers • New York and London

Sixth Printing, 1969

ATLAS OF DESCRIPTIVE HISTOLOGY
Copyright © 1965 by HOEBER MEDICAL DIVISION
HARPER & ROW, PUBLISHERS, INCORPORATED
Printed in the United States of America

All rights reserved. For information address
HOEBER MEDICAL DIVISION · HARPER & ROW, PUBLISHERS
49 East 33rd Street, New York, N.Y. 10016

Library of Congress catalog card number: 65-25786
69   70   71   6

CONTENTS

PREFACE   ix

INTRODUCTION   1

EPITHELIUM   2
   1. Squamous Epithelia   4
   2. Cuboidal, Columnar, and Pseudostratified Columnar
      Epithelia   6
   3. Transitional Epithelium, "Nonsurface" Epithelium, and
      Epithelioid Cells   8

CONNECTIVE TISSUE   11
   4. Loose Connective Tissue   14
   5. Dense Connective Tissue   16
   6. Regular Connective Tissue   18
   7. Special and Embryonic Connective Tissue   20

SUPPORTING TISSUE   23
   8. Cartilage   24
   9. Cartilage, Fetal Skeleton   26
  10. Cartilage and Spongy Bone   28
  11. Fibrocartilage   30
  12. Compact Bone   32
  13. Endochondral Bone Formation I   34
  14. Endochondral Bone Formation II   36
  15. Intramembranous Bone Formation   38

MUSCLE TISSUE   40
  16. Smooth Muscle   42
  17. Striated Muscle   44
  18. Cardiac Muscle I   46
  19. Cardiac Muscle II   48

NERVOUS SYSTEM   50
  20. Sympathetic Ganglion   52
  21. Dorsal Root Ganglion   54
  22. Peripheral Nerve   56
  23. Cerebrum   58
  24. Cerebellum   60
  25. Spinal Cord   62

CONTENTS

CARDIOVASCULAR SYSTEM   *64*
26. Heart   *66*
27. The Aorta   *68*
28. Muscular Arteries and Veins   *70*
29. Arterioles and Lymphatic Vessels   *72*

LYMPHATIC TISSUE AND ORGANS   *75*
30. Tonsil and Lymph Node I   *76*
31. Lymph Node II   *78*
32. Spleen I   *80*
33. Spleen II   *82*
34. Thymus   *84*

INTEGUMENT   *87*
35. Skin I   *88*
36. Skin II   *90*

DIGESTIVE SYSTEM   *92*
37. Tongue I   *94*
38. Tongue II   *96*
39. Soft Palate   *98*
40. Salivary Glands I   *100*
41. Salivary Glands II   *102*
42. Developing Tooth   *104*
43. Esophagus   *106*
44. Esophagus and Cardia   *108*
45. Stomach, Fundic Region   *110*
46. Stomach, Pyloric Region   *112*
47. Small Intestine   *114*
48. Duodenum   *116*
49. Villi   *118*
50. Intestinal Glands and Muscularis Externa   *120*
51. Appendix and Large Intestine   *122*
52. Mucosa of Large Intestine   *124*
53. Liver I   *126*
54. Liver II   *128*
55. Gall Bladder   *130*
56. Pancreas   *132*

RESPIRATORY SYSTEM   *135*
57. Olfactory Mucosa   *136*
58. Trachea and Bronchus   *138*

CONTENTS

59. Bronchus and Bronchiole   *140*
60. Respiratory Bronchiole, Alveolar Duct, Alveolar Sac, and Alveolus   *142*

URINARY SYSTEM   *145*
61. Kidney I   *146*
62. Kidney II   *148*
63. Kidney III   *150*
64. Ureter   *152*
65. Urinary Bladder   *154*

MALE REPRODUCTIVE SYSTEM   *157*
66. Testis I   *158*
67. Testis II   *160*
68. Efferent Ductules and Epididymis   *162*
69. Ductus Deferens and Seminal Vesicle   *164*
70. Prostate Gland   *166*

FEMALE REPRODUCTIVE SYSTEM   *169*
71. Ovary I   *170*
72. Ovary II   *172*
73. Corpus Luteum   *174*
74. Uterine Tube   *176*
75. Uterus   *178*
76. Mammary Gland, Inactive   *180*
77. Mammary Gland, Proliferative   *182*
78. Mammary Gland, Lactating   *184*

ENDOCRINE SYSTEM   *187*
79. Thyroid Gland   *188*
80. Parathyroid Gland   *190*
81. Pituitary Gland I   *192*
82. Pituitary Gland II   *194*
83. Adrenal Gland I   *196*
84. Adrenal Gland II   *198*
85. Pineal Body   *200*

INDEX   *203*

PREFACE

This book is designed to assist the student in the laboratory. It was not designed to present the theoretical subject matter of histology as it is found in standard textbooks, but rather to present an account of microscopic appearance in the language of the histologist.

Histology involves not only the analysis of three dimensional structure by the examination of two dimensional specimens, but also the application of whatever methods and techniques help the histologist to understand structure, function, and cellular interrelationships in a more dynamic way. Autoradiography, tissue culture, histo- and cytochemistry, electron microscopy, X-ray diffraction, etc. have all been incorporated into the thinking of the histologist and much of this information has been incorporated into histology textbooks. The student is concerned not only with the necessity of becoming familiar with much of this information, but also with the necessity of learning how to "read" slides. Yet, one of the perplexing features of textbook accounts is that very often they do not make a sharp distinction between microanatomy and actual microscopic appearance. Cellular details are often described in textbooks, but the details may not be evident in a routine H & E section. When a student looks through a microscope to examine a slide he wants to know what is on the slide and what interpretations can be made from it. This book is designed to assist the student in the laboratory when he is confronted with these questions.

A series of extensively labeled photomicrographs have been selected which usually include illustrations at low magnification, thereby providing a panoramic view of the section, and then, significant areas were selected for examination at higher magnification. In the descriptive accounts much emphasis is placed on characteristics of the histologic section and particularly on the reasons why a structure is identified as such.

The interpretation of a histologic slide involves primarily the recognition of forms, general organization, and location of parts. Identification by specific color reaction is less important. This point is emphasized by the use of black and white in the atlas. The histologist can recognize cross striations of muscle regardless of whether they are stained red with eosin, dark blue with iron hematoxylin, or unstained and examined with phase contrast optics; he can recognize nuclei regardless of whether they are stained dark blue by hematoxylin of an H & E stain, or whether they are stained red by the acid fuchsin of a trichrome. He does this by considering their form, arrangement, and location. The histology student should attempt to develop this skill for he will quickly learn that a particular organ or tissue stained at different times, by different people, may not have quite the same color characteristics. This is not to say that the histologist does not make use of staining reactions;

he does. However, he depends more on differences rather than specific color reaction. It should be noted that whereas the black and white reproductions do show the differences in staining reaction, they emphasize the more important criteria, namely, shape, location, and organization.

The student will find this atlas useful chiefly in the laboratory. However, he will also find it useful in preparing for examinations at home, especially those that involve a "practical" for, in reality, the photomicrographs are the closest thing to an actual slide and far closer to the slide than composite illustrations.

EDWARD J. REITH, PH.D.
MICHAEL H. ROSS, PH.D.

New York, N. Y.

ATLAS OF DESCRIPTIVE HISTOLOGY

INTRODUCTION

The illustrations in this book are all photomicrographs of routine histological sections. All, except two, are paraffin sections, and most of them have been stained with hematoxylin and eosin (H & E). In order to adequately interpret the illustrations (or a specimen on a slide), it is necessary to know how specimens are routinely prepared, because during preparation, tissue undergoes a number of alterations. Water soluble materials are lost while the specimen is in aqueous solutions; lipids are lost while it is in lipid solvents; shrinkage occurs during a number of steps; and finally, fixation (the first step) has a profound effect on the staining of certain tissue components.

Immediately after its removal, the tissue is placed in a fixative, which is intended to preserve the structure of the tissue and to prepare it for future treatments.

After the tissue has been fixed, it is ready to prepare for cutting. In order to cut adequately thin sections, the tissue must be embedded in a hard substance such as paraffin. This introduces several additional steps since paraffin is not miscible with water. Therefore, the water must be removed from the tissue and replaced by a liquid which is miscible with paraffin. To accomplish this, the specimen is dehydrated through a graded series of alcohol solutions and placed in a nonaqueous liquid, e.g., xylene. It is then infiltrated with melted paraffin. The paraffin (containing the tissue) is allowed to cool and is then trimmed to form a block. Sections are cut from the block with a microtome. These are placed on a slide, a small amount of albumin serving as an adhesive. They are, however, still unsuitable for examination with the microscope since paraffin is infiltrated throughout the tissue, moreover, the tissue section is colorless and must be stained. For this, the paraffin is dissolved out, and the tissue is rehydrated (by being passed through a graded series of alcohol solutions to water). The tissue is then stained. At this point the slide is still not ready for microscopic examination, for in order to obtain a permanent preparation, the stained tissue section must be dehydrated again, "mounted" in Canada balsam or some similar material, and covered with a coverslip.

As stated above, hematoxylin and eosin are commonly used dyes in preparing routine stained specimens. Hematoxylin stains nuclei, some cytoplasmic components, such as the ergastoplasm, and some extracellular materials, such as the matrix of cartilage. Eosin stains the cytoplasm of muscle cells, most cytoplasmic materials, and extracellular fibers.

In addition to hematoxylin and eosin, a large number of other staining procedures can be applied to tissue sections. Some of these are employed to illustrate materials which are not adequately visualized by H & E. However, these special methods should be thought of as supplementing, not replacing, the H & E preparations.

EPITHELIUM

EPITHELIUM consists of cells that are closely applied to each other with no intervening fibrous material. Epithelium is found on surfaces and as the functional units (parenchyma) of glands. The outer surface of the body, the body tubes, and the body cavities (except joint cavities and bursae) are lined by epithelium. Epithelium rests on a supporting connective tissue; the part of the connective tissue which is actually contacted by the epithelium is the basement membrane. The blood vessels of the connective tissue do not enter the epithelial layer; therefore, surface epithelium is described as being avascular.

Glands develop from epithelial surfaces by growing into the underlying connective tissue. In some cases, the connection of the gland to the surface is retained, as in the salivary glands; in other cases the connection is lost, as in the thyroid gland. In most glands, the gland cells are separated from the connective tissue and its blood vessels by a basement membrane. However, in some glands (e.g., liver), the relationship between epithelium and blood vessels becomes extremely intimate. Some glandular tissue within the body does not develop from surfaces. For example, the theca lutein cells of the corpus luteum are derivatives of the connective tissue that surrounds the Graafian follicle. Yet these cells assume most of the characteristics of glandular epithelium. The interstitial cells of Leydig also develop from connective tissue (mesenchyme), and they too assume some of the characteristics of epithelial cells.

Epithelial cells engage in chemical work for the body. They absorb materials from the lumen of the alimentary canal and the lumen of kidney tubules. Epithelial cells engage in a wide range of synthetic activity throughout the body. They synthesize an intracellular protein, keratin, which covers the surface of the body; they synthesize mucus to lubricate body tubes; they synthesize digestive enzymes and hormones; and in the liver, they subject many materials that are absorbed from the alimentary canal to a host of chemical transformations before these materials pass into the systemic circulation. The preceding are only some examples of epithelial cell activities.

Epithelium is classified according to the arrangement and shape of its cells. Epithelium which is only one cell deep is called *simple;* epithelium which is more than one cell deep is called *stratified.* On the basis of cell shape, epithelium is designated as *squamous, cuboidal,* or *columnar.* In a number of glands the epithelial cells have a pyramidal shape; these may be classified as either cuboidal or columnar.

In two locations, epithelium has special names, *endothelium* and *mesothelium.* Endothelium lines the inner surface of the heart, blood vessels, and lymphatic vessels. Mesothelium lines the serous membranes of the body.

EPITHELIUM

The free surface of epithelial cells may contain cilia, stereocilia, or microvilli according to the function of the cells. Many cells possess motile cilia, which enable the cells to move mucus or other materials along the surface. Stereocilia are special surface modifications that are found in the ductus epididymis and the ductus deferens. Microvilli are found on the surface of cells that engage in absorptive activity. Although they cannot be identified individually with the light microscope, the microvilli in the intestines are arranged as closely packed cylindrical projections of about the same height and constitute the striated border. In the kidney, the microvilli are also closely packed, somewhat longer than in the intestines but not so uniform in height; collectively, these appear as the brush border of kidney cells.

Plate 1. Squamous Epithelia

The flat face of simple squamous epithelium (mesothelium) of the peritoneum is shown in Figure 1. The specimen was prepared by stripping off the surface of the peritoneum and then treating the spread with silver and a light stain to reveal the nuclei (**N**). The silver appears as the black precipitate. It marks the extent of the cytoplasm (**C**). These cells are extremely thin plates, and when they are sectioned at right angles to the surface (Fig. 2), the nuclei (**N**) appear as elongated structures which produce a slight bulging of the cell, and the cytoplasm (**C**) appears as a thin band along the surface. Under the epithelium is the supporting connective tissue (**CT**). (Below the connective tissue are smooth muscle (**SM**) cells cut in cross section.)

The simple squamous epithelium (endothelium) lining a lymphatic vessel is shown in Figure 3. The nuclei (**N**) of the endothelial cells are the dark-staining elongated structures which bulge slightly into the lumen. The cytoplasm (**C**) appears as the linear extension that continues from the extremities of the nuclei. Actually, this thin line represents two cell membranes and a small amount of intervening cytoplasm. Over the nuclei, the cytoplasm is so attenuated that the nuclei appear to be naked and exposed to the lumen. It is not possible to determine where one endothelial cell ends and the next begins.

Mesothelium, endothelium, and other simple squamous epithelia all have the same appearance. Any differences in appearance between the epithelia in Figures 2 and 3 are not to be regarded as significant. Histologically, mesothelium and endothelium are distinguished from each other on the basis of their location, not their appearance.

Stratified squamous epithelium of the tongue is shown in Figure 4. The surface cells and their nuclei (**arrows**) are flat—therefore the name squamous—the deeper cells are less flat, and the deepest cells are columnar, cuboidal, or polyhedral. The boundaries (**arrowheads**) between the cells can be seen in the middle of the layer. Note that the cells are in intimate contact with each other. The

KEY

BL, basal layer of epithelium
C, cytoplasm
CT, connective tissue
N, nuclei
SM, smooth muscle
arrows, flat nuclei of surface cells
arrowheads, boundaries between epithelial cells

Fig. 1 (rabbit), x 640; Fig. 2 (monkey), x 640; Fig. 3 (human), x 640; Fig. 4 (monkey), x 640.

epithelial cells that are at the epithelial-connective tissue junction are referred to as the basal layer (**BL**).

Provision must be made for the replacement of surface cells that are lost for one reason or another. In the case of mesothelial cells, these can be replaced by underlying connective tissue cells and presumably from neighboring mesothelial cells. However, the replacement of epithelium by underlying connective tissue cells is unique and is confined to mesothelium. Endothelial cells are replaced by neighboring endothelial cells. For all stratified epithelia, surface cells are replaced by cells which move up from the basal layer in which they are produced.

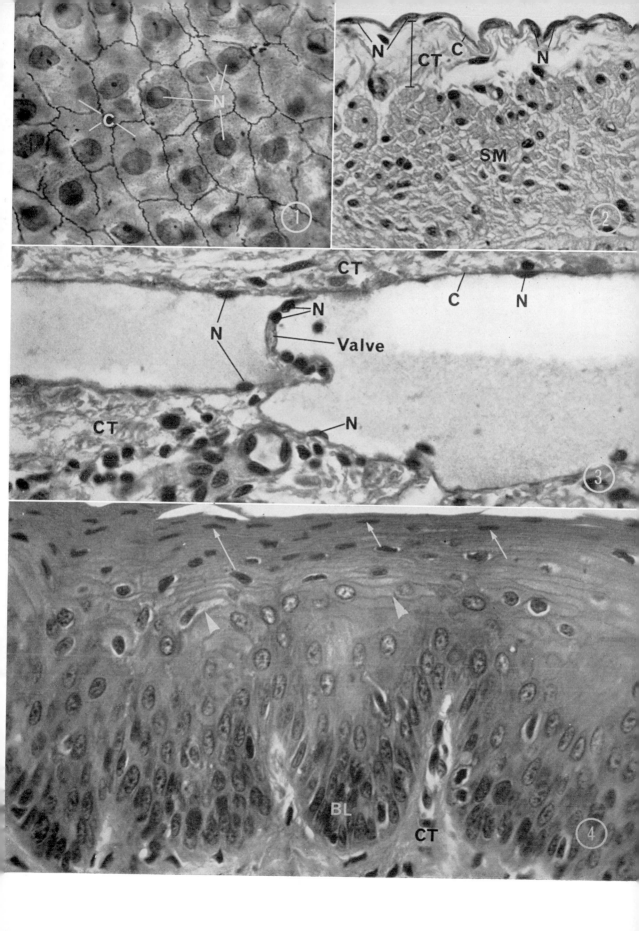

Plate 2. Cuboidal, Columnar, and Pseudostratified Columnar Epithelia

The cuboidal epithelium (**Ep**) that lines the surface of the ovary is shown in Figure 1. A small amount of cytoplasm surrounds each nucleus. The boundaries between the cells are not distinct and the epithelium appears as a row of nuclei. Under the epithelium is the supporting connective tissue (**CT**).

The columnar epithelium of the gall bladder is shown in Figure 2. The part of the cell which contacts the basement membrane is referred to as basal; it contains the elongated nucleus. The part of the cell near the surface is referred to as apical. The cytoplasm of these cells appears homogeneous and stains with eosin. The cells are closely packed; the cell boundaries are evident in some places. The columnar epithelium of the small intestines is shown in Figure 3. Here, two kinds of cells are present: columnar absorptive cells and goblet cells (**GC**). The absorptive cells are tall and thin, and possess a striated border (**SB**) on their free surface. The nuclei of these cells are elongated; the cytoplasm stains with eosin. The round nuclei within the epithelial layer belong to lymphocytes (**Lym**). The goblet cells contain a "cup" of mucus in their apical portions, just beyond the nucleus. The cytoplasm in the basal portion of these cells is very attenuated, and in one of the cells (**arrow**), it appears as a cytoplasmic stalk which extends down to the basement membrane. The basement membrane (**BM**) appears as the thin line on which the epithelial cells rest. It should be noted, however, that basement membranes, while always present, are not usually seen in routine H & E sections.

Figure 4 shows the ciliated pseudostratified columnar epithelium of a bronchus. Each cilium is connected to a basal body (**BB**), which collectively appear as the dark band at the base of the cilia (**C**). Three cell types are present in this epithelium: columnar cells, goblet cells (**GC**), and basal cells (**BC**). Basal cells are close to the basement membrane. They have only a small amount of cytoplasm, which is confined to the vicinity of the nucleus and does not reach the surface. In this preparation, the nuclei of the basal cells are spherical; the nuclei of the columnar

KEY

BB, basal bodies
BC, basal cells
BM, basement membrane
C, cilia
CT, connective tissue
Ep, epithelium
GC, goblet cells
Lym, lymphocytes
S, stereocilia
SB, striated border
TB, terminal bars
arrow, cytoplasmic "stalk" of goblet cell

Figs. 1–4 (monkey), x 640; Fig. 5 (rabbit), x 640.

cells are slightly larger and ovoid; the nuclei of the goblet cells appear as the dark, elongated, horizontally oriented structures at the base of the mucous cup. Although this epithelium appears to be stratified, it is designated pseudostratified columnar because all of the cells contact the basement membrane.

The pseudostratified columnar epithelium of the ductus epididymis is shown in Figure 5. Most of the cells in this figure are columnar. Some basal cells (**BC**) are also present. The surface projections of the columnar cells are stereocilia (**S**). These are long, branching microvilli which assume a wavy, tapering appearance during the course of tissue preparation. The cell boundaries and terminal bars (**TB**) are evident in this preparation.

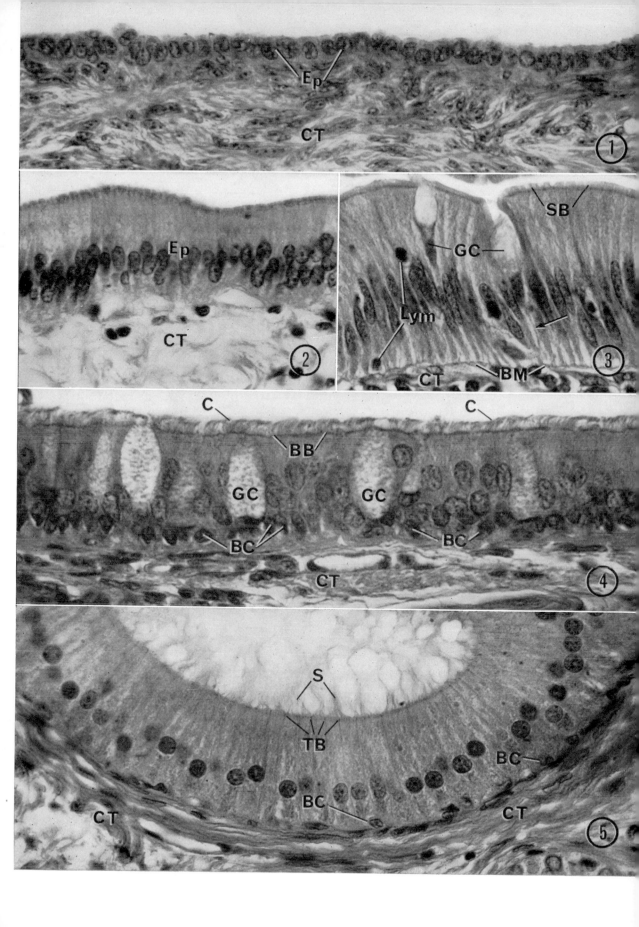

Plate 3. TRANSITIONAL EPITHELIUM, "NONSURFACE" EPITHELIUM, AND EPITHELIOID CELLS

Transitional epithelium is present on the inner surface of the renal pelvis, the ureters, the urinary bladder, and part of the urethra. Figure 1 shows the transitional epithelium (**Ep**) from an empty urinary bladder and the underlying connective tissue (**CT**). The epithelium appears to be about four or five cells deep. The cells on the surface are large and dome shaped and occasionally two nuclei (**arrow**) are seen in a single cell. The cells immediately under the surface cells are pear shaped and slightly smaller than the surface cells. The deepest cells are smaller than the surface cells, and as a consequence the nuclei of these cells appear more crowded. When the bladder is distended, the epithelial cells are flattened and the epithelium appears to be only two or three cells deep. It should be noted, however, that a specimen of the bladder wall is usually in a contracted state when it is removed, unless special steps have been taken to preserve it in a distended state.

Figure 2 shows cuboidal cells of the liver that are arranged as interconnecting sheets. When sectioned, the sheets appear as cords of cells one or more cells deep according to the plane of section. The nuclei of these cells are spherical; they are surrounded by a granular cytoplasm. The elongated spaces between the cords of cells are vascular channels (sinusoids) (**S**). Although liver cells do not occupy a surface, their epithelial nature is indicated by the fact that they contact each other by their lateral borders, a minimum of intercellular "cementing" material is between the cells, and obviously no fibrous material is between the cells. These cells are glandular epithelium (of the liver) which have developed from the endoderm. They retain a connection with the alimentary canal by extremely small canals that can barely be seen with the light microscope (see Plate 54).

Figure 3 shows cells which assume certain epithelial characteristics. The cells (**Epd**), however, do not develop from a surface, but rather, they develop from connective-tissue-type cells. They are referred to as epithelioid because of the following characteristics: The

KEY

Ep, epithelium
Epd, epithelioid cells
CT, connective tissue
S, sinusoid
arrow (Fig. 1), binucleate cell
arrows (Fig. 4), nuclei of epithelioid cells of the thymus gland
Figs. 1–3 (monkey), x 640; Fig. 4 (human, 7 mos.), x 640.

nuclei are spherical and vesiculated, and they are surrounded by a discernible amount of cytoplasm. Moreover, the cell borders can be seen and the cells contact similar neighboring cells much the same as epithelial cells contact each other.

Figure 4 shows cells which are also referred to as epithelioid. They develop from the endodermal epithelium; however, they come to assume certain connective tissue characteristics. These are the "reticular" cells or the epitheloid cells of the thymus gland. They possess relatively large, pale-staining nuclei (**arrows**). These stand out among the more numerous, smaller, intensely staining nuclei of the lymphocytes (thymocytes). In some cases, the cytoplasm of the epithelioid cells can be seen; however, the cells are not seen to contact similar neighboring cells in the typical manner of epithelial cells.

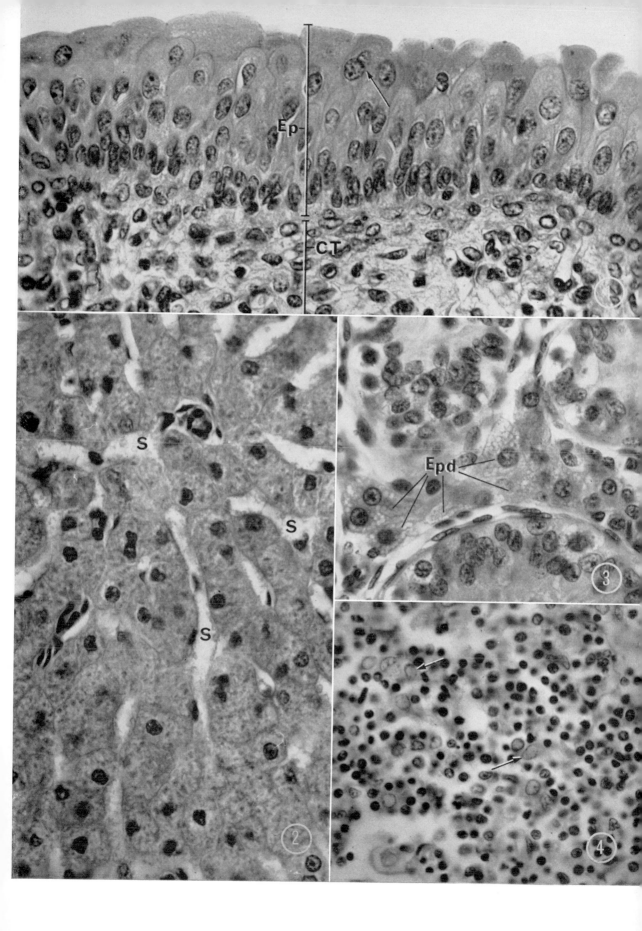

CONNECTIVE TISSUE

CONNECTIVE TISSUE consists of cells and extracellular material, namely, fibers and ground substance. The various combinations of cells and extracellular material account for the different kinds of connective tissue. For purposes of convenience, connective tissues can be classified as follows:

A. Connective Tissue Proper*
   General
   1. loose
   2. dense
   Special
   3. regular
   4. elastic
   5. adipose
   6. reticular
   Embryonic
   7. mesenchyme
   8. mucous
B. Supporting Tissue (see page 23)
   1. cartilage
   2. bone

1, 2. Both *loose* and *dense* connective tissue contain fundamentally the same components. The difference between them is in the ratio of cells to extracellular fibers. Loose connective tissue contains relatively more cells and fewer fibers; dense connective tissue contains fewer cells and more fibers. Moreover, the fibers in loose connective tissue are thinner and more delicate.

Ground substance occupies the space between the cells and fibers of connective tissue. It is not a conspicuous feature of routine H & E sections because it is easily lost during the tissue preparation. Ground substance consists of polysaccharides of different types. Some of these polysaccharides may contain "acid" groups, such as sulfate, which stain with basic dyes. Special preparations are usually employed to demonstrate this material.

Three kinds of fibers are present in connective tissue: collagenous fibers, elastic fibers, and reticular fibers. *Collagenous fibers* form interlacing bundles and are sometimes also referred to as white fibers. These fibers are produced by connective tissue cells called fibroblasts. The same cell would be called a fibrocyte when it is not actively engaged in the production of collagen (the protein substance which constitutes collagenous fibers). Collagenous fibers and fibrocytes are the most characteristic components of connective

---

* Unless otherwise indicated, the term "connective tissue" hereafter refers to general connective tissue.

11

tissue. Collagenous fibers stain with eosin. *Elastic fibers,* as the name suggests, impart elastic properties to a tissue. These are less numerous than collagenous fibers. Although elastic fibers may stain lightly with eosin, special elastic stains which contain orcein or resorcin fuchsin are usually employed for their demonstration. *Reticular fibers* are small collagenous fibers which are surrounded by nonacidified ground substance. They are present where connective tissue meets epithelium, and they form networks around small blood vessels and nerves, muscle cells, and fat cells. Reticular fibers are extremely small and they are not conspicuous in H & E preparations. Special silver methods may be employed to demonstrate reticular fibers; they appear black in these preparations. The periodic acid-Schiff (PAS) reaction may also be used to demonstrate reticular fibers.

Several cell types are present in connective tissue: fibrocytes, mast cells, histiocytes, fat cells, and white blood cells which have migrated from the nearby blood vessels. Connective tissue is also described as containing undifferentiated cells which retain the ability to develop into other cell types. However, one current opinion holds that some so-called differentiated cell types also retain the ability to transform into other cell types.

As mentioned above, *fibrocytes* are the most characteristic cells of connective tissue. They (as fibroblasts) are associated with the production of collagenous, elastic, and reticular fibers. *Histiocytes* are connective tissue macrophages. They may be fixed or wandering. *Mast cells* are found throughout connective tissue. However, they are especially numerous around small blood vessels. The cytoplasm of these cells is filled with granules which have staining characteristics similar to those of heparin and certain kinds of ground substance. *Fat cells* have the ability to store large amounts of lipid.

It is not practical to try to identify each of the various connective tissue cell types in H & E preparations. However, the following points may be helpful. One can usually distinguish a fixed cell from a wandering cell (see Plate 5). Fat cells can be identified because of their large size and empty appearance. Fibrocytes, fixed macrophages, and mast cells are difficult to distinguish from one another. The cytoplasm of these cells is generally difficult to delineate from the extracellular fibrous material, and the cells frequently appear as naked nuclei. The question of identifying cell types, however, is not a matter of considering the cells as if they were isolated units. In a histology slide, cells are seen in relation to other structures, and the position of connective tissue cells with respect to these other structures, e.g., blood vessels, surfaces, and fibers, may serve as an indication to their identification. For example, in very fibrous tissue, the fibrocyte is the predominant cell type, and this fact in itself serves as a major factor in its identification. Whereas fibrocytes are also present in extremely cellular tissues, such as one often sees under epithelial surfaces, other cell types may be equally or more numerous. Mast cells are relatively more numerous in the vicinity of small blood vessels. In special circumstances, the cell types can be identified with more assurance. Thus, macrophages can be identified if they contain phagocytized material within their cytoplasm. Mast cells can be identified by taking special precautions to preserve the granules and then staining them with a basic dye. Fibrocytes usually possess small, flattened nuclei. However, when it is actively engaged in the production of collagen, the nucleus of the cell (now a fibroblast) becomes enlarged and pale staining; moreover, the cytoplasm becomes conspicuous. The cytoplasm of the fibroblast presents a stellate profile, and parts of it stain with hematoxylin or basic dyes.

The term *lamina propria* is applied to the connective tissue which serves as a supporting framework for the epithelium of mucous membranes. This connective tissue is usually very cellular. In some places it contains large numbers of lymphocytes, and in these cases it is referred to as diffuse lymphoid tissue. Plasma cells are frequently found in the lamina propria. These cells are related to lymphocytes and are associated with antibody production. They have a spherical nucleus which is eccentrically located and traditionally described as being "cartwheel." The cytoplasm of plasma cells is more extensive than the cytoplasm of lymphocytes, and it stains with hematoxylin, except for the part in the center which contains the Golgi apparatus.

3. *Regular connective tissue* consists of bundles of parallel collagenous fibers. This kind of tissue with its inelastic property constitutes tendons and ligament.

4. *Elastic tissue* contains a predominance of elastic material. This need not be in the form of fibers, but rather, it may be in the form of broad and interconnecting bands, or else as fenestrated membranes. The two locations in which large amounts of elastic material are found are the walls of the elastic arteries and the elastic ligaments of the spinal cord (ligamenta flava, and ligamentum nuchae).

5. In certain locations, the connective tissue of the body contains large numbers of fat cells. This tissue no longer retains the characteristics of general connective tissue, but has a distinctive histological appearance, and is called *adipose tissue*.

6. The designation *reticular tissue* is applied to the reticular fibers and special cells (reticular cells) which form the framework of lymphoid organs and bone marrow. *Blood* is a derivative of connective tissue (bone marrow and lymphoid organs) in which the intercellular material is liquid.

7, 8. *Mesenchyme* is embryonic connective tissue; *mucous connective tissue* is embryonic connective tissue with a large amount of ground substance which gives it a jellylike quality.

Plate 4. Loose Connective Tissue

The tissue which surrounds the epithelial elements of an inactive mammary gland lobule serves as an example of loose connective tissue (**LCT**) (Fig. 1). In an H & E preparation, the nuclei of the connective tissue cells appear as the dark-staining bodies (**arrows**). The cytoplasm, however, cannot be distinguished from the thin, irregularly arranged collagenous fibers that are between the cells. The small, walled, ringlike structures within the connective tissue are blood vessels (**BV**). Surrounding the inactive lobule and its loose connective tissue is dense connective tissue (**DCT**). As stated in the introduction, both contain fundamentally the same elements; however, loose connective tissue is more cellular and less fibrous, whereas dense connective tissue is relatively less cellular and more fibrous. In the loose connective tissues, the fibers are extremely thin; in the dense connective tissue the fibers are thick. This is readily apparent in Figure 1.

It should be emphasized that the classification of loose and dense connective tissue is based on relative factors and many intermediate forms exist. An example of an intermediate form is shown in Figure, 2, the connective tissue of the rete testis. This moderately dense connective tissue (**CT**) contains a variety of connective tissue cells and interlacing bundles of collagenous fibers which separate the cells. For most of the cells, only the nuclei are evident; the cytoplasm is difficult to delineate from the extracellular fibrous material. On the basis of the nuclear shapes, staining, and arrangement, it is evident that the cells are not grouped or organized in any special pattern. To summarize, the microscopic appearance of connective tissue includes the presence of several cell types not organized in any special pattern, and, between the cells, interlacing bundles of fibers. The inclusion of some epithelium (**Ep**) permits one to compare epithelium and connective tissue. The epithelial cells are arranged to form a surface. They are closely applied, and are not separated by fibers.

It is not possible to identify the ground substance in routine H & E preparations, and

KEY

BV, blood vessels
CT, connective tissue
DCT, dense connective tissue
Ep, epithelium
LCT, loose connective tissue
arrows, nuclei of connective tissue cells
Fig. 1 (human), x 160; Fig. 2 (human), x 480.

it is extremely difficult and usually impractical to try to identify elastic material. It is safe to say, however, that the predominance of fibrous material is collagenous.

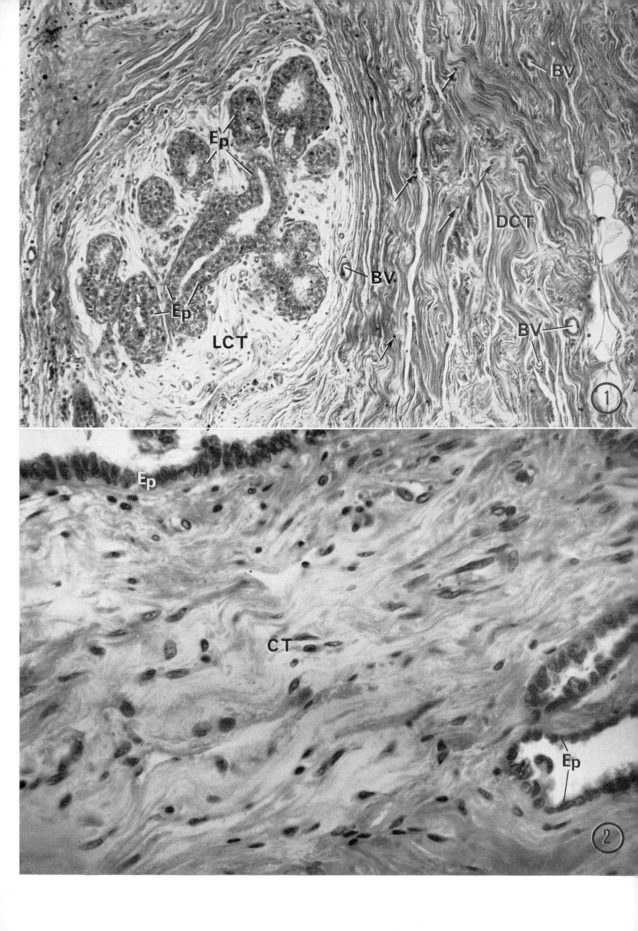

Plate 5. DENSE CONNECTIVE TISSUE

A section of dense connective tissue is shown in Figure 1. It consists of thick bundles of interlacing collagenous fibers and, scattered about, connective tissue cells. The collagenous fibers are by far the most prominent feature of the specimen. Although elastic fibers are also present, special methods are required for their demonstration. Reticular fibers are present around the small blood vessels; however, they also require special methods for their demonstration. A small blood vessel (**arrow**), cut longitudinally, is present on the left. At this magnification (Fig. 1), the connective tissue cells can be identified chiefly on the basis of their nuclear staining. The nuclei appear as small dark bodies throughout the field.

Figure 2 shows a field of dense connective tissue at higher magnification. The thick collagenous fibers that are seen at low magnification are comprised of large numbers of thin fibrils. Although it is not practical to try to identify the various kinds of connective tissue cells, some generalizations can be made. A cell in which the nucleus is surrounded by a definable amount of cytoplasm is not a fixed cell. Two such cells (**arrowheads**) are shown in Figure 2. The nucleus of each is surrounded by a clearly defined amount of cytoplasm. A nonfixed macrophage has this appearance, and these are probably macrophages. However, such an identification is somewhat tenuous unless phagocytized material can be identified within the cytoplasm. The nuclei of several other connective tissue cells are also evident. The cytoplasm, however, is not evident. These cells are identified as fibrocytes.

The inset shows a lymphocyte next to the type of cell which has been identified as a macrophage-type cell. The lymphocyte has a small, spherical, intensely staining nucleus. A small amount of cytoplasm is discernible around the nucleus. However, it should be noted that one does not always see cytoplasm around a lymphocyte in a histological section.

KEY

arrow, blood vessel
arrowheads, nonfixed (wandering) cells
Fig. 1 (human), x 160; Fig. 2 and inset (human), x 640.

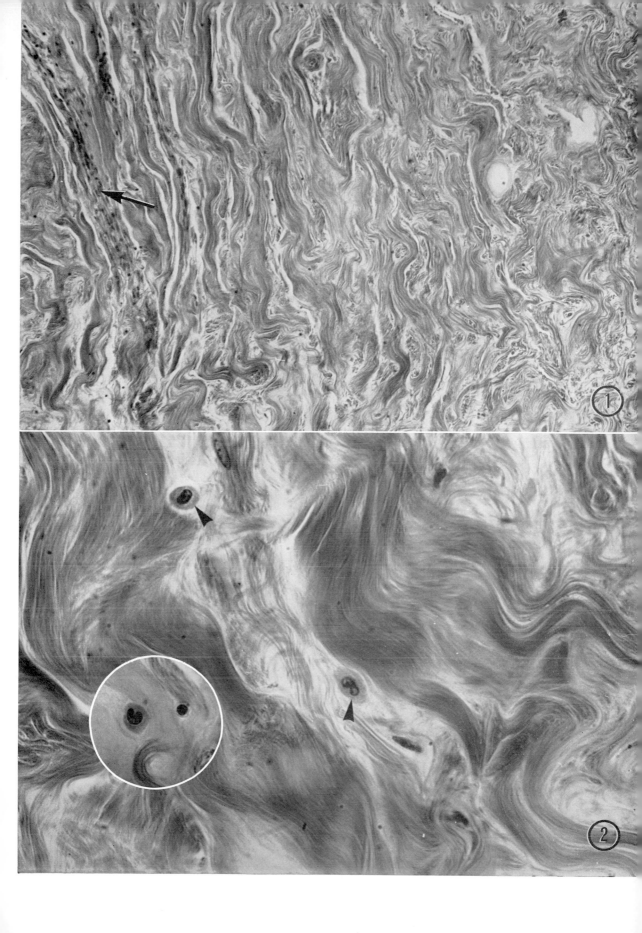

Plate 6. REGULAR CONNECTIVE TISSUE

Regular connective tissue consists of connective tissue in which the fibrous elements are organized in a parallel array. This is epitomized in ligaments and tendons.

Figure 1 is a longitudinal section of a ligament. It shows rows of collagenous fibers separated by rows of cells. The lateral extent of the collagenous bundles is not always clear; however, it is suggested by the location of the cells. The nuclei stand out, although, the cytoplasm of the cells is not evident. One regularly sees folds and even cracks in routine H & E preparations of ligaments (and also tendons). These folds are frequently at right angles to the long axis of the collagenous bundles. They are probably the result of the vibrational impact of the cutting knife. Indeed, even smaller cross-directional folds may be present, and these should not be confused with the cross striations of striated muscle.

Examination of Figure 2, a higher magnification of a ligament, indicates that the cells between the collagenous bundles are of one type; they are fibrocytes. The nuclei of these cells are shaped like oval plates. Therefore, when the broad face of the nucleus is viewed, it appears oval, and when the nucleus is viewed on edge, it appears flat. Ligaments are described as being less regularly organized than tendons.

A tendon is illustrated in Figure 3. It also consists of parallel bundles of collagenous fibers which are separated by rows of cells. The nuclei of these cells are viewed on edge and they appear as the thin, dark-staining profiles. A small amount of striated muscle (**StM**) is shown where it connects to the tendon. Although both tendon and muscle appear as oriented fibers and nuclei, the muscle contains cross striations, but the tendon does not.

The capsules of organs also contain rather organized bundles of collagenous fibers. These are more likely to be disposed in sheets rather than in cords. Therefore, the term "lamellated" is sometimes applied to this form of connective tissue.

KEY

StM, striated muscle

Fig. 1 (cat), x 160; Fig. 2 (cat), x 440; Fig. 3 (human), x 440.

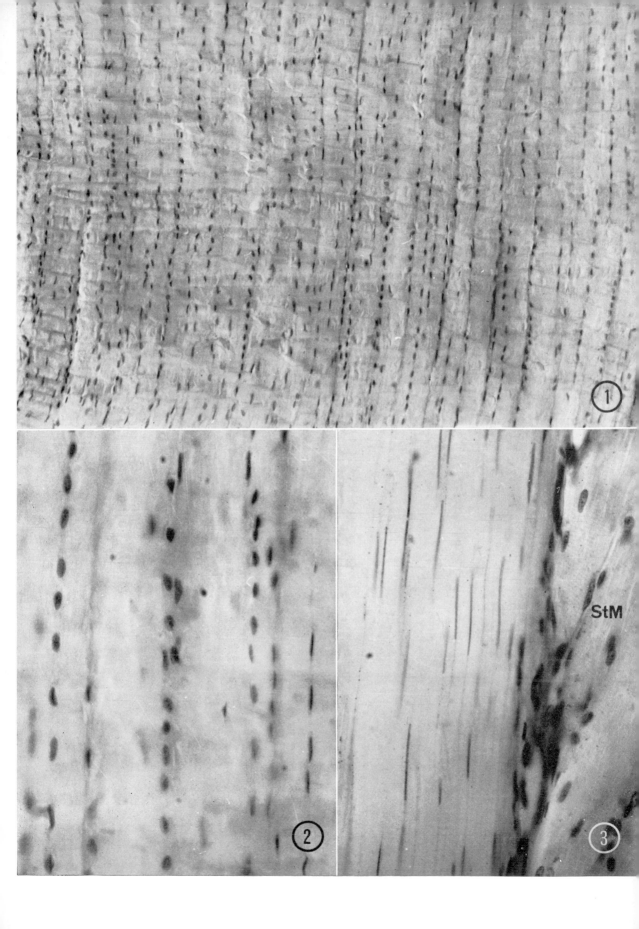

Plate 7. SPECIAL AND EMBRYONIC CONNECTIVE TISSUE

Elastic fibers are present in loose and dense connective tissue throughout the body, but in lesser amounts than collagenous fibers. Figure 1 is a section of the connective tissue of skin. This specimen was prepared to show elastic fibers; it was then stained with H & E. The connective tissue at the top of the figure is loose (papillary layer) and contains delicate elastic fibers (**arrows**). (These should not be confused with the nuclei of the connective tissue cells which also appear dark). The connective tissue in the bottom part of the figure is dense (reticular layer), and the elastic fibers (**arrowheads**) are thicker and more coarse. This connective tissue, however, is not classified as elastic because the preponderance of fibrous material is collagenous.

Figure 2 shows the wall of an elastic artery (pulmonary artery) which has been stained to illustrate the elastic material. The elastic material appears black and is a conspicuous component of the arterial wall. It is organized in the form of fenestrated membranes rather than as fibers. Tissues of the body containing large amounts of elastic material are limited in distribution to the walls of elastic arteries and some ligaments that are associated with the spinal column.

Mesenchyme is embryonic connective tissue. It is highly cellular and contains a minimum of fibers, none of which are organized into thick bundles. (This is in contrast to adult connective tissue wherein the cells may be few and the collagenous bundles thick.) Figure 3 shows the mesenchyme from the cheeks of a fetal head. The nuclei of the mesenchymal cells stain with hematoxylin and are readily evident. The cytoplasm, however, is difficult to distinguish from the extracellular material. Extremely delicate strands of collagenous fibers are present between the cells. The specimen also shows some developing striated muscle cells (**StM**), blood vessels (**BV**), and the epithelial surface (**Ep**).

Mucous connective tissue is embryonic connective tissue that is characterized by the presence of large amounts of ground substance which gives it a jellylike quality. It is present in many parts of the embryo, for

KEY

BV, blood vessel
Ep, epithelium
StM, developing striated muscle
arrows, delicate elastic fibers
arrowheads, coarse elastic fibers

Fig. 1 (human), x 160; Fig. 2 (human), x 150; Fig. 3 (fetal pig), x 400; Fig. 4 (human), x 400.

example, under the skin and in the umbilical cord. A section of the umbilical cord is shown in Figure 4. The cells are widely scattered. The cytoplasm of the cells cannot always be distinguished from the intercellular fibrous material and precipitated mucoid material.

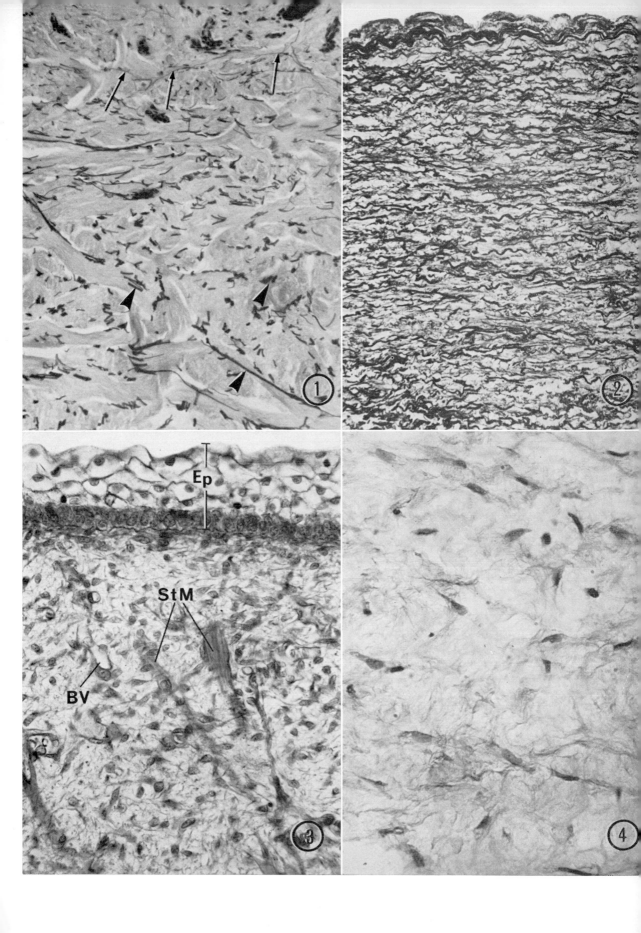

SUPPORTING TISSUE

CARTILAGE AND BONE are the essential weight-bearing components of the skeleton and for this reason they are also referred to as supporting tissues. Cartilage, in common with other connective tissue, consists of cells and intercellular material, except that in cartilage the intercellular material is solidified and the cells are of one type, called chondrocytes. Cartilage cells elaborate a matrix which contains both collagenous fibers and sulfated polysaccharide ground substance. The cells surround themselves with this matrix and occupy spaces called lacunae. (Elastic fibers are also present in the matrix of elastic cartilage.) Cartilage is unique among the various members or relatives of the connective tissue family in that it is not vascularized. Three chief kinds of cartilage can be distinguished: hyaline cartilage, elastic cartilage, and fibrocartilage.

Bone is a modified form of connective tissue in which the intercellular matrix becomes calcified. The intercellular matrix of bone contains polysaccharide ground substance and collagenous fibers. Two types of bone can be distinguished: dense or compact, and spongy or cancellous. The essential features in both spongy and compact bone are the presence of a mineralized matrix, small canals (canaliculi), and spaces (lacunae) which contain bone cells (osteocytes). In cancellous bone the matrix, lacunae, and osteocytes are organized to form spicules or trabeculae; however, in dense bone there is a special arrangement of blood vessels and bone elements which forms structural units called Haversian systems or osteons.

Special preparations are needed to examine bone because of its mineral content. Two of the most common are ground sections and decalcified sections. Ground sections are prepared by removing as much soft tissue and organic matter from the bone as possible and allowing the bone to dry. Thin slices are then cut with a saw, and these are ground to adequate thinness with fine grinding stones. The specimen may be treated with India ink to highlight the spaces that were formerly occupied by organic matter, e.g., cells and connective tissue components. In such preparations, the canaliculi, lacunae, and Haversian canals appear black (except where the India ink is lost). Ground sections display the architecture of dense bone and especially the organization of Haversian systems by revealing the mineralized material. However, the relationship of bone to soft tissue is destroyed in routine ground preparations. In decalcified sections, the cellular and organic components are retained, and the mineral is removed by treating the tissue with demineralizing solutions such as acids or chelating agents. After the bone has been demineralized it is processed in the same manner as other tissues. These preparations usually retain the relationships between the bone and related soft tissue. It may also be necessary to decalcify cartilage of aged tissue.

Plate 8. CARTILAGE

Hyaline cartilage is found in the adult as the structural basis for a number of parts of the respiratory system. Figure 1 is a portion of the trachea; Figure 2, a portion of a bronchiole. In both of these cases, the cartilage appears as a nonvascular expanse of tissue surrounded by a perichondrium (**P**). This is the fibrous capsule-like cover of hyaline cartilage. The perichondrium is shown to completely surround the hyaline cartilage of the bronchiole. It also surrounds the hyaline cartilage of the trachea, but this cannot be seen. Perichondrium is more than a simple capsule, however, in that it serves as a source of new chondrocytes during growth of cartilage. The outer part of the perichondrium is more fibrous; the inner part is more cellular. It is this more cellular inner part that is chondrogenetic.

A more detailed examination of hyaline cartilage reveals the following features (Fig. 3): Cartilage consists of a homogeneous appearing matrix (**M**) in which are small spaces, called lacunae (**L**), that contain chondrocytes (**Ch**). The matrix contains collagenous fibers which are masked by the solidified ground substance and are not evident in routine H & E sections. The ground substance contains, among other components, sulfated polysaccharides. Because of this, the matrix of cartilage stains with hematoxylin or basic dyes, and is said to be basophilic. If the sulfated material is not adequately retained during the preparative processes, the matrix may stain with eosin. The matrix immediately surrounding a lacuna stains more intensely and is referred to as the capsule (**Cap**). In a number of instances the capsule and cartilage cell can be clearly distinguished (**arrowhead**, Fig. 3). In other cases, this is not clear. Frequently, two or more lacunae are extremely close, and separated only by a thin partition of matrix. The matrix that surrounds such a group of related lacunae (territorial matrix) (**TM**) stains somewhat less than the capsule, but more intensely than the more removed matrix (extraterritorial matrix). Cartilage cells are often distorted during tissue preparation and in some cases fall out of their space, so

that occasional empty lacunae (**arrows**) are seen. Cartilage cells characteristically contain glycogen, but special methods are required for its demonstration.

Cartilage is capable of appositional growth, i.e., growth at the surface, and interstitial growth, i.e., growth within the substance of the cartilage. During appositional growth and development of cartilage, fibroblasts in the cellular part of the perichondrium begin to elaborate matrix which ultimately surrounds the cell. It follows, then, that these cells which have just become cartilage cells are close to the perichondrium. They are also flatter and smaller, and in smaller lacunae than the more deeply located cells. In the process of interstitial growth, cells which have recently divided are close to each other and may even be in the same lacuna.

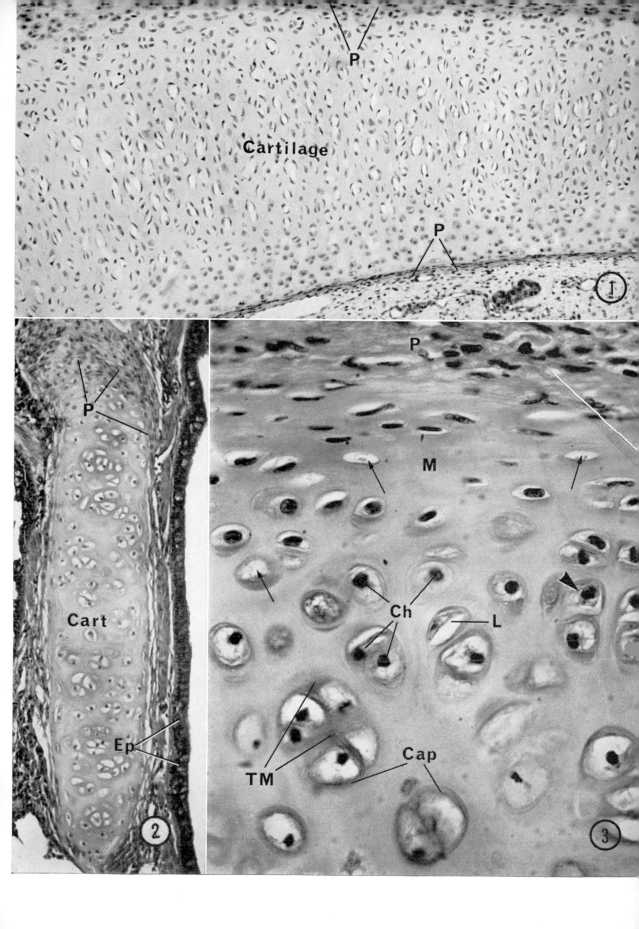

Plate 9. CARTILAGE, FETAL SKELETON

Hyaline cartilage is present as a precursor to bones in the fetus. Most of this cartilage will be replaced by bone tissue, except where one bone rubs against another bone, as in a joint. In these locations, cartilage persists as an articular structure. Evidently bone is not able to rub against bone and form a freely movable joint, whereas cartilage is able to do this. In addition, cartilage, being capable of interstitial growth, persists in weight-supporting bones as a "growth plate" as long as growth in length occurs. The role of cartilage on articular surfaces and in bone growth is considered in the following plate.

Figure 1 is a section through a fetal foot. The cartilage matrix appears extremely dark because it is stained intensely with hematoxylin. The intensity of staining is due to either or a combination of two factors, sulfated mucopolysaccharides and calcium. The matrix of cartilage that is about to be replaced by bone becomes impregnated with calcium salts and the calcium stains intensely with hematoxylin. It should be noted that the multitude of light spaces within the matrix are due to the lacunae.

The cartilage is surrounded by perichondrium, except where it faces a joint cavity (**JC**). Here the naked cartilage forms a surface. In a number of places, developing ligaments (**L**) can be seen where they join the cartilage. The nuclei of the fibroblasts are conspicuous. They are aligned in rows and are separated from other rows of nuclei by collagenous material. Some blood vessels (**BV**) can be seen in various parts of the section, but not in the cartilage; this is avascular.

Figure 2 is a more magnified view of the rectangle in Figure 1. In reference to the joint, note the following: The joint cavity (**JC**) is a space between the cartilage, whose boundaries are completed by a wall of connective tissue (**CT**). This connective tissue surface will constitute the synovial membrane in the adult and contribute to the formation of a lubricating fluid (synovial fluid) that is present in the joint cavity. Therefore, all the surfaces which will enclose the adult joint cavity derive originally from mesenchyme. This is at least one major

KEY

BV, blood vessels
CT, connective tissue
JC, joint cavity
L, ligament
Fig. 1 (rat), x 65; Fig. 2 (rat), x 160; Fig. 3 (rat), x 640.

exception to the general principle that epithelium is found on surfaces, and should be kept in mind. Synovial fluid is a viscous fluid and contains, among other things, polysaccharide material that is related to other connective tissue polysaccharides.

Figure 3 provides a closer view of the cartilagenous surface and shows closely situated lacunae with their chondrocytes. The nuclei of the chondrocytes appear spherical and are clearly distinguishable. However, the cytoplasm is not always evident so that in some cases it appears that only a nucleus is present in the lacuna. The capsules of lacunae near the surface are evident. In a number of cases, it is evident that cell division has recently occurred because two cells occupy the same lacuna. In other cases, two lacunae are extremely close with only a thin plate of matrix separating them. This is also an indication of recent cell division.

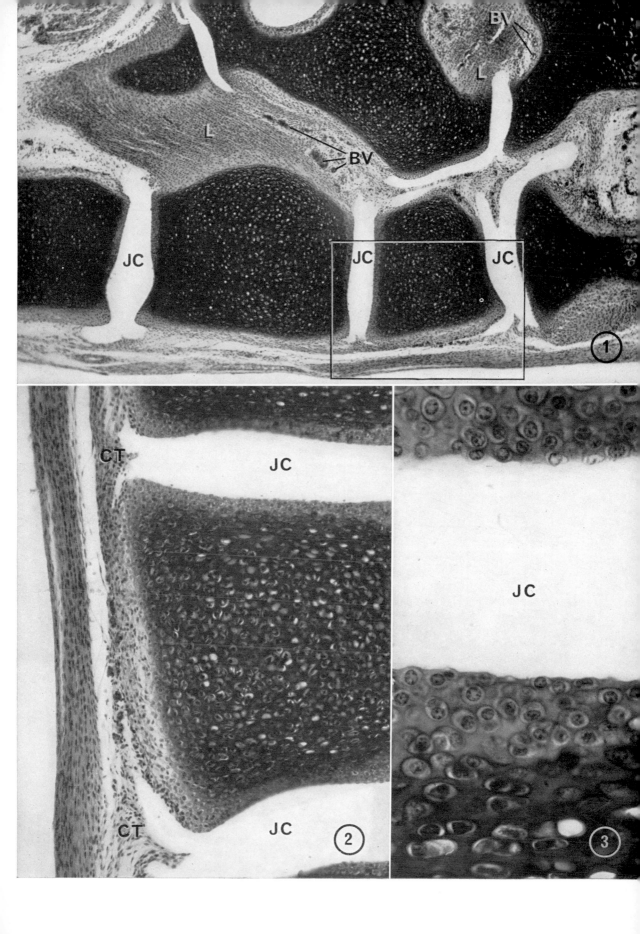

Plate 10. CARTILAGE AND SPONGY BONE

Cartilage is retained on the articular surface of bones as a friction plate in a synovial joint (Fig. 1). This is hyaline cartilage (**HC**), but it is not surrounded by a perichondrium. One surface of the cartilage is free and serves for articulation; the other surface is in contact with bone of the spongy or cancellous type. The general features of cartilage are evident in Figure 1, namely, a more or less homogeneous-appearing matrix which contains lacunae and their cells. However, certain features relating to the histological appearance of cartilage and its comparison to bone are brought out in this specimen, and for this reason a brief consideration of spongy bone will be given below.

Spongy bone (**SB**) consists of trabeculae and spicules of mineralized matrix in which are small spaces, the lacunae. Each lacuna contains a bone cell (osteocyte). The nuclei of the bone cells stain with hematoxylin and stand out against the eosinophilic staining of the matrix. Between the trabeculae and spicules are the numerous round cells of the red bone marrow (**RBM**).

When comparing cartilage and bone, note the following: In articular cartilage the lacunae and cells near the surface are smaller and flatter in comparison to the more deeply located lacunae and cells. However, there are intermediate sizes between these two extremes. In bone, on the other hand, the lacunae are essentially the same size and spaced in a characteristic manner. Moreover, in the bone, if the spicules exceed a certain size, blood vessels (**BV**) tunnel through the trabeculae. A somewhat less regular feature of bone is the wavy nature of its matrix. These wave patterns are called "bone lines" (**arrows**). This is not a dependable characteristic; however, it is familiar to those who regularly examine bone. The boundaries between bone and the articular cartilage are marked by **arrowheads**.

Hyaline cartilage (**HC**) is also present in developing long bones as a growth unit called the epiphyseal disc. Because of its capacity for interstitial growth, which is not shared by bone tissue, the epiphyseal disc (Fig. 2) is an essential feature of bone that is growing in

KEY

BV, blood vessels
HC, hyaline cartilage
L, lacunae
P, perichondrium
RBM, red bone marrow
SB, spongy bone
arrowheads, boundary between bone and hyaline cartilage
arrows, bone lines

Figs. 1 and 2 (dog), x 160; Fig. 3 (dog, Weigert stain), x 160.

length. In this specimen bone is in contact with the top of the cartilaginous growth plate and once this happens, removal of cartilage from this surface ceases.

Elastic cartilage differs from hyaline cartilage inasmuch as the matrix contains elastic fibers (Fig. 3). These impart unique properties of elasticity to elastic cartilage that are not shared by hyaline cartilage. Elastic cartilage is found in the auricle of the external ear, in the auditory tube, and in part of the larynx.

Figure 3 shows the perichondrium (**P**), lacunae (**L**), cartilage cells and matrix of elastic cartilage. The cells have shrunk and separated from the walls of the lacunae, and in many instances, the nuclei and cytoplasm of the chondrocytes are clearly evident. The elastic fibers appear as the black fibers within the matrix. Note again that the cells and lacunae nearer the perichondrium are smaller than those more centrally situated, and that intermediate sizes are present.

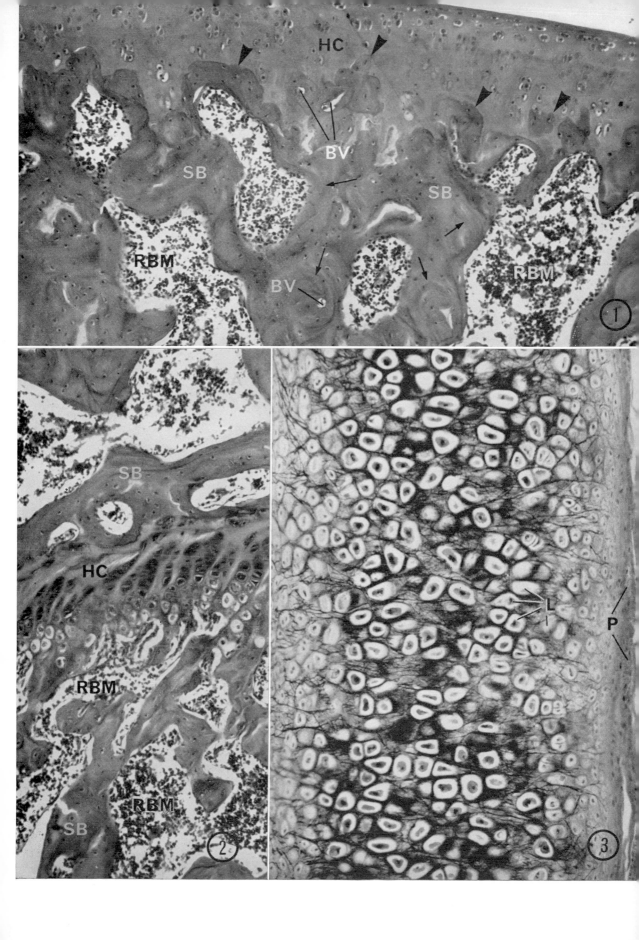

Plate 11. FIBROCARTILAGE

Fibrocartilage is an intermediate between fibrous (collagenous) tissue and hyaline cartilage. It is regularly present where fibrous tissue is subjected to pressure, namely, at the intervertebral discs and the symphysis pubis. It is also present at a number of other places. For example, it is present at the knee joint, mandibular joint, sternoclavicular joint, shoulder joint, and it may be present along the grooves or insertions for tendons or ligaments.

Histologically, fibrocartilage appears as fields of cartilage imperceptibly blending with regions of fibrous tissue or, sometimes, hyaline cartilage. No perichondrium is present. A low magnification view of fibrocartilage is shown in Figure 1. Much of the field has a fibrous appearance, and nuclei of fibrocytes are to be seen scattered about. However, even at this low magnification, at least one field appears to show characteristics of cartilage (**rectangle**). This is examined at higher magnification in Figure 2. Examination of this figure shows a region where the intercellular material is homogenous (**HM**) and typical of cartilage. Lacunae (**L**) with distinct capsules can be identified. However, even in places where the intercellular material is fibrous (**FM**), some distinct lacunae, chondrocytes, and capsules can be seen (**arrows**). The presence of a capsule around a cell is indicative of a cartilage cell and cartilage, and when fibrous material shares the field with these cells and their capsules, one can identify the tissue as fibrocartilage. The nuclei of other cells which are not apparently contained in a lacuna and surrounded by a capsule are also seen. These are nuclei (**F**) which belong to fibrocytes.

KEY

F, fibrocyte nuclei
FM, fibrous matrix
HM, homogenous matrix
L, lacunae
arrows, lacunae and chondrocytes in fibrous matrix
Fig. 1 (dog), x 160; Fig. 2 (dog), x 640.

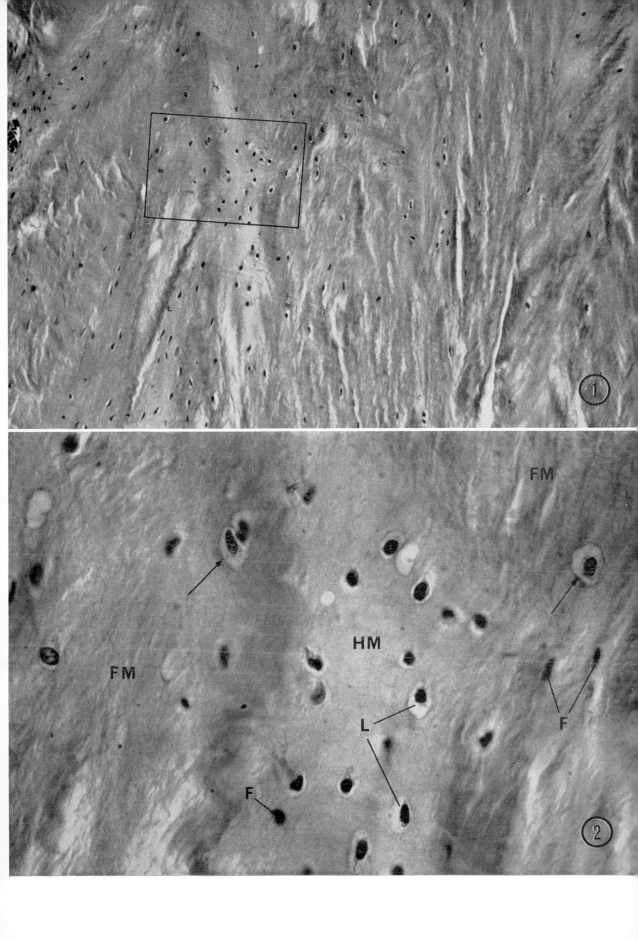

Plate 12. COMPACT BONE

Haversian systems, or osteons, are roughly cylindrical structures which may branch. In the shaft of a long bone, the long axis of the osteons are oriented parallel to the long axis of the bone, so that a cross section through the shaft of a long bone would also cut the osteons in cross section.

Figure 1 is a ground section of dense bone which was treated with India ink. The center of each Haversian system contains a canal, called the Haversian canal (**HC**), which travels through its long axis. This is surrounded by concentric layers of mineralized material which, in cross section, appear as rings much the same as growth rings of a tree. The Haversian canal is also surrounded by concentric arrangements of lacunae. These appear as the small dark oval structures with their long axis oriented circumferentially. Although the Haversian canals may vary somewhat in size, the lacunae are much smaller, far more numerous, and relatively uniform in size. Small canals (canaliculi) radiate outward from the Haversian canals to the lacunae. These appear as the delicate black radiations from the Haversian canal that pass through the lamellae to the lacunae (see inset, Fig. 1). The canaliculi also connect neighboring lateral lacunae, but these connections are less conspicuous.

In Figure 1, a number of Haversian systems appear complete; these have been most recently formed. Other Haversian systems show incomplete outer lamellae (**arrows**); these belong to older Haversian systems which have been partly resorbed. In some cases, only small parts of older Haversian systems remain between the complete newer ones. These remains are called interstitial lamellae (**IL**).

The Haversian canal contains small blood vessels and delicate connective tissue. The blood vessels reach the Haversian canals from either the periosteum or bone marrow through other tunnels called Volkmanns canals (**VC**) (Fig. 1). These can be distinguished from the Haversian canals in that they cut through lamellae, whereas the Haversian canals are surrounded by concentric rings of lamellae.

The general features of dense bone are

KEY

HC, Haversian canal
IL, interstitial lamellae
VC, Volkmann's canal
arrows (Fig. 1), incomplete lamellae
arrows (Fig. 3), canaliculi
Fig. 1 (dog), x 65, (inset), x 260; Figs. 2 and 3 (dog), x 160.

shown in Figure 2, a decalcified section. In the center of each osteon is a Haversian canal (**HC**) and, in some cases, the blood vessels can be seen. The matrix stains pink with eosin; the nuclei of osteoblasts stain with hematoxylin and stand out sharply against the pink background of the matrix.

The ring-like arrangement of the lamellae is not conspicuous in Figure 2, but is particularly striking in Figure 3. Figures 2 and 3 are photographs of the same slide (and same field), except that phase contrast optics were employed for Figure 3. The canaliculi are also evident in Figure 3 (**arrows**). Collagenous fibers travel spirally in the lamellae, but while those in a particular lamella travel in the same direction, those in neighboring lamellae travel in a different direction. This accounts for the striking appearance of the lamellae when viewed with phase contrast optics.

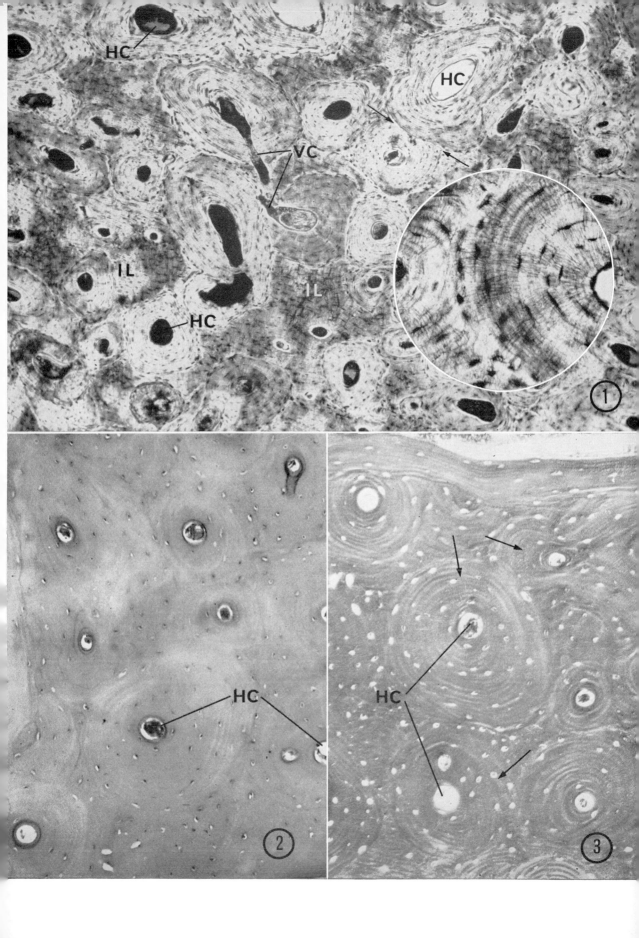

Plate 13. ENDOCHONDRAL BONE FORMATION I

Endochondral bone formation involves the simultaneous removal of cartilage and the formation of bone. Moreover, as a bone grows, it undergoes changes in shape, i.e., remodeling. These changes include the formation of a large medullary cavity. Two specialized cell types have been identified with the processes of bone growth and remodeling, osteoblasts and osteoclasts. Osteoblasts are the cells that are engaged in the formation of bone. Although the removal of bone is not as well understood, it has been established that multinucleated cells, called osteoclasts, are engaged in the removal of bone in some situations.

The early steps of endochondral bone formation are illustrated in the cartilage model on the left side of Figure 1. These steps are: (1) The cartilage cells in the center become enlarged, i.e., hypertrophic (**HC**). (2) The matrix of the cartilage becomes calcified (**CM**). The calcified matrix stains intensely with hematoxylin and appears as the black material between the white spaces of the enlarged cartilage cells. (3) A Collar of bone forms around the circumference of the center of the cartilage bar. This bone is called periosteal bone (**PB**) because the osteoblasts develop from the periosteum (at this very early stage it might be called perichondral bone). It should be noted that the periosteal bone (or perichondral bone) is in fact intramembranous bone since it develops within the membrane that surrounds the bone (or cartilage).

The cartilage model on the right side of Figure 1 shows the next events and a continuation of the earlier ones. A vascular bud (not shown) and accompanying connective tissue from the periosteum invade the calcified cartilage and bring about its dissolution, thereby forming a cavity (**Cav**). Careful examination at higher power would reveal that the cells in the center of this cavity are not all cartilage cells; some of them are connective tissue cells. While this new step occurs, the earlier steps continue: (1) the cartilage cells proliferate, thereby providing for an increase in the length of the developing bone; (2) the perios-

KEY

AC, articular cartilage
Cav, cavity
CM, calcified matrix
EB, endochondral bone
EpC, epiphyseal plate
HC, hypertrophic cartilage cells
PB, periosteal bone
P Bud, periosteal bud

Fig. 1 (monkey), x 40; Fig. 2 (human), x 40; Fig. 3 (monkey), x 16.

teal bone (**PB**) continues to form; (3) the cartilage cells facing the cavity become hypertrophic (**HC**); (4) the matrix becomes calcified (**CM**) and erosion of cartilage occurs at the two extremities of the expanding cavity, and (5) bone forms on the spicules of cartilage. This is endochondral bone.

All of these processes are seen at a more advanced stage in Figure 2. Note the thicker and more extensive periosteal bone (**PB**) which stains with eosin, the enlarged cavity (**Cav**), the edge of the eroded cartilage, and the endochondral bone (**EB**) which has formed around the desquamated cartilage. This bone also stains with eosin, whereas the calcified cartilage stains intensely with hematoxylin. Some intensely staining calcified cartilage is still present in the endochondral bone spicules.

At some point, as the continuous processes described above proceed, one end of the cartilage model (the epiphysis) is invaded by a periosteal bud (**P Bud**) and it undergoes the same changes that occurred in the shaft (Fig. 3). This same process then occurs at the other end of the long bone. Consequently, at each end of a developing long bone a cartilaginous plate (epiphyseal plate) (**EpC**) is between two sites of bone formation. The rectangle in Figure 3 is shown at higher magnification in Plate 14.

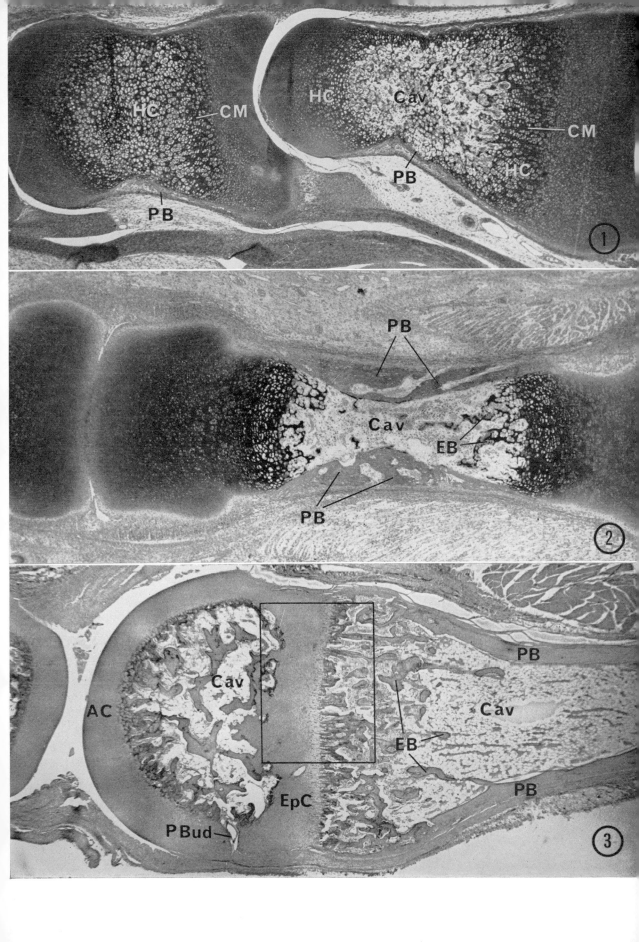

Plate 14. ENDOCHONDRAL BONE FORMATION II

A higher magnification of the rectangle in Plate 13 is shown as Figure 1. The cartilage of the epiphyseal plate can be divided into different zones which reflect the progressive changes that occur in active endochondral bone formation. These zones are not sharply delineated and the boundary between them is somewhat arbitrary. They lead toward the marrow cavity, so that the first zone is furthest from the cavity. The zones are:

1) The zone of reserve cartilage (**RC**). The cells of this zone have not yet begun to participate in the growth of the bone; they are reserve cells. These cells are small, usually only one to a lacuna, and not grouped. At some time, some of these cells will proliferate and undergo the changes outlined in the next zone. *2)* Zone of proliferating cartilage (**PC**). The cells of this zone are increasing in number; they are slightly larger than the reserve cells, close to their neighbors, and they begin to form rows. *3)* Zone of hypertrophic cartilage (**HC**). The cells of this zone are aligned in rows and are significantly larger than the cells in the preceding zone. *4)* Zone of calcified matrix (**CM**). In this zone the matrix becomes impregnated with calcium salts and, because of this, it stains intensely with hematoxylin. *5)* Zone of resorption (**arrows**, Fig. 2). This zone is where an edge of eroded cartilage is in direct contact with the connective tissue. Spicules of cartilage are formed because the connective tissue invades and resorbs in spearheads rather than along a straight front. Endochondral bone (**EB**) formation occurs on the surfaces of these spicules of calcified cartilage.

Osteoblasts (**Ob**) are aligned on the surface of the spicule where bone formation is actively in progress. In most cases, a thin band of material, called osteoid, can be seen on the surface of the spicule in direct contact with the osteoblasts. The osteoid is the recent product of the osteoblasts; it stains with eosin, and is paler or lighter staining than the bone matrix. It is more evident in the illustrations on the following plate. Cartilage cells (**CC**) are still present in the center of some spicules, especially near the epiphyseal

KEY

B, bone
C, cartilage
Cav, marrow cavity
CC, cartilage cells
CM, calcified matrix
CT, connective tissue
EB, endochondral bone
EBF, endochondral bone formation
HC, hypertrophic cartilage
M, marrow cells
Ob, osteoblasts
Oc, osteocytes
PC, proliferating cartilage
RC, reserve cartilage
arrows, resorption of cartilage

Fig. 1 (monkey), x 40; Fig. 2 (monkey), x 160; Fig. 3 (monkey), x 160.

cartilage (Fig. 2). The smaller cells in the plate, are osteocytes (**Oc**). Between the spicules in Figures 1 and 2 is loose cellular connective tissue (**CT**).

Figure 3 shows the epiphyseal plate when bone formation is going on at a reduced rate and only on one side of the epiphyseal plate. The functional zones are similar to those described above, but they are reduced in extent, along with the reduction of the thickness of the epiphyseal plate (Figures 2 and 3 are the same magnification). The histological signs of endochondral bone formation (**EBF**) are present on the diaphyseal side of the epiphyseal plate, but not on the epiphyseal side. This is indicated because bone (**B**) contacts the cartilage (**C**) on the epiphyseal side, whereas connective tissue (**CT**) is in contact with the cartilage on the diaphyseal side. The connective tissue between the spicules contains large numbers of round cells, or marrow cells (**M**).

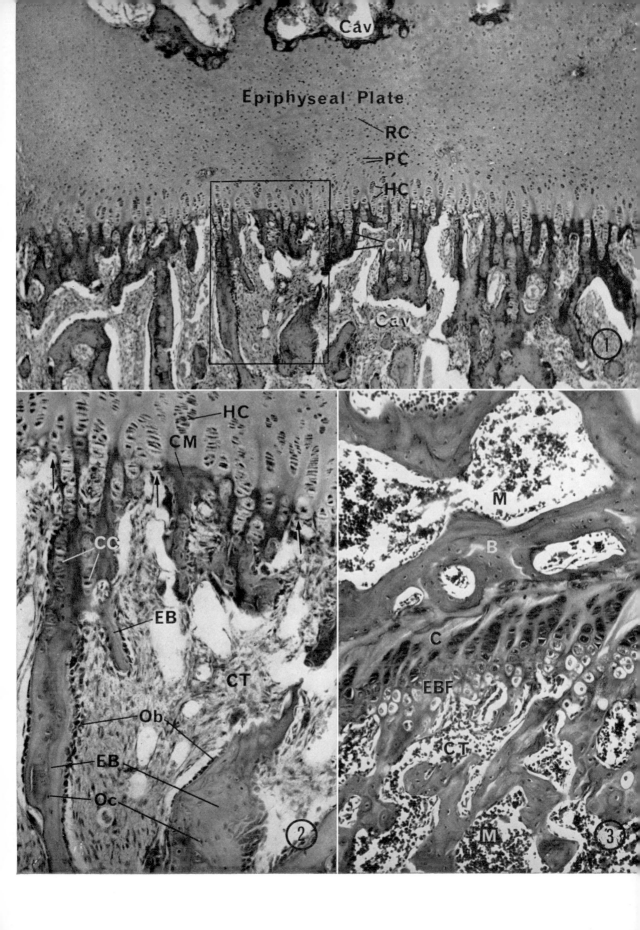

Plate 15. INTRAMEMBRANOUS BONE FORMATION

The flat bones of the skull, the mandible, and the clavicle ossify, at least in part, via an intramembranous route. The bones which form via an intramembranous route do not provide structural support compared to the support that is required of bones that ossify via an endochondral route.

The formation of intramembranous bone in the mandible is shown in Figure 1. This is a low-power panoramic view which shows some developing spicules of bone and their relationship to the surface of the face. The bone spicules (**BS**) appear as the elongated irregular dark profiles in the connective tissue. The oval structure is Meckel's cartilage (**MC**).

The sequence of events in intramembranous bone formation can be studied by examining a spicule (**rectangle**) at higher magnification (Fig. 1, inset). The earliest steps are illustrated at the top and later events at the bottom. During intramembranous bone formation, cells from the connective tissue differentiate into osteoblasts (**Ob**) and become concentrated at the site of future bone. The osteoblasts engage in the production of osteoid (**Os**); osteoid consists of collagenous fibers and a homogeneous matrix. Osteoid can be recognized because it is situated on the surface of bone spicules, osteoblasts are usually in contact with it, and it stains less intensely with eosin than does the "matrix" of the bone. Osteoid becomes calcified and is then bone. When osteoblasts have surrounded themselves with their product and come to lie in lacunae, they are called osteocytes.

Intramembranous bone formation and the remodeling of the skull are illustrated in Figure 2. Note that osteoblasts and osteoid are present along almost the entire surface of bone on the skin side. Lines can be seen in the spicules which reflect the general contours and pattern of bone deposition. These lines are intact on the side of the spicule upon which bone is being deposited, but they are interrupted where bone is being resorbed (**arrow**).

Figure 3 shows developing intramembranous bone at higher magnification. The nuclei of the osteocytes (**Oc**) stain with hematoxylin and

KEY

BS, bone spicules
BV, blood vessels
MC, Meckel's cartilage
Ob, osteoblasts
Oc, osteocyte
Ocl, osteoclast
Os, osteoid
arrow, edge where bone was resorbed
Fig. 1 (pig), x 65; Fig. 2 (human), x 65; Fig. 3 (human), x 160; Fig. 4 (rabbit), x 640.

stand out against the pink staining matrix. The osteoblasts (**Ob**) are located on the surface of the bone spicule, immediately adjacent to the lightly staining osteoid (**Os**) which they have just formed. Two osteoclasts (**Ocl**) can be seen on the under surface of one of the spicules. Loose connective tissue is between the bone spicules, and blood vessels (**BV**) are located within this connective tissue at approximately an equal distance from the neighboring bone spicules.

Osteoclasts are multinucleated cells which engage in the removal of bone. They are immediately adjacent to the bone which is actually being removed (Fig. 4). A striated border is present at the cell bone junction, but this can only be seen in the most favorable preparations. After osteoclasts have been at work for some time, they form a slight concavity on the surface of the bone. This concavity is called Howship's lacuna.

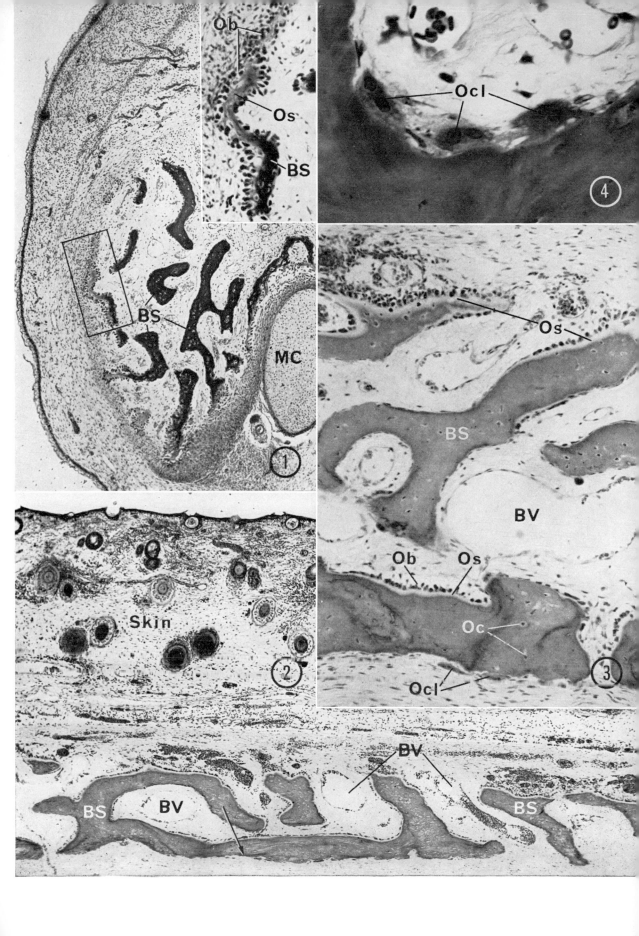

MUSCLE TISSUE

MUSCLE consists of long protoplasmic fibers which are specialized to contract. The muscle fibers are cellular elements and should not be confused with connective tissue fibers, which are extracellular and nonprotoplasmic. For convenience, histologists have traditionally classified muscle into three groups: smooth muscle, striated muscle, and cardiac muscle.

Smooth muscle consists of cells that are almost invariably spindle shaped. They possess a single, elongated nucleus. The cytoplasm of smooth muscle cells contains a variety of organelles; however, in routine H & E preparations, the cytoplasm stains rather evenly with eosin, and the organelles are not visualized. Examination of the cytoplasm with the electron microscope shows longitudinally oriented threadlike structures called myofilaments. These are the contractile elements within the cytoplasm.

Smooth muscle is found in many locations within the body. It is found in large amounts in the wall of the viscera (and for this reason it is also called visceral muscle); it is present in the walls of blood vessels; it is present in small bundles or as single cells in the skin, endocardium, intestinal villi etc., and it is associated with many glands and their ducts. If the muscle cells that are associated with the glands (or their ducts) are on the epithelial side of the basement membrane they are called myoepithelial cells. (It should be noted that the myoepithelial cells develop from the same source as the epithelium itself.)

Muscle cells within a bundle or layer are usually oriented in the same direction, but neighboring bundles or layers may be oriented in different directions. For example, in the intestines, two of the muscle layers are oriented at right angles to each other.

Striated muscle consists of extremely long multinucleated fibers. When viewed with the light microscope, the cytoplasm is seen to be bounded by a thick membrane. This membrane was called the sarcolemma by classical histologists and was regarded as being the cell membrane. However, ultrastructural studies reveal that it consists not only of a cell membrane, but of basement membrane material and delicate collagenous fibers. In current usage the term sarcolemma is used to mean only the cell membrane. The nuclei are located immediately under the sarcolemma. Striated muscle fibers possess cross striations. The striations are the most characteristic histologic features of this kind of muscle, and are the basis for the name striated muscle. The cytoplasm of striated muscle cells contains longitudinal subunits called myofibrils. These can be seen in *favorable* histologic preparations; they are especially evident in cross sections of the muscle fibers, where they give the cut edge of the fiber a stippled appearance.

The cross striations that are seen in routine preparations are a property of the myofibrils. Banded portions of neighboring myofibrils are in register and give the entire muscle fiber its cross striated appearance. Examination of the myofibrils with the electron microscope reveals that they are comprised of myofilaments.

Striated muscle is the contractile component of the skeletal muscles. In addition, striated muscle is also found in the muscles of the face, in the muscles that move the eyeballs, in the tongue, in the pharynx, and in the upper part of the esophagus. In the latter two locations, the striated muscle is obviously in a visceral location.

It should be noted that the term striated muscle refers to muscle tissue. A skeletal muscle, on the other hand, is an organ of locomotion in which striated muscle is a functional component. The muscle tissue in skeletal muscles, i.e., the striated muscle, is sometimes called skeletal muscle.

Cardiac muscle is the muscle that is found in the wall of the heart. It consists of long fibers which branch and meet with neighboring fibers. Within the wall of the heart, groups of fibers travel in different directions. Therefore in most histological sections, some groups of fibers are cut longitudinally, and others are cut in cross section or obliquely.

Cardiac muscle fibers, like striated muscle, possess cross striations. However, cardiac muscle is not included with striated muscle in most classifications.

The nuclei of cardiac muscle fibers are located at regular intervals in the center of the fiber. Cross bands, different from the cross striations, are also present in cardiac muscle. These are the intercalated discs. Examination of these discs with the electron microscope reveals that they are thickened opposing cell membranes. The fibers of cardiac muscle, then, are distinctly different from the fibers of striated muscle. In cardiac muscle, the cells are aligned end to end to form the functional "fibers" which are seen with the light microscope. On the other hand, a fiber of striated muscle is a single protoplasmic unit.

Some of the cardiac muscle fibers are specialized to conduct impulses; these are called Purkinje fibers.

Plate 16. SMOOTH MUSCLE

In longitudinal section, smooth muscle cells appear as elongated fibers, all of which are oriented in the same direction (Fig. 1). Their nuclei (**N**) are also elongated and conform to the general shape of the cell. In this preparation the nuclei appear slightly twisted, like a corkscrew; this is as they appear in contracted cells. The cells are slightly separated from each other and this allows one to delineate the cell boundaries. However, the boundaries cannot always be seen in H & E sections (see Fig. 4).

A cross section through smooth muscle cells from the same specimen is shown in Figure 2. The nuclei (**N**) are included in some cells. These appear as the dark spherical structures. In most of the cells, however, the nuclei have been missed, and only the eosinophilic cytoplasm appears. Because the cells are staggered, some are cut through the thick central portion, others are cut through the tapering ends. The difference in diameter between neighboring cells is one of the most characteristic features of smooth muscle that is cut in cross section. This also applies to the nuclei, but to a much lesser degree. The two elongated nuclei belong to connective tissue cells (**arrows**).

Interlacing bundles of smooth muscle cells are shown in Figure 3. One bundle has been cut longitudinally (**L**). This can be recognized by the elongated shape of the nuclei. Other bundles of smooth muscle cells have been cut in cross section or obliquely (**X**). Because the muscle cells within a bundle are oriented in the same direction, they have essentially the same appearance regardless of the plane of section. Therefore, when the bundle is cut longitudinally, the cells and their nuclei all appear elongated; when the bundle is cut in cross section, they appear polygonal. This point is more evident in Figure 4, which is a higher magnification of the same specimen shown in Figure 3. Note where the smooth muscle cells are cut longitudinally, the nuclei (**N**) are elongated; where they are cut in cross section or obliquely, the nuclei are spherical or oval.

Connective tissue (**CT**) is between the

KEY

CT, connective tissue
L, smooth muscle, longitudinal section
N, nuclei of smooth muscle cells
X, smooth muscle, cross or oblique section
arrows, connective tissue cell nuclei

Fig. 1 (intestine, monkey), x 640; Fig. 2 (intestine, monkey), x 640; Fig. 3, (uterus, human), x 160; Fig. 4 (uterus, human), x 640.

bundles of smooth muscle cells. Connective tissue can be distinguished from the muscle in several ways: Smooth muscle cells are regularly oriented, but the connective tissue fibers are arranged in a somewhat irregular and wavy pattern; the nuclei of the smooth muscle cells have essentially the same shape in a particular bundle, the nuclei of the connective tissue cells, on the other hand, present a variety of shapes; the muscle cytoplasm stains more intensely than the connective tissue fibers; and finally, when examining smooth muscle, one sees a characteristic number of nuclei per unit area of tissue.

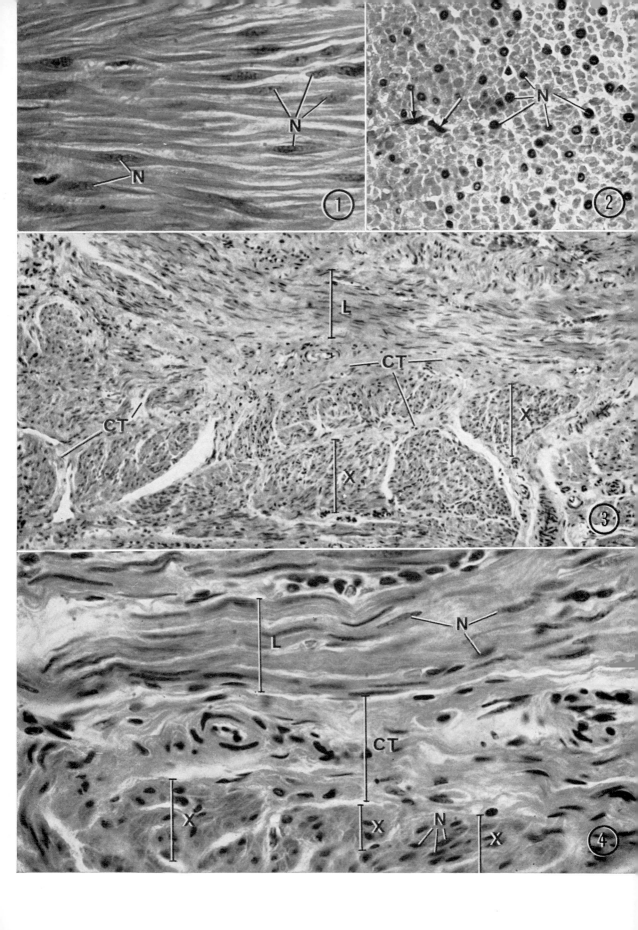

Plate 17. STRIATED MUSCLE

Longitudinally sectioned striated muscle is shown in Figure 1. The fibers are oriented vertically in the illustration. The cross striations are the bands which appear at right angles to the long axis of the fibers. They are the most striking feature of striated muscle when viewed through the microscope. (The visualization of cross striations may be enhanced by reducing the diameter of the condenser diaphragm.) Although the individual myofibrils are not conspicuous, the suggestion that longitudinal subunits exist is obtained in many places where the myofibrils are slightly out of register. Between the muscle fibers is a small amount of delicate connective tissue, called *endomysium.* This contains an extensive capillary network which travels lengthwise, between the muscle fibers. During maximal muscular activity, the capillaries are all patent; in a less active state, only some are patent at a particular time. The capillary walls are not evident, but the closely packed red blood cells are evident (**arrows**). In fact, the arrangement of blood cells in this slide serves as an indication as to the location of the capillaries.

Striated muscle cells are multinucleated. The nuclei (**N**) of the striated muscle cells are seen advantageously in Figure 2. The nuclei appear as the elongated structures at the edge of the fiber. In some cases, when they are viewed face down, the nuclei appear to be in the center of the cell. Although the cross striations are conspicuous, the longitudinal myofibrils are not clearly delineated, and only in some places are there suggestions of longitudinal subunits. Delicate connective tissue, endomysium (**CT**), is between the fibers; the blood vessels are not evident in this illustration.

A cross section of striated muscle is shown in Figure 3. The fibers appear as polygonal profiles of eosinophilic areas. The cut ends of the myofibrils (also called sarcostyles) give the cut surface a stippled appearance. In many fibers, clefts separate groups of myofibrils into distinct areas called *Cohnheim's fields.* The clefts are now regarded as artifacts and little significance is attached to the Cohnheim's

---

KEY

CT, connective tissue
N, nuclei
arrows, red blood cells in capillaries
arrowheads, sarcolemma
Fig. 1, x 400; Fig. 2, x 640; Fig. 3, x 640.

---

fields. The peripheral location of the nuclei (**N**) is well displayed in cross sections. The sarcolemma (**arrowheads**) appears as the thin line which surrounds the fiber. Separation has occurred between some of the muscle fibers. This reveals the delicate connective tissue (**CT**) which constitutes the endomysium.

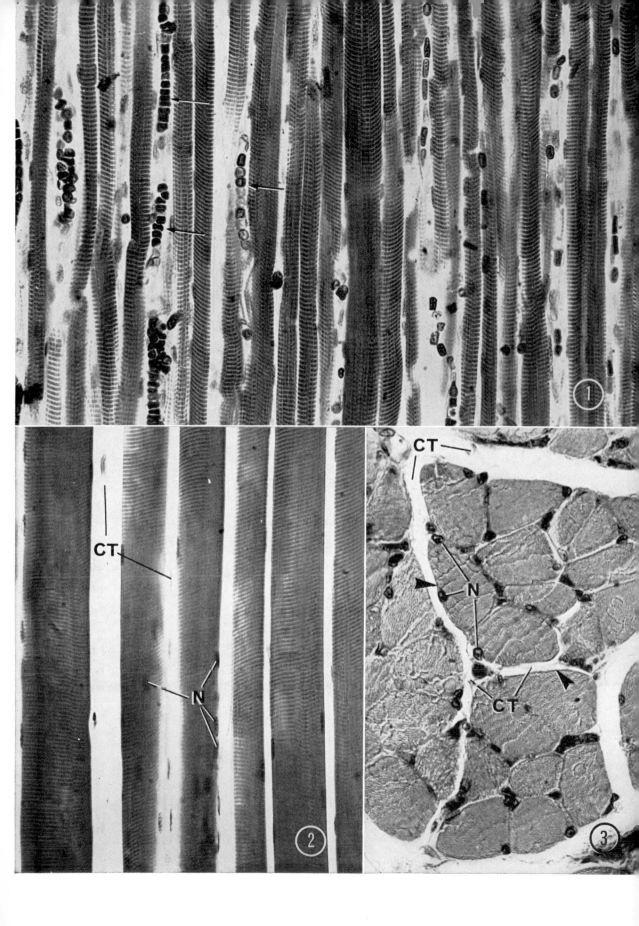

Plate 18. CARDIAC MUSCLE I

A section of cardiac muscle is shown in Figure 1. Most of the fibers are cut longitudinally (**L**), however some are cut obliquely (**X**). The branching nature of cardiac muscle is readily evident in this figure (**arrows**). The nuclei are located in the center of the fibers. This is evident not only where the fibers have been cut longitudinally but also where they are cut obliquely or in cross section. Between the fibers are many small nuclei which belong to connective tissue cells (**CT**), or cells which make up the blood vessels (**BV**).

The cross striations and intercalated discs can be seen if longitudinal sections of cardiac muscle are examined at higher magnification (Fig. 2). The intercalated discs (**ID**) appear as the dense bands. Intercalated discs are not always evident in H & E preparations. They are frequently difficult to see in human specimens. The discs represent thickened opposing cell membranes. In this respect, cardiac muscle fibers differ significantly from striated muscle fibers. The cardiac muscle fibers are end to end alignments of cells; each striated muscle fiber, on the other hand, is a single protoplasmic unit. The myofibrils appear as the longitudinal subunits.

Figure 3 shows cardiac muscle cut in cross section. The field shows the cross-sectioned muscle fibers and connective tissue between the fibers. The muscle fibers have irregular profiles because of the branching that is characteristic of this muscle. A small blood vessel (**BV**) crosses the upper half of the field.

The myofibrils can be seen in cross sections if the magnification is sufficiently high as in Figure 4. They appear as the small eosinophilic bodies which give the cut edge of the muscle fiber a stippled appearance.

KEY

BV, blood vessel
CT, connective tissue
ID, intercalated discs
L, longitudinally sectioned fibers
X, obliquely sectioned fibers
arrows, branching of cardiac muscle fibers

Fig. 1 (human), x 160; Fig. 2 (dog), x 640; Fig. 3 (human), x 160; Fig. 4 (human), x 640.

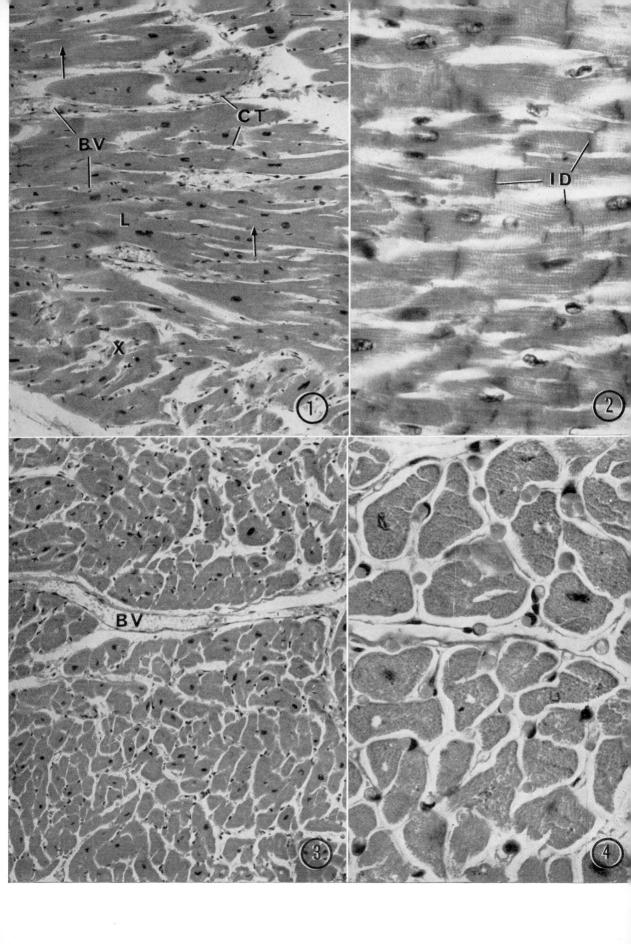

Plate 19. CARDIAC MUSCLE II

Some of the muscle cells within the heart are specialized to conduct impulses from the AV node through the ventricular septum and into the ventricles. These are the *Purkinje fibers.* Within the ventricular septum, they are grouped into a bundle, the AV bundle. This quickly branches into two main components, one going into each ventricle.

A cross section through cardiac muscle and Purkinje fibers is shown in Figure 1. This is a relatively low-power view and the cardiac muscle fibers (**CM**) appear small. They are grouped at the periphery of the figure. The Purkinje fibers are in the center of the field. Connective tissue (**CT**) separates groups of Purkinje fibers from each other and from the cardiac muscle. Some small blood vessels (**BV**) are within the connective tissue.

The arrangement of Purkinje fibers is seen more advantageously at higher magnification (Fig. 2). They are arranged as groups of four or five fibers which are in intimate contact. These groups of Purkinje fibers are separated by connective tissue from other similar groups. The boundaries between the individual Purkinje fibers are not clear in most of the bundles that are shown in Figure 2, however, in some cases they are marked by small clefts and are indicated by arrows. A nucleus (**N**) of a Purkinje cell is shown. Between the bundles of the Purkinje fibers is delicate connective tissue (**CT**). The cytoplasm of a Purkinje cell contains large amounts of glycogen. The glycogen rich areas (**G**) appear homogenous and frequently occupy the center portion of the fiber. The myofibrils (**M**) are located at the periphery of the cell and have a stippled appearance.

A longitudinal section through Purkinje fibers is shown in Figure 3. The Purkinje fibers resemble swollen cardiac muscle cells and the myofibrils appear as the longitudinal subunits. The nuclei are in the homogeneous, glycogen-rich part of the cell.

KEY

BV, blood vessels
CM, cardiac muscle fibers
CT, connective tissue
G, glycogen rich areas
M, myofibrils,
N, nucleus of Purkinje cell
arrows, clefts between Purkinje cells

Fig. 1 (sheep), x 160; Fig. 2 (sheep), x 400; Fig. 3 (sheep), x 400.

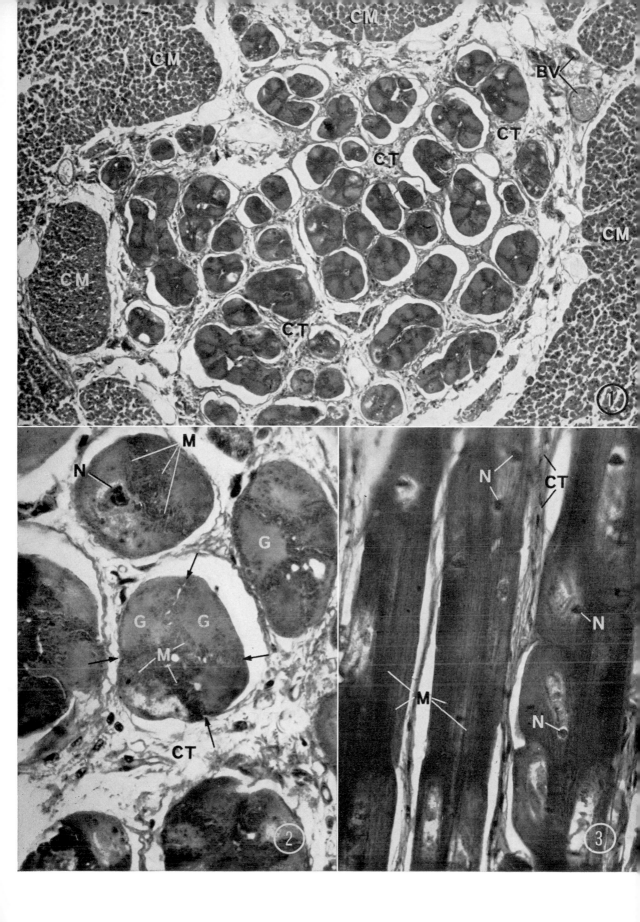

NERVOUS SYSTEM

THE STRUCTURAL UNIT of the nervous system is the neuron or nerve cell. These cells are specialized to conduct impulses. Neurons vary greatly in shape in different parts of the nervous system. All of them, however, contain a cell body and cytoplasmic processes.

The cell body (*perikaryon*) is the part of the neuron which contains the nucleus. In many cases the cell body is extremely large. The processes are the cell specializations which are associated with the conduction of impulses. Two kinds of processes exist: *dendrites* and *axons*. The dendrite is defined as the process which conducts impulses toward the cell body. The axon conducts the impulse away from the cell body. Each neuron has only one axon. The term "fiber" is applied to any long process, whether it be an axon or a dendrite. From a practical standpoint the term "fiber" is most useful since in many instances one cannot distinguish histologically between axons and dendrites. (In referring to the constituents of nerves, the terms axon and nerve fiber are often used interchangeably, despite the fact that some of the fibers may be peripheral processes of sensory neurons. It should be noted that the peripheral process of a sensory neuron is often classified as a dendrite because it conducts impulses toward the cell body.)

Within the central nervous system, cell bodies are found in grey matter. The fibers are found both in the grey matter, and in the white matter. In many parts of the white matter the fibers are grouped and form discrete bundles whose origin and destination are known. In this case they are referred to as *tracts*. This is especially true in the spinal cord. The supporting cells, throughout the central nervous system, are called neuroglia. Three kinds of neuroglia are present: astrocytes, oligodendrocytes, and microglia. Microglial cells are capable of phagocytic activity. They probably develop from mesoderm. Astrocytes and oligodendrocytes are spoken of as supporting cells; however, they should not be thought of as providing only structural support, but rather as participating also in cooperative metabolic functions. The cells which line the cavity of the central nervous system are epithelial-like and are called *ependyma*. All of these cells, except the microglia, develop from the ectoderm.

Within the peripheral nervous system, cell bodies are located in *ganglia*; the nerve fibers constitute the conducting components of the nerves. The fibers are surrounded by a thin cellular tube called the *neurilemma* or *Schwann cell*. It is also called the *Sheath of Schwann*. In most cases, the cell membrane of the Schwann cell is modified to form an additional cover of the nerve fiber called *myelin*. Nerve fibers which have such a cover are referred to as *myelinated;* fibers without a myelin cover are called *nonmyelinated* (fibers that go to the viscera are nonmyelinated). Although the myelin is an extension of the Schwann cell, it consists of layers of cell membrane wrapped around the fiber. The term "Schwann cell" or "Sheath of Schwann" is meant to indicate the cytoplasmic part of the cell that is external to the myelin. In forming the cellular tube that surrounds the nerve fiber, each Schwann cell (and its myelin) covers a segment of the nerve fiber. The place where adjacent Schwann cells meet is called the *node of Ranvier.*

Plate 20. Sympathetic Ganglion

Sympathetic ganglia are peripheral motor ganglia which contain cell bodies of neurons (post-synaptic neurons) that conduct impulses to smooth muscle, cardiac muscle, and glands. Figure 1 is a low magnification view of a sympathetic ganglion "stained" by a silver method. Numerous cell bodies (ganglion cells) (**CB**) and bundles of nerve fibers (**F**) are seen. In addition, some blood vessels (**BV**) and connective tissue (**CT**) are evident. The area enclosed within the **rectangle** includes a cell body which is shown at higher magnification in Figure 2.

The cell bodies in the ganglion appear as relatively large spherical structures. Because of their size, the nucleus may not always be included in the section. The nucleus (**N**) that is shown in Figure 2 is large, spherical, and pale staining. The nucleolus appears as the smaller spherical body within the nucleus. The cytoplasm of this cell body contains a black deposit. This is due to a yellow pigment, lipofuchsin (**L**), which blackens in silver preparations. The lipofuchsin can also be seen in many of the cell bodies that are shown in Figure 1. Other components of the cytoplasm (Golgi, mitochondria, and Nissl bodies) are not evident in these preparations because they each require special methods for their demonstration. The neuron in Figure 2 shows a number of processes (**P**) connected to the cell body. These neurons are designated as multipolar neurons because many processes join to the cell body.

As noted above, numerous bundles of fibers are also demonstrated in the silver preparation (Fig. 1). They appear as the dark, threadlike structures (**F**). Although in this specimen it is not possible to distinguish the nerve fibers from the connective tissue fibers, most of them are actually nerve fibers, and one can conclude with a reasonable degree of assurance, that those fibers that are organized as discrete bundles are nerve fibers.

Figure 3 is an H & E preparation from the same block of tissue as seen in Figures 1 and 2, but with several sections removed. The cell bodies (**CB**), some with nuclei and nucleoli, are clearly seen. The dark structures which

KEY

BV, blood vessel
CB, cell body
CT, connective tissue
F, nerve fiber longitudinal section
F¹, nerve fiber cross section
L, lipofuchsin
N, nucleus
P, process

Fig. 1 (human), x 160; Fig. 2 (human), x 640; Fig. 3 (human), x 160.

are in the immediate vicinity of the cell bodies (Fig. 3) are nuclei of supporting cells. These will be seen to greater advantage in Plate 21. Supporting cells are also associated with the nerve fibers. The nuclei of these supporting cells stain with hematoxylin in an H & E preparation and give the bundles of nerve fibers a slightly different appearance from those of the silver preparation. When a bundle of fibers is cut longitudinally (**F**), and stained with H & E, the nuclei of the supporting cells appear elongated in the same direction as the fibers. When the nerve bundles are cut in cross section (**F¹**), the nuclei of supporting cells appear spherical. The nuclei of supporting cells are not evident in the silver preparation that is shown in Figure 1.

It should be noted that the multipolar nature of these ganglion cells is readily determined in the silver preparation, but not in the H & E preparation and one is hard pressed to find several processes joined to a cell body in an H & E preparation.

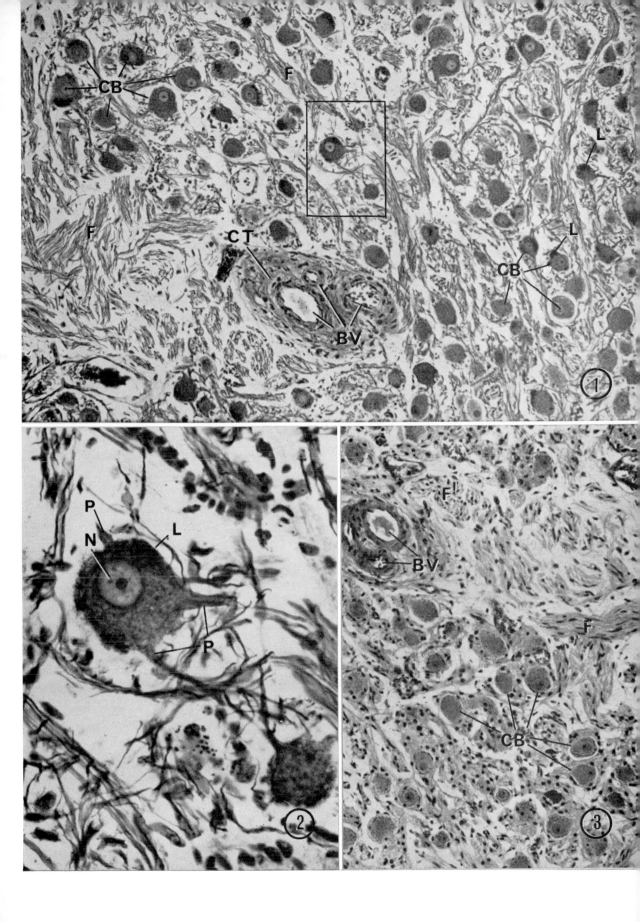

Plate 21. Dorsal Root Ganglion

Dorsal root ganglia differ from autonomic ganglia in a number of ways. Whereas autonomic ganglia contain multipolar neurons and have motor synaptic connections, dorsal root ganglia contain unipolar neurons, are sensory, and have no synaptic connections.

Figure 1 shows a dorsal root ganglion and the nerve root (**NR**) at low power. Even at this magnification it is possible to identify the cell bodies (ganglion cells) (**CB**) which appear as the large spherical structures in the upper part of the figure. Surrounding the ganglion and nerve root is loose connective tissue (**CT**) and blood vessels (**BV**).

A higher magnification of the ganglion is shown in Figure 2. Frequently the ganglion cells are arranged so that rows of cell bodies are separated by bundles of fibers (**NF**). While this may not be a rigid feature, when evident, it often aids in distinguishing dorsal root ganglia from autonomic ganglia. The cell bodies are generally spherical in shape. They also contain a large spherical nucleus. The nuclei are pale staining and usually show a densely staining round nucleolus. Many of the cell bodies are cut in such a plane that the nucleus and nucleolus are not included in the section. Again, the cytoplasmic organelles (Golgi, mitochondria, Nissl) are not revealed in routine H & E preparations.

Figure 3 is an enlargement of the rectangle in Figure 2. A cell body is shown with a large spherical nucleus (**N**) and its darkly staining nucleolus (**Nl**). Surrounding the cell body are nuclei of supporting cells which are called *satellite cells* (**SC**). These nuclei are much smaller than the nuclei of nerve cells. The cytoplasm of satellite cells is usually not well delineated, so that the boundary between the satellite cell and the nerve cell cannot be identified. Other cells immediately beyond the satellite cells have elongated nuclei; these belong to *capsule cells* (**CC**).

In Figure 3, the large **arrowheads** show the central nerve fiber, the small **arrows** show the neurilemma or where it should be. The clear region in between was occupied by myelin.

Dorsal root ganglion cells are designated unipolar neurons because only one process joins the cell body. The axon and dendrite unite just before joining the cell body. It is, however, extremely difficult to find the point where the cell body and process join. During early development the processes join the cell body separately. Because of this, the designation pseudo-unipolar is sometimes used for these neurons.

KEY

BV, blood vessels
CB, cell body
CC, capsule cells
CT, connective tissue
N, nucleus
Nl, nucleolus
NF, nerve fibers
NR, nerve root
SC, satellite cells
arrows, neurilemma
arrowheads, nerve fiber

Fig. 1 (cat), x 40; Fig. 2 (cat), x 160; Fig 3 (cat), x 640.

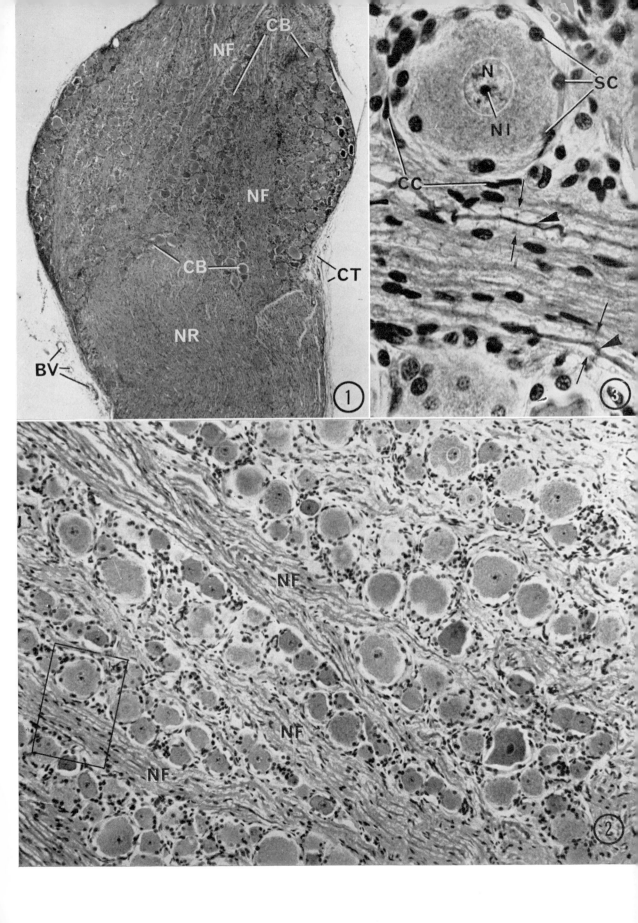

Plate 22. PERIPHERAL NERVE

Nerves are comprised of bundles of nerve fibers held together by connective tissue. The conducting component of the nerve is the nerve fiber. It may be an axon of a motor neuron or a dendrite of a sensory neuron. The nerve fibers are surrounded by a cellular tube called the neurilemma, or Sheath of Schwann. They may be myelinated or non-myelinated. The myelin, if present, is immediately around the nerve fiber, and surrounded by the neurilemma. The connective tissue that binds the nerve fibers together is designated as endoneurium, perineurium, and epineurium. *Endoneurium* consists of the delicate connective tissue which separates individual nerve fibers and their covers. The *perineurium* forms a sheath which surrounds a bundle of nerve fibers and its endoneurium. The *epineurium* separates and surrounds the perineurial bundles.

A cross section through a femoral nerve is shown in Figure 1. The nerve fibers are grouped in bundles (**NFB**) of different size. Epineurium (**Epn**) separates and surrounds the different bundles. It contains some fat cells and blood vessels (**BV**), and is surrounded by adipose tissue (**AT**) in which are larger blood vessels. The perineurium (**Pn**) is thin in the specimen that is illustrated in Figure 1. The bundles of nerve fibers have separated somewhat from the perineurial sheath, causing a space to appear between the nerve fibers and its perineurium; this is a common occurrence in sections of nerves. The nerve fibers appear wavy, and in the section, some are cut in cross section, whereas others are cut longitudinally or obliquely.

The area that is marked by the rectangle in Figure 1 is examined at higher magnification in Figure 2. The nerve fiber (**F**) occupies a central position; it is surrounded by the myelin space (**M**). Most of the myelin is lost during the preparation of the tissue and that which remains appears as radiations which extend from the fibers to the neurilemma. The Sheath of Schwann appears as the thin ring which surrounds the remains of the myelin. In some cases the nucleus (**arrows**) of the Schwann cell is included in the section.

This appears as the dark-staining thick portion of the neurilemmal sheath. When the fiber and its covers are sectioned longitudinally, the same relationship of fiber (**F**), myelin (**M**), and neurilemma (**SS**) is to be seen, except that these appear as parallel tracts.

The endoneurium can be seen in some places. It appears as the delicate strands between the nerve fibers. The nuclei (**arrowheads**) of some endoneurial cells are also evident. Small blood vessels are frequently seen in the endoneurium.

56

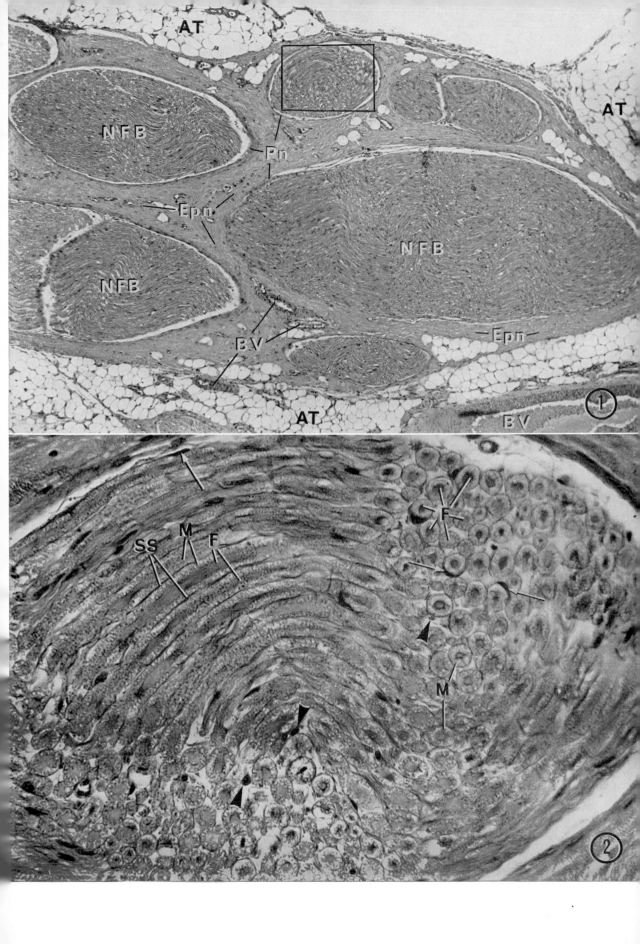

Plate 23. CEREBRUM

The cerebral cortex is described as containing six distinguishable layers. No sharp boundaries separate these layers, rather, they are distinguished on the basis of predominance of cell type and fiber (axons and dendrites) arrangement. While the various layers can be recognized in H & E preparations, these preparations do not provide information regarding the fiber arrangement.

Figure 1 is a low power view of the cerebral cortex and includes a small amount of white matter below the lowest broken line. At a glance, it is possible to recognize the two areas, inasmuch as the white matter contains many more nuclei than the cortex, and in addition, they are all of approximately the same size. These are nuclei of neuroglial cells (**NN**) and are shown at higher magnification in Figure 5. Figure 5 also shows that the cytoplasm of the neuroglial cells is not distinguishable and these cells appear as naked nuclei in a "no man's land," referred to as the neuropil (**Np**). Small blood vessels (**BV**) are also evident in the white matter.

The six layers of the cortex are marked in Figure 1, and are best seen on the right side of the figure. None of these layers is sharply delineated; the horizontal lines represent only rough approximations. From the surface, the layers are: (I) The plexiform or molecular layer. This consists largely of fibers, most of which travel parallel to the surface, and relatively few cells. (II) The layer of small pyramidal cells (or outer granular layer). This consists mainly of small cells, many of which have a pyramidal shape. (III) The layer of medium pyramidal cells (or layer of outer pyramidal cells). This layer is not sharply marked from layer II. However, the cells are somewhat larger and possess a typical pyramidal shape. (IV) The granular layer (or inner granular layer). This is characterized by the presence of many small stellate shaped cells (granule cells). (V) The layer of large pyramidal cells (or inner layer of pyramidal cells). This layer contains pyramidal cells which, in many parts of the cerebrum, are smaller than the pyramidal cells of layer III, but which, in the motor area, are extremely large

KEY

BV, blood vessel
Cap, capillary
NN, neuroglial cell nuclei
Np, neuropil
PC, pyramidal cell
Pol C, polymorphic cell body
arrow, cytoplasm of neuron

Fig. 1 (human), x 65; Figs. 2–5 (human), x 640.

and referred to as Betz cells. (VI) The layer of polymorphic cells. This layer contains cells with diverse shapes, many of which have a spindle or fusiform shape. These cells are called fusiform cells.

Three cell types have been referred to above: pyramidal cells, stellate cells (or granule cells), and fusiform cells. Two other cell types are also present in the cerebral cortex, but not illustrated. They are the horizontal cells of Cajal, which are present only in layer I and send their processes laterally, and cells of Martinotti, which send their axons toward the surface (opposite to that of pyramidal cells).

Layer 1 is illustrated at higher magnification in Figure 2 and reveals a blood capillary (**Cap**) and several nuclei. Most of these nuclei belong to neuroglial cells (**NN**). This conclusion is based on the fact that the cytoplasm belonging to these nuclei cannot be distinguished. One nucleus, however, is surrounded by cytoplasm (**arrow**) and is thus identified as part of a neuron cell body.

The rectangle in Figure 1 is examined at higher magnification in Figure 3. The pyramidal cells (**PC**) contain an oval nucleus in which is located a small intensely staining round nucleolus. The cytoplasmic limits of the cell body appear roughly triangular. The base of the cell faces the white matter and sends a single axon in that direction. This process, however, is not evident. The apex of each cell body shows a large dendritic process that extends toward the surface of the gray matter.

Figure 4 shows the small polymorphic cell bodies (**Pol C**) of layer VI and, again, neuroglial nuclei (**NN**).

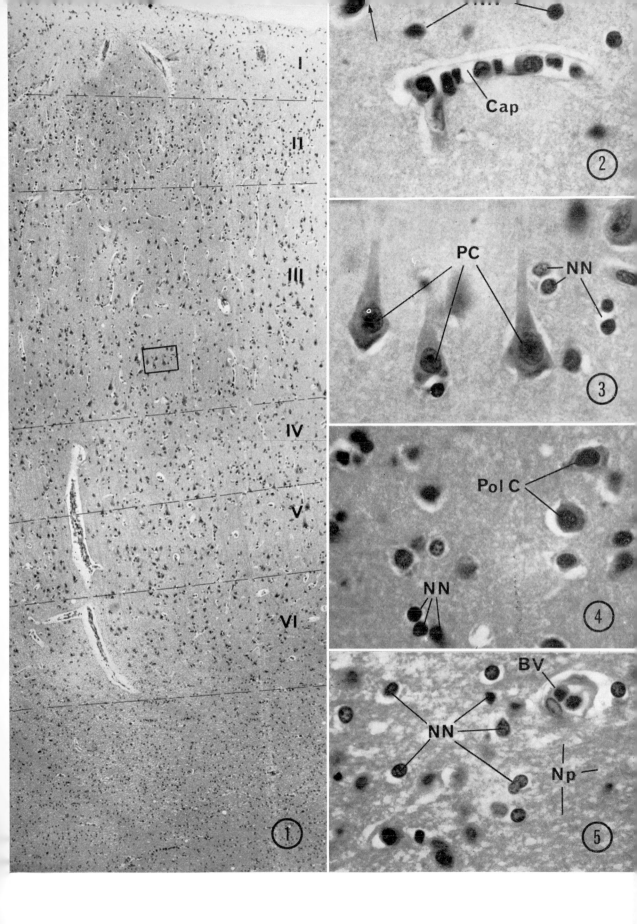

Plate 24. CEREBELLUM

The cerebellar cortex is more or less the same in appearance, regardless of which region is examined. Figures 1 and 2 are low power views of the cerebellum stained by H & E and toluidine blue, respectively. In both, the cortex can be seen to consist of an outer region, the *molecular layer* (**Mol**) (or plexiform layer), and an inner region, the *granular layer* (**Gr**). At the junction between the two are the large *Purkinje cells* (**Pkj**) which are characteristic of the cerebellum.

The rectangle in Figure 1 is examined at higher magnification in Figure 3. This shows the Purkinje cells between the molecular and granular layers. The cells of the molecular layer are widely spaced; in contrast, the cells of the granular layer are closely packed and result in the intensity of staining of this layer. The fibrous cover on the cerebellar surface is the pia mater (**Pia**). Some blood vessels (**BV**) can be seen in this layer. The white matter (**WM**), stains differently in the two preparations. Its fibrous nature can be recognized in Figure 1, due to the light staining with eosin.

The Purkinje cells are large flask-shaped cells with extensively branched dendrites that extend into the molecular layer. A suggestion of the dendritic branching is obtained in the silver preparation (Fig. 5). A large nucleus with its nucleolus is evident in each cell body of the H & E preparation (Figs. 3 and 4). The Purkinje cell sends its axon through the granular layer into the white matter. This is not revealed in these illustrations.

Several cell types are found in the molecular layer. Some of these are *basket cells* (**BC**). These characteristically show a small amount of cytoplasm around the nucleus. Basket cells have both axons and dendrites in the molecular layer. The axons travel parallel to the plane of the Purkinje layer and send basket-like nets around the cell bodies of a number of adjacent Purkinje cells. Some of these are probably among the fibers (**F**) that are shown in Figure 5. The molecular layer also contains *stellate cells* near the cerebellar surface, but they are not evident here. The processes of the stellate

KEY

BC, basket cells
BV, blood vessel
F, fibers
G, Golgi II cell
Gr, granular layer
Mol, molecular layer
Pia, pia mater
Pkj, Purkinje cells
WM, white matter
arrows, glomeruli

Fig. 1 (human), x 40; Fig. 2 (human), x 40; Fig. 3 (human), x 160; Fig. 4 (human), x 400; Fig. 5 (cat), x 160.

cells remain in the vicinity of the cell body.

As noted previously, the granular layer contains numerous small cells called *granule cells*. They appear as the numerous small dark bodies. Granule cells receive incoming impulses from other parts of the central nervous system. They send axons into the molecular layer where they branch in the form of a T so that the axons contact the dendrites of several Purkinje cells. The granular layer shows clear areas, called *glomeruli* (**arrows**), which are among the places where incoming fibers contact granule cells. Only the glomeruli are evident; the details of fiber connection are not. The granular layer also contains another cell type, the *Golgi type II* cell (**G**). These are larger than the granule cells (Figs. 3 and 4). They have dendrites in the molecular layer and extensively branching axons in the granular layer. The cell bodies are usually near the Purkinje layer.

It should be emphasized that the details of fiber pathways and connections cannot be ascertained by examination of isolated unrelated sections. Only the location and some characteristics of the cell body can be learned from such sections. Fiber pathway and connection can only be established by a combination of experimental and special staining methods.

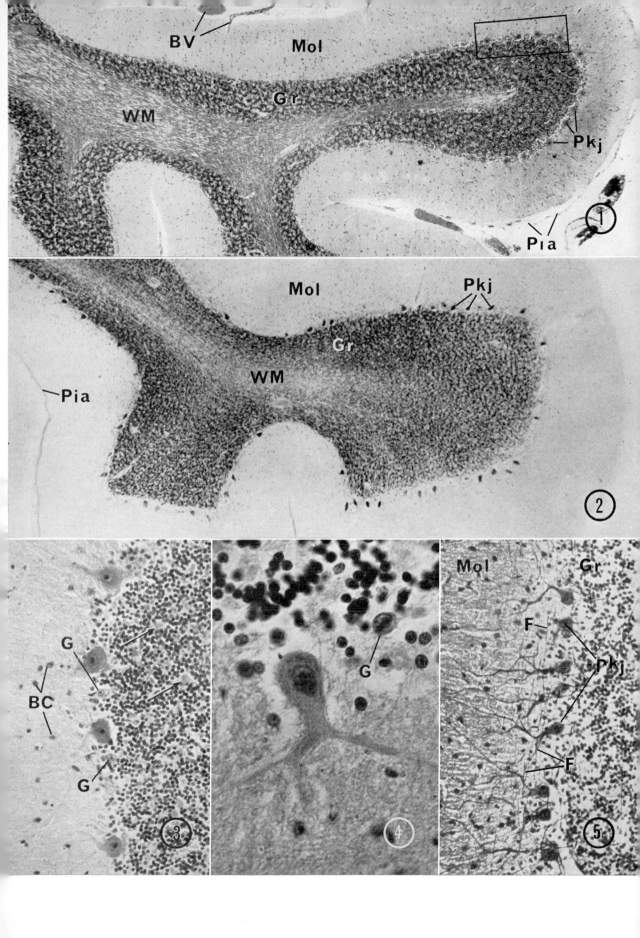

Plate 25. SPINAL CORD

The spinal cord is organized into two discrete parts. The outer part contains ascending and descending nerve fibers. This constitutes the white matter of the cord. The inner part contains cell bodies of neurons and nerve fibers. This is the grey matter of the spinal cord. Neuroglial cells are in both the white matter and the grey matter.

A cross section through the cervical region of the spinal cord (human) is shown in Figure 1. The preparation is designed to stain the myelin which surrounds the ascending and descending fibers. Although the fibers which have common origins and destinations in the physiological sense are arranged in tracts, these tracts cannot be distinguished unless they have been marked by special techniques such as causing injury to the cell bodies from which they arise.

The grey matter of the spinal cord appears roughly in the form of an H. The anterior and posterior prongs are referred to as anterior horns (**AH**) and posterior horns (**PH**), respectively. The connecting bar is called the grey commissure (**GC**). The neuron cell bodies that are within the anterior horns (anterior horn cells) are so large that they can be seen even at extremely low magnifications (**arrows**). The pale-staining fibrous material which surrounds the spinal cord is the pia mater (**Pia**). It follows the surface of the spinal cord intimately and dips into the large ventral fissure (**VF**) and into the shallower sulci. Blood vessels are present in the pia mater. Some ventral (**VR**) and dorsal (**DR**) roots of the spinal nerves are included in the section.

An H & E preparation of the spinal cord is shown in Figure. 2. The nucleus (**N**) of the anterior horn cell appears as the large spherical pale-staining structure within the cell body. It contains a spherical, intensely staining nucleolus. The anterior horn cell contains many processes, two of which are seen in Figure. 2. The illustration also shows a number of other nuclei (**NN**) which belong to neuroglial cells. The cytoplasm of these cells is not evident. The remainder of the field consists of nerve fibers and neuroglial cell cytoplasm whose organization is hard to

KEY

AH, anterior (ventral) horn
DR, dorsal roots
GC, grey commissure
N, nucleus of anterior horn cell
NB, Nissl bodies
NN, nuclei of neuroglial cells
Np, neuropil
PH, posterior (dorsal) horn
Pia, pia mater
VF, ventral fissure
VR, ventral roots
arrows, cell bodies of anterior (ventral) horn cells
Fig. 1 (human), x 16; Fig. 2 (human), x 640; Fig. 3 (human), x 640.

interpret. This is called the neuropil (**Np**). A capillary crosses through the field below the cell body.

A toluidine blue preparation of the spinal cord (a comparable area to that of Fig. 2) is shown in Figure 3. This stains the Nissl bodies (**NB**) which appear as the large, dark-staining bodies in the cytoplasm. Nissl bodies do not extend into the axon hillock. (The axon leaves the cell body at the axon hillock.) The nuclei (**NN**) of neuroglial cells are evident, the cytoplasm is not. The neuropil stains very faintly.

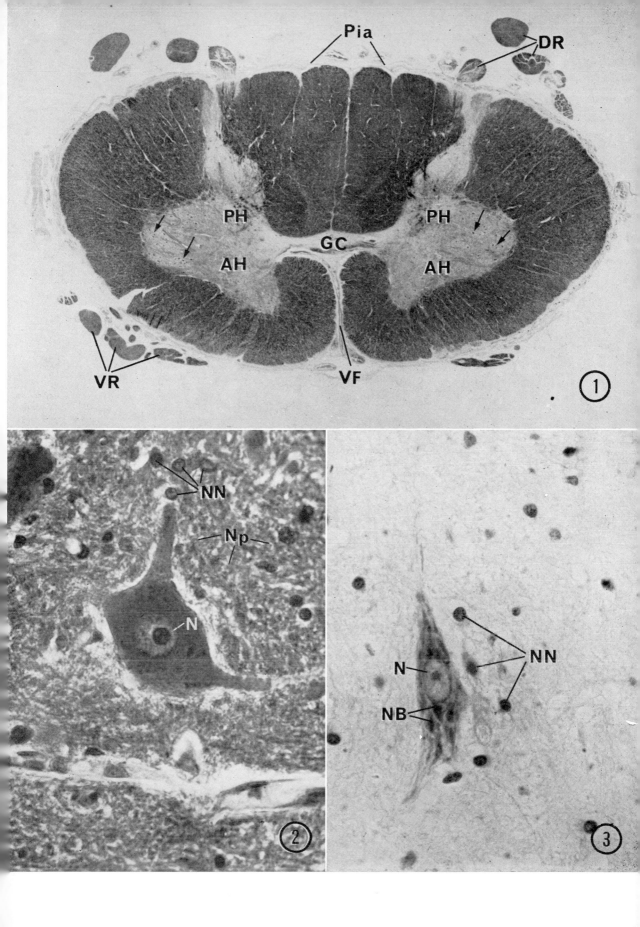

CARDIOVASCULAR SYSTEM

THE CARDIOVASCULAR SYSTEM consists of the blood vessels, through which blood flows, and the heart, which pumps the blood. Arteries conduct blood away from the heart; veins return blood to the heart. Capillaries join the arterial system to the venous system; however, arteriovenous shunts which bypass capillaries, also exist. An additional set of vessels, the lymphatic vessels, help to return protein and other large material from the tissue spaces.

The wall of the heart contains a large amount of muscle, the contraction of which forces blood into the arteries at high pressure. The pressure is dissipated so that in vessels returning to the heart it is very low. In the capillaries, the pressure is such that it favors the passage of materials through the vessel wall. In reference to the passage of materials it should be noted that the capillary wall is extremely thin. It consists of a single layer of squamous epithelium which is arranged as a tube. The epithelium which forms the capillary and which lines the inner surface of the heart, arteries, veins, and lymphatic vessels is called *endothelium.*

The arteries closest to the heart contain a large amount of elastic material and, because of this, they are called elastic arteries. The elastic material enables the vessel wall to be expanded by the blood which is ejected by the heart. The recoil of the expanded vessel during the time that the heart is relaxed contributes somewhat to the movement of blood. It also minimizes the extreme difference between systolic and diastolic pressure which would prevail if there were no elastic material within the arterial wall.

Further along the arterial tree, the elastic tissue is reduced and smooth muscle becomes more predominant. The arteries are then called muscular arteries. After considerable branching and reduction in size, smooth muscle constitutes the bulk of the vascular wall and the vessels are called arterioles.

Arterioles are the major "stopcocks" which serve to shunt blood to one or other of the vascular territories of the body (skin, striated muscle, abdominal viscera, thoracic viscera, etc.). Moreover, arterioles constitute one of the major factors in the maintenance of blood pressure in that they are largely responsible for what is referred to as peripheral resistance.

Veins conduct blood under much lower pressure than is present in the arteries, and the walls of veins are significantly thinner than the walls of the arteries which they accompany. Small veins are called venules.

The lymphatic vessels begin as lymphatic capillaries within connective-tissue spaces. These drain into larger lymphatic vessels, which ultimately open into the veins at the base of the neck. Lymph nodes are placed within the paths of the lymphatic vessels. The fluid within lymphatic vessels is called lymph.

Both veins and lymphatic vessels possess valves which serve to direct blood toward the heart (or lymph toward the large veins). Valves are especially important in the movement of fluid against gravity. It should be noted, however, that the veins of the portal system do not possess valves.

Plate 26. HEART

A section through the wall of the atrium is shown in Figure 1. The outermost part is the *epicardium* (**Epi**); the thick middle portion is the *myocardium* (**Myo**), and the inner part is called the *endocardium* (**Endo**). The myocardium is by far the thickest component. It consists of bundles of cardiac muscle. These do not all travel in the same direction, therefore in most sections cardiac muscle fibers may be cut longitudinally, in cross section, or obliquely. Connective tissue (**CT**) separates the bundles of cardiac muscle. A large amount of connective tissue is in the vicinity of the blood vessel (**BV**) that is in the periphery of the myocardium. The myocardium is considered on pages 46 and 48.

The epicardium (**Epi**) is shown at higher magnification in Figure 2. It is surfaced by mesothelium. Under the mesothelium is the supporting connective tissue (**CT**), the fibrous elements of which are loosely arranged. Elastic fibers are present in the connective tissue; however, they are not evident in routine H & E preparations. A small nerve (**N**) is present in the connective tissue between the muscle bundles. The nerve appears as a bundle of thin wavy fibers which are significantly thinner than the muscle fibers.

The endocardium (**Endo**) is shown at higher magnification in Figure 3. It can be divided into three layers: (**1**) an inner layer, which is comprised of endothelial cells that rest on a subendothelial layer of delicate collagenous fibers; (**2**) a middle layer, which is somewhat thicker and contains not only collagenous fibers, but also smooth muscle cells (**SM**) and elastic fibers (the elastic fibers are not visualized in H & E preparations); and (**3**) an outer layer, which consists of loose connective tissue and is called the subendocardial layer. The subendocardial layer is continuous with the connective tissue of the myocardium. The subendocardial layer contains blood vessels (**BV**), collagenous and elastic fibers, but no smooth muscle.

The ventricles have essentially the same structure as the atria except that the myocardium is much thicker. In addition, the subendocardial layer of the ventricles con-

KEY

BV, blood vessel
CT, connective tissue
Endo, endocardium
Epi, epicardium
Myo, myocardium
N, nerve
SM, smooth muscle
1, endothelium and subendothelial connective tissue
2, middle layer of endocardium
3, subendocardial layer
Fig. 1 (human), x 44; Figs. 2 and 3 (human), x 160.

tains special muscle fibers which belong to the intrinsic conducting system of the heart (Purkinje fibers, see page 48).

The epicardium can be distinguished from endocardium in several ways. The larger blood vessels and nerves that supply the heart wall are in the epicardium; large amounts of adipose tissue are invariably present in the epicardium in the vicinity of the vessels; the endocardium is layered and contains smooth muscle cells; the blood vessels in the endocardium are considerably smaller than the blood vessels of the epicardium; and finally Purkinje fibers may be seen in or near the subendocardial layer of the endocardium.

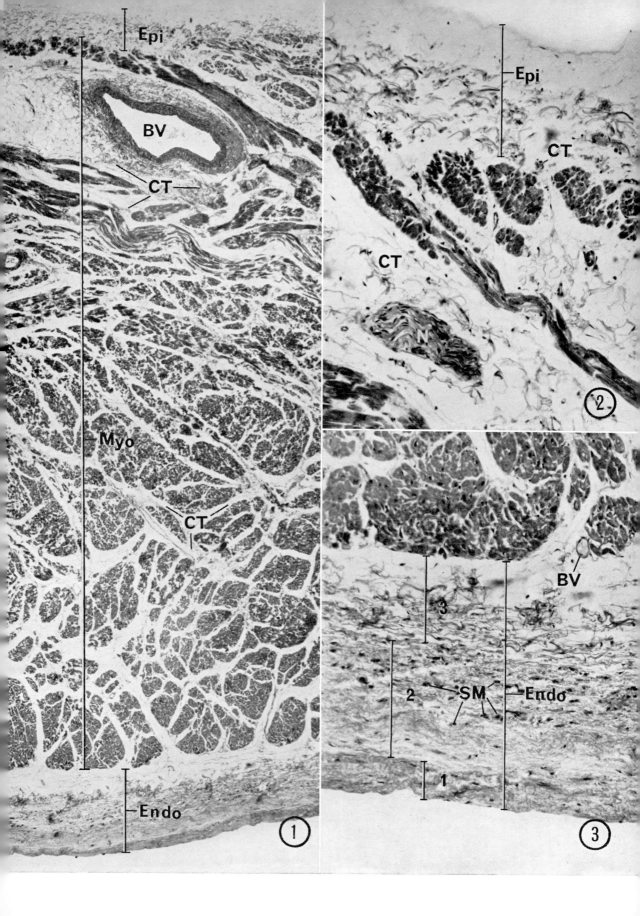

Plate 27. THE AORTA

The aorta is the artery that carries blood away from the left ventricle. Because of the large amount of elastic tissue which it contains, it is referred to as an elastic artery. The elastic tissue, however, is not evident without special preparations (see page 20).

The layers which make up the wall of the aorta are shown in Figure 1. This is a longitudinal section through the entire thickness of the arterial wall near its origin. Three layers can be recognized. They are designated the *tunica intima* (**TI**), *tunica media* (**TM**), and *tunica adventitia* (**TA**). The adventitia is the outermost part. It consists mainly of connective tissue, and contains the blood vessels (**BV**) (vasa vasorum) and nerves (nerva vasorum) (**NV**) which supply the arterial wall.

The tunicae intima and media are shown at high magnification in Figure 2. The tunica intima consists of a lining of endothelial cells (**E**) which rest on a layer of connective tissue (**CT**). Both collagenous and elastic fibers are in the connective tissue. Some smooth muscle cells may also be in the intima of the aorta.

The tunica media contains an abundance of smooth muscle; however, the distinctive feature of the wall is the large amount of elastic material which is also present. The elastic material is present not in the form of fibers, but rather in the form of fenestrated "membranes." The smooth muscle cells are arranged in a closely wound spiral between the elastic membranes. In longitudinal sections through the wall of the aorta, the smooth muscle cells appear to be cut in cross section (inset). Therefore, some cells appear to have a nucleus (**N**) while other cells (**C**) do not appear to have a nucleus. This difference in appearance occurs because muscle cells are of considerable length, and when they are cross-sectioned, the nuclei are not included in every cell.

The smooth muscle cells of the tunica media are particularly evident when the aorta is cut longitudinally as it is in Figures 1 and 2. It should be noted that practically all of the smooth muscle in Figure 1 has been cut in cross section. This indicates that the smooth

KEY

BV, blood vessels
C, cytoplasm of smooth muscle cells
CT, connective tissue
E, endothelium
N, nuclei of smooth muscle cells
NV, nerve (nerva vasorum)
TA, tunica adventitia
TI, tunica intima
TM, tunica media
arrows, area showing longitudinally arranged smooth muscle
Fig. 1 (human), x 65; Fig. 2 (human) x 160; inset (human), x 640.

muscle cells are arranged in a circular fashion (actually a closely wound spiral). In Figure 2 some of the smooth muscle cells have been cut longitudinally, which indicates that they are not arranged in the spiral. This area (**arrows**) is adjacent to the semilunar valve and is not typical of most of the aorta. It should be realized that in a cross section of the aorta, the smooth muscle cells are not as striking as in a longitudinal section, and indeed they may be difficult to distinguish from the connective tissue elements.

Other elastic arteries are the brachiocephalic, the subclavian, the beginning of the common carotid, and the pulmonary arteries. The elastic arteries are also called *conducting arteries.*

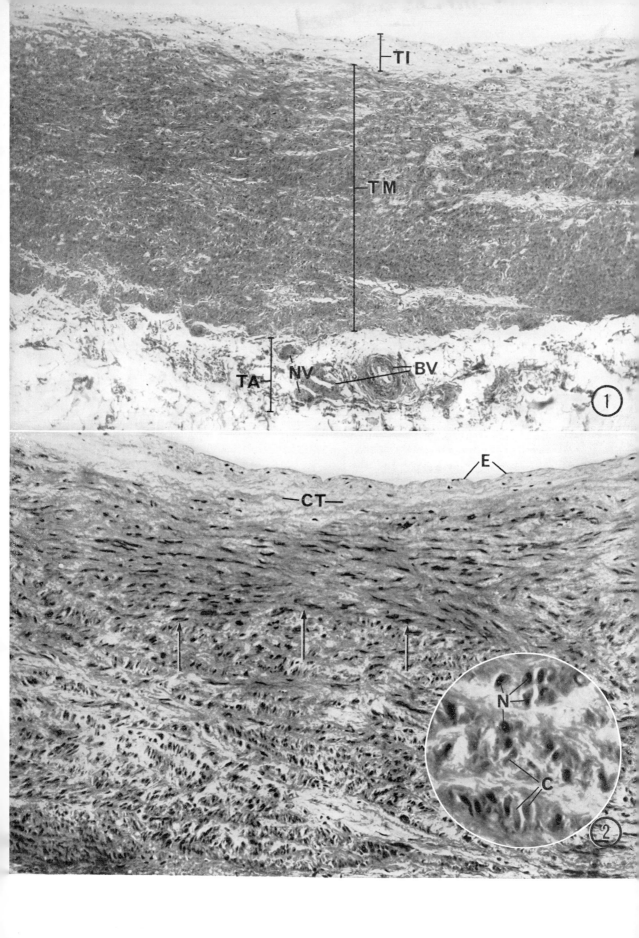

Plate 28. Muscular Arteries and Veins

As the arterial tree is traced further from the heart, the elastic tissue is considerably reduced in amount, the tunica media consists mainly of smooth muscle, and the arteries are called muscular arteries or arteries of medium caliber. A cross section through a muscular artery is shown in Figure 1. Some blood cells are in the lumen. The wall of the artery can be divided into three layers: tunica intima (**TI**), tunica media (**TM**), and tunica adventitia (**TA**). Figure 2 is an enlargement of the rectangle in Figure 1.

The tunica intima is comprised of an endothelial lining [**E(N)**], an extremely small amount of connective tissue, and the internal elastic membrane (**IEM**). The internal elastic membrane has a scalloped appearance and is highly refractile. The connective tissue is extremely scant and the endothelial cells appear to rest directly on the internal elastic membrane. The agonal contraction of the artery causes the internal elastic membrane to assume its scalloped formation and this contracts the endothelial cells so that the endothelial nuclei appear rounded and perched on the internal elastic membrane.

The tunica media consists mainly of circularly arranged smooth muscle cells. The nuclei of the smooth muscle cells [**SM(N)**] are elongated and oriented in the same direction. Their twisted appearance indicates that the smooth muscle cells are in a contracted state. The material between the nuclei is mainly cytoplasm of the muscle cells, however, the cytoplasmic boundaries are not evident. The refractile corkscrew material in the tunica media is elastic material (**EM**). Reticular fibers are also present, but they are not visualized in H & E preparations.

The tunica adventitia (**TA**) consists of connective tissue. The refractile scalloped sheet at the junction of the tunica media and adventitia is the external elastic membrane (**EEM**). The nuclei [**F(N)**] of some fibrocytes can be seen; the cytoplasm of these cells cannot be distinguished from the extracellular material.

The walls of veins which accompany muscular arteries can be divided into tunica in-

KEY

AT, adipose tissue
BV, small blood vessels in surrounding connective tissue
E, endothelium
EEM, external elastic membrane
EM, elastic material
E(N), endothelial nuclei
F(N), fibrocyte nuclei
IEM, internal elastic membrane
SM(N), smooth muscle nuclei
TA, tunica adventitia
TI, tunica intima
TM, tunica media

Fig. 1 (monkey), x 160; Fig. 2 (monkey), x 640; Fig. 3 (monkey), x 65; inset (monkey), x 640.

tima, tunica media, and tunica adventitia. Although there is elastic material in the wall, it is significantly less in amount than in the artery. Figure 3 enables one to compare a muscular artery with its accompanying vein. The lumen of the vein is larger than that of the artery, but the wall is thinner and the vessel frequently appears collapsed or flattened. The tunica intima (**TI**) is extremely thin (inset) and consists of a endothelial (**E**) lining that rests on a small amount of connective tissue. The tunica media (**TM**) is much thinner than that of the artery; the tunica adventitia (**TA**) is thicker. The tunica media consists largely of smooth muscle. The nuclei of the smooth muscle cells [**SM(N)**] are elongated and oriented, but the cytoplasmic boundaries cannot be identified.

The key to identifying a blood vessel that appears alone is that the arteries possess an internal membrane, whereas veins do not.

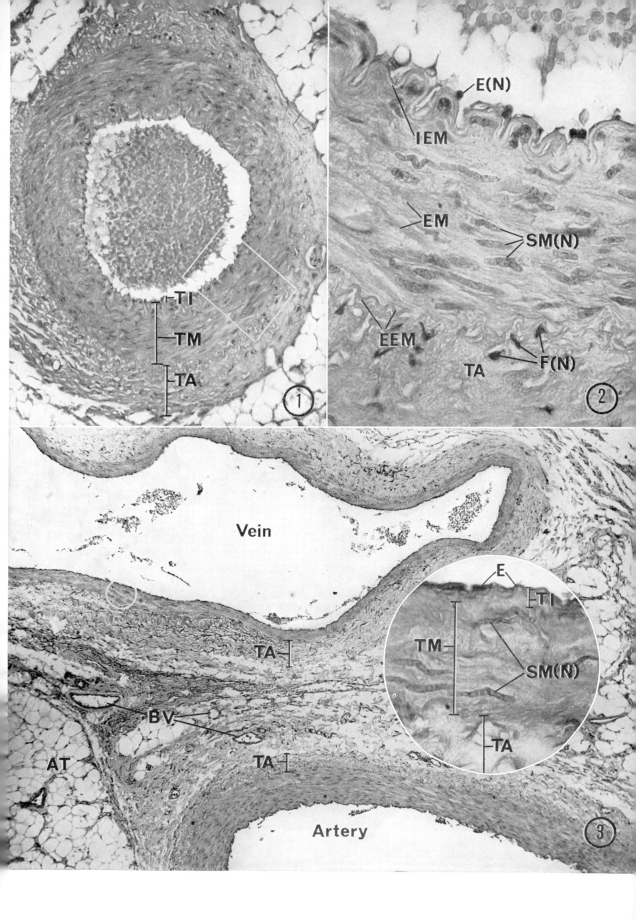

Plate 29. ARTERIOLES AND LYMPHATIC VESSELS

Arterioles. The terminal components of the arterial tree, just before the capillary bed or the arteriovenous shunt, are the arterioles. Arterioles contain an endothelial lining and smooth muscle in the wall. The muscle component is limited in thickness to one or two cells. There may or may not be an internal elastic membrane, according to the size of the vessel.

A longitudinal section through an arteriole is shown in Figure 1. It branches on the right. The elongated nuclei which line the lumen belong to endothelial cells (**arrows**). An elastic membrane cannot be seen. The round nuclei located in the wall of this vessel belong to smooth muscle cells [**SM(N)**] which have been cut in cross section. They should not be confused with cuboidal cells. Figures 2 and 3 show how, by changing the focus of the optical system, one can obtain information relevant to this point. In Figure 2 one sees the elongated nuclei of the endothelial cells *(***arrows***)* as in Figure 1. Round nuclei are aligned in rows in the wall of the vessel. Four nuclei (**A**) are indicated on the left and seven (**B**) on the right. Notice the "shadows" related to the four nuclei on the left. By changing the focus (Fig. 3) one comes to realize that the round appearing nuclei are really elongated nuclei which are wrapped around the vessel wall in a circular fashion. Note how the length of the four nuclei in Figure 3 corresponds to the four nuclear "shadows" that are illustrated in Figure 2.

Lymphatic vessels have extremely thin walls. A lymphatic vessel from the mucosa of the pharynx is shown in Figure 4. It has been cut longitudinally and two valves (**V**) are included in the section. One of the valves is shown at high magnification in Figure 5. The wall of the lymphatic vessel consists of almost nothing but an endothelial lining. The nuclei (**arrows**) of the endothelial cells appear to be exposed to the lumen. This is because the cytoplasm is so attenuated. At the nuclear poles the cytoplasm continues as a thin thread. It is not possible to determine when one endothelial cell ends and the next begins. Connective tissue (**CT**) surrounds the lym-

KEY

A, smooth muscle cell nuclei at different focus levels in Figures 2 and 3
B, smooth muscle cell nuclei at different focus levels in Figures 2 and 3
CT, connective tissue
SM(C), smooth muscle cell cytoplasm
SM(N), smooth muscle cell nuclei
V, valves of lymphatic vessel
arrows, endothelial cell nuclei

Figs. 1–3 (monkey), x 640; Fig. 4 (human), x 160; Fig. 5 (human), x 640.

phatic vessel. Some lymphocytes and precipitated lymph are within the lumen of the vessel. As a general statement, lymphatic vessels possess lumens of very large caliber in comparison to the thickness of the wall.

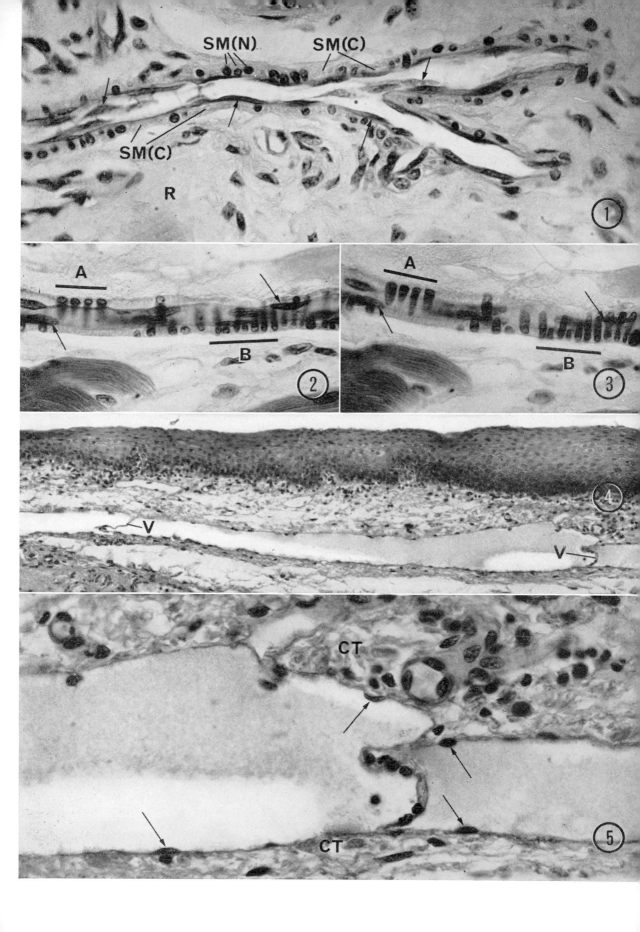

LYMPHATIC TISSUE AND ORGANS

LYMPHATIC TISSUE, or lymphoid tissue, is a modified form of connective tissue characterized by the presence of large numbers of lymphocytes. The lymphocytes are arranged as nodules. In histological sections, the nodules appear as circular or oval formations of closely packed cells, and frequently a lighter center is present. The lighter center is referred to as a germinal center, since this is the region where new lymphocytes are being formed. The germinal center may also be called a secondary nodule, in which case the outer arrangement of cells would be designated a primary nodule. Germinal centers are not evident in newborn animals. Their formation can be induced by subjecting the animal to certain antigens and for this reason they are also referred to as reaction centers.

The stroma of lymphatic tissue consists of reticular fibers and their associated reticular cells. Reticular cells are fixed cells. They are phagocytic; moreover, they retain the potential to become free macrophages, to develop into lymphocytes, or to form new reticular cells.

Lymphatic tissue occurs as dense aggregations of lymphocytes (dense lymphoid tissue) in the tonsils, nodules of the alimentary canal, lymph nodes, the spleen, and the thymus gland. Moreover, lymph nodules may be seen in the various loose connective tissues of the urinary system, digestive system, and respiratory system.

Whereas lymph nodules may be regarded as units of lymphoid tissue, the lymph nodes, spleen, and thymus should be regarded as lymphoid organs. They represent different forms, or degrees, of organization. For example, lymph nodes are placed in the path of lymphatic vessels and therefore come into close contact with the lymph; the spleen is placed in the path of blood vessels and thus it comes into close contact with the blood. The tonsils and other lymph nodules may be looked upon as being in close contact with tissue fluid. The thymus is not related to body fluids in the same manner as lymph nodes or spleen, and it does not respond to circulating antigen in the same manner. This is presumably due to blood tissue barriers, because it does respond if antigen is injected through the capsule directly into the gland.

The mucosa of parts of the alimentary canal and respiratory tract contains a highly cellular lamina propria. Many of the cells within this lamina propria are lymphocytes. However, they are not organized in any characteristic pattern. This highly cellular lamina propria, containing large numbers of lymphocytes, is called diffuse lymphoid tissue.

Plate 30. TONSIL AND LYMPH NODE I

Tonsil. The palatine tonsils (fauceal tonsils) (Fig. 1) consist of dense accumulations of lymphocytes in the mucous membrane of the fauces (the junction of oral cavity and oropharanx). The epithelium (**Ep**) that forms the surface of the tonsil dips into the underlying connective tissue (**CT**) in numerous places forming crypts, the *tonsillar crypts.*

A number of lymph nodules (**LN**) are shown in Figure 1. Each has a *germinal center* (**GC**). Between the nodules are territories which are more or less densely packed with lymphocytes. An epithelial crypt (**arrow**) appears in the center of the illustration. This retains a surface of stratified squamous epithelium. However, in this specimen, and as is often the case, the epithelium is heavily infiltrated with lymphocytes and is difficult to identify. This process of lymphatic invasion of the epithelial surface is illustrated more effectively in Figure 2.

The epithelial surface (**EP**) is clearly evident on the right side of Figure 2 and is easy to distinguish from the underlying connective tissue (**CT**). On the left, however, lymphocytes have invaded the epithelial surface and have obscured the epithelial-connective tissue boundary. The **arrowheads** indicate areas where the base of the epithelium can be recognized.

In addition to the palatine tonsils, similar aggregations of lymphatic tissue are present under the epithelium of the tongue (called *lingual tonsils*) and under the epithelium of the roof of the nasopharanx (called *pharyngeal tonsils*).

Lymph node I. Lymph nodes are small lymphatic organs that are located in the path of lymph vessels; they are exposed to the lymph as it passes through. A panoramic view of a section through a lymph node (Fig. 3) illustrates the following characteristic features. A connective tissue capsule (**Cap**) surrounds the entire mass of lymphoid tissue. Trabeculae extend from the capsule into the substance of the lymph node to form part of the supporting stroma. Part of the surface of the lymph node is slightly concave and contains a hilus (**arrowhead**). At this point, blood

KEY

BV, blood vessels
Cap, capsule
CS, cortical sinus
CT, connective tissue
EP, epithelium
GC, germinal center
LN, lymph node
arrow, tonsilar crypt
arrowhead (Fig. 2), epithelial-connective tissue junction
arrowhead (Fig. 3), hilus of lymph node
Fig. 1 (human), x 40; Fig. 2 (human), x 65; Fig. 3 (monkey), x 40.

vessels (**BV**) enter and leave, and efferent lymphatics leave the lymph node.

The outer part of the lymph node, the *cortex* (Fig. 3), has a greater concentration of cells than the inner part, the *medulla*. Some lymph nodules with germinal centers can be recognized in the cortex (**rectangle**). This area will be examined at higher magnification in Plate 31.

Immediately under the capsule (**Cap**) is an area where there are fewer cells than in the densely packed region of the cortex. This is a lymph sinus which, because of its location, is designated as the *cortical sinus* (**CS**) (or subcapsular sinus). Lymph enters the cortical sinus via afferent vessels, passes through the node and leaves via efferent vessels near or at the hilus.

The medulla contains both cords of lymphocytes and channels of lymph sinuses. The lymph sinuses (also called *medullary sinuses*) appear lighter than the cords of tissue (medullary cords), and communicate with the cortical sinus.

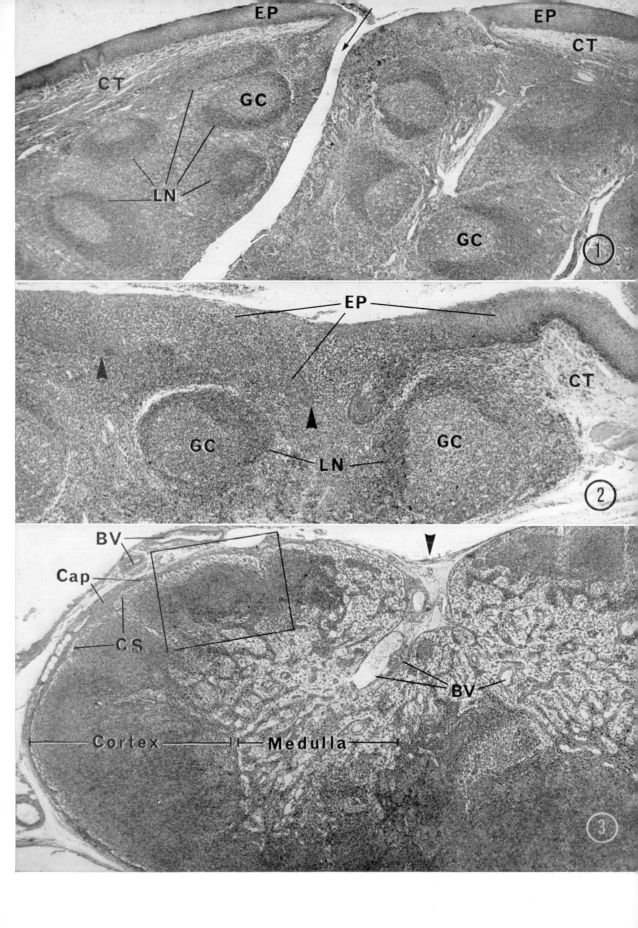

Plate 31. LYMPH NODE II

The cortical region of the lymph node (from rectangle on Plate 30) is examined at higher magnification in Figure 1. A lymph nodule (**LN**) with a germinal center (**GC**) occupies the center of the field. Above this is the cortical sinus (**CS**), and the capsule (**Cap**). A trabeculum (**T**) is shown leaving the capsule to form part of the supporting stroma of the lymph node. The cortical sinus follows the trabeculum into the substance of the lymph node; thus the trabeculum will be separated from the dense aggregation of lymphocytes in the cortex and medulla by a lymph sinus on all sides. **Arrowheads** indicate the sinus on each side of the trabeculum.

The area within the **rectangle** in Figure 1 is examined at higher magnification in Figure 2. It shows the cortical sinus (**CS**), the outer part of the cortex and the capsule (**Cap**). The stroma of the lymph node consists of reticular fibers and their associated reticular cells, and trabeculae. Reticular cells, though present throughout the node, are readily identified in the cortical sinus since, here, they are not obscured by large numbers of lymphocytes. The nuclei of reticular cells (**RC**) are usually elongated and pale staining. A small amount of cytoplasm can be seen immediately surrounding the nucleus, and this sends out cytoplasmic processes which extend beyond the vicinity of the nucleus. Actually the cytoplasmic extensions of reticular cells are wrapped around the delicate reticular fibers and it is not possible in H & E preparations to determine where the reticular cell cytoplasm ends and the fiber begins. Reticular cells are fixed cells. The lymphocytes appear as the free, unattached cells with densely staining nuclei and a thin but evident ring of surrounding cytoplasm. Other cell types such as monocytes are also present in lymphatic tissue, but they are often difficult to identify. Reticular cells are regarded as relatively undifferentiated cells which can transform into other cell types, such as lymphocytes and macrophages. Even though they are fixed and associated with reticular fibers, reticular cells are phagocytic.

Part of the lymph nodule and its germinal

KEY

Cap, capsule
CS, cortical sinus
GC, germinal center
LN, lymph nodule
RC, reticular cells
T, trabeculum
arrowheads (Fig. 1), lymph sinus
arrowheads (Fig. 3), large lymphocytes
white circle, small lymphocytes
black circle, medium-sized lymphocytes

Fig. 1 (monkey), x 170; Figs. 2 and 3 (monkey), x 640.

center are examined at higher magnification in Figure 3. The outer part of the nodule is shown at the top of the figure; the germinal center is at the lower half. At least three types of lymphocytes can be distinguished: (1) Small lymphocytes (**white circle**). These are closely packed at the outer part of the nodule, but are also found throughout the node. They have small nuclei which stain intensely with hematoxylin. (2) Medium-sized lymphocytes (**black circle**). These are the most numerous cell type in the germinal center; they have pale-staining nuclei somewhat larger than those of the small lymphocytes and often show distinct nucleoli. (3) Large lymphocytes (**arrowheads**). These are not as numerous as the medium-sized cells and have nuclei that may be twice as large as those of the medium lymphocytes. Intermediate cell types are also present but are difficult to classify.

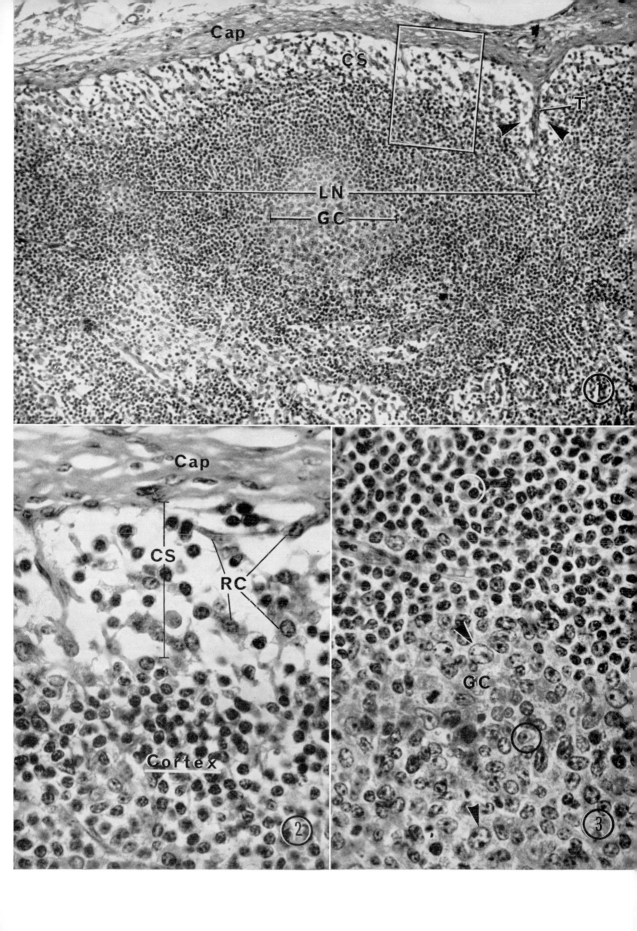

Plate 32. SPLEEN I

The spleen is a lymphoid organ surrounded by a capsule and placed in the path of the blood stream (splenic artery and vein). Two major territories are evident in a low magnification view of a spleen section, *red pulp,* and *white pulp.*

The red pulp (**RP**) presents an overall red-staining response because of the large numbers of red cells that are present. The white pulp (**WP**), on the other hand, consists of many closely packed lymphocytes. The predominant components of the red pulp are the *venous sinuses,* and "cords" of splenic tissue, called *Billroth's cords.* It is not always easy to distinguish the venous sinuses from the Billroth's cords at low magnification, and in parts of the field (?) this cannot be done with assurance. In the lower left, however, the sinuses (**VS**) are dilated and the contents are somewhat separated from the walls, thereby highlighting the profiles of some sinuses. When the venous sinuses are delineated as they are in the lower left, the Billroth's cords can be identified as the tissue between the sinuses. Red blood cells are typically present in both the venous sinuses and the Billroth's cords.

The red pulp is viewed at higher magnification in Figure 2. Some sinuses (**VS**) are evident because the luminal contents appear to be separated from the vessel wall. Billroth's cords (**BC**) are between the venous sinuses. In some preparations, the venous sinuses may be packed with red cells, and in these cases the islands of predominantly red cells direct attention to the location of the sinuses.

The large number of cells in the white pulp (Fig. 3), and the intense nuclear staining makes the white pulp appear as islands of spotted blue in H & E preparations. The cells of the white pulp are actually grouped around an artery, and surround it along its length after the artery has left the trabecula. Therefore, in each island or bar of white pulp there may be an artery, called the central artery (**CA**). This is usually eccentrically located. The cluster of lymphocytes surrounding the arteries expands at intervals and the expansions are referred to as *splenic*

KEY

BC, Billroth's cords
CA, central artery
Cap, capsule
RP, red pulp
T, trabeculae
VS, venous sinuses
WP, white pulp
?, areas of red pulp where venous sinuses and Billroth's cords are difficult to distinguish
Fig. 1 (monkey), x 65; Fig. 2 (monkey), x 160; (inset), x 640; Fig. 3 (monkey), x 640

nodules, or *Malpighian corpuscles.* The splenic nodules may contain germinal centers.

The capsule (**Cap**) of the spleen consists of fibroelastic tissue and scattered smooth muscle cells. On its surface is a layer of mesothelial cells (**circular inset**). Trabeculae (**T**) extend from the capsule into the substance of the spleen. These also contain fibroelastic tissue and smooth muscle. The capsule and trabeculae bring about changes in the size and volume of the spleen due to the contraction of the muscle.

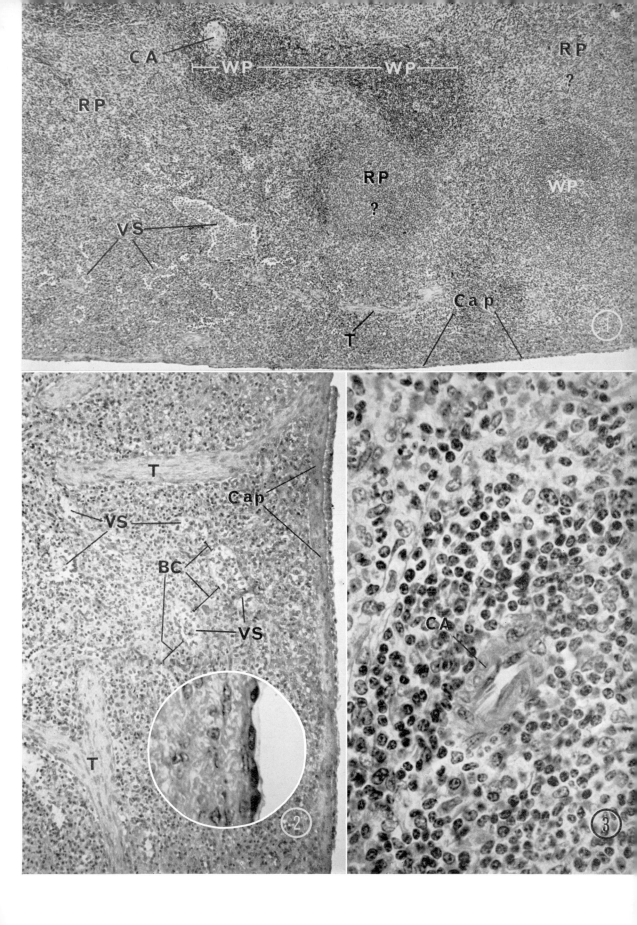

Plate 33. SPLEEN II

The red pulp of the spleen is shown in greater detail in Figure 1. Venous sinuses (**VS**) and Billroth's cords (**BC**) fill the field. The venous sinuses can be recognized by their outline. They are unique vascular channels that are shaped like a sausage or elongated balloon and present circular profiles when cross sectioned. Their wall consists of elongated rod-like cells which are oriented parallel to each other in the long axis of the sinus. Therefore, when the venous sinus is cut in cross section, as a number of them are in Figure 1, the rod-shaped lining cells are also cut in cross section, and the cut edges form a ring that constitutes the profile of the sinus (**arrows**). Occasionally a nucleus is included in the cross section through a lining cell. The nucleus protrudes into the lumen and it is sometimes difficult to distinguish the nucleus of a lining cell from the contents of the sinus. The rod-shaped lining cells serve not only as a wall for the sinus, but they are also phagocytic. Billroth's cords can be identified as the territories between the venous sinuses. They can be delineated best by locating the boundary of neighboring sinuses. The cords are filled with a variety of cell types, among which are numerous red blood cells. These red cells have obviously left the vascular channels, i.e., they are extravascular.

The framework of the spleen consists of a capsule, trabeculae and a reticular stroma. The reticular stroma is illustrated in Figures 2 and 3 (silver preparations). In the red pulp (**RP**), the reticular fibers are arranged in ring-like formations around the venous sinuses. These fibers appear as irregular but characteristic ladders when cut longitudinally. This ring-like arrangement is not present in the white pulp (**WP**) where there are no venous sinuses. In the white pulp, the reticular stroma consists of a delicate irregular network of reticular fibers.

It is still not known whether an open or closed circulation prevails in the spleen. A brief outline of the splenic circulation will pinpoint this problem and help in an understanding of splenic structure. The splenic artery enters the spleen at the hilus. Branches

KEY

BC, Billroth's cords (pulp cords)
RP, red pulp
VS, venous sinus
WP, white pulp
arrows, cross sections of venous lining cells
Fig. 1 (monkey), x 640; Fig. 2 (human), x 160; Fig. 3 (human), x 640.

travel via trabeculae until as a consequence of branching, the arteries are reduced in diameter. They leave the trabeculae to be surrounded by lymphocytes. The accumulations of lymphocytes around these arteries constitute the white pulp, and the artery is called the central artery. The arterioles then enter the red pulp and form a cluster of branches, which is called a penicillus. While in the red pulp, three successive segments of each branch are described: 1) arteries of the pulp, 2) sheathed arteries (they are only slightly developed in man, but are conspicuous in the dog and certain other vertebrates), and 3) terminal capillaries (also called arterial capillaries). At this point there is still uncertainty as to whether the arterial capillaries continue directly into the venous sinuses (closed circulation) or open into splenic cords (open circulation), or whether both situations prevail. The venous sinuses are large channels which flow into veins that ultimately enter the trabeculae and leave the spleen as the splenic vein. It should be noted that the venous sinuses are extremely numerous, whereas arterioles of the red pulp are fewer in number and more difficult to find.

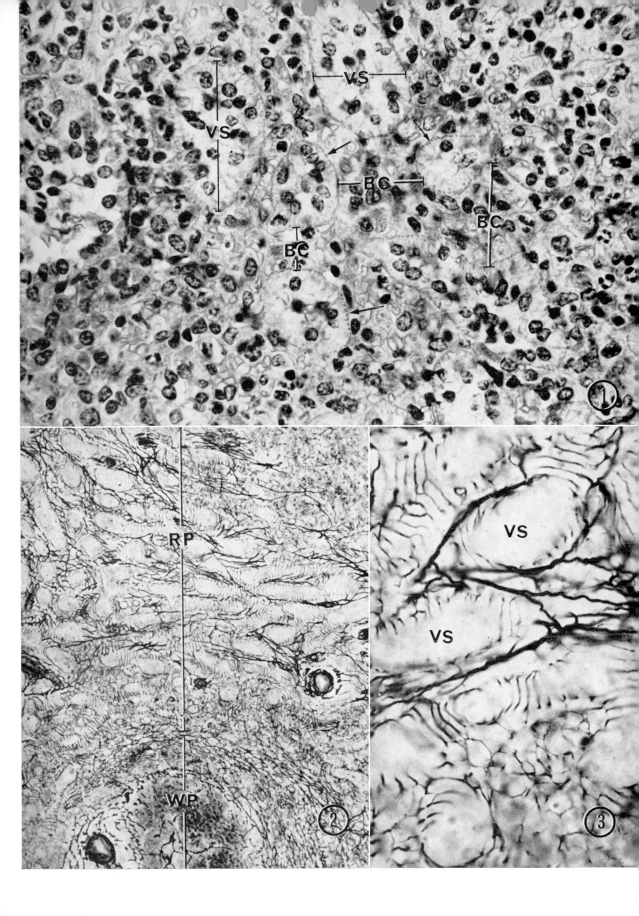

Plate 34. THYMUS

The thymus gland is a lymphoid organ with special properties. For example, the supporting element differs from the supporting elements of other lymphoid tissue. It consists of "epithelioid cells" which developed from endodermal epithelium. These cells are not phagocytic in the same manner as the reticular cells of other lymphoid tissue; moreover, reticular fibers are not associated with these cells. The lymphocytes develop from the entodermal cells as they separate from the pharyngeal pouches and multiply.

The thymus gland has a cortex which contains densely packed lymphocytes and a medulla in which the cells are not as tightly packed. As a consequence, the cortex appears darker in H & E preparations. A capsule (**Cap**) surrounds each lobe (there are two lobes) of the thymus and sends septa (**S**) into the substance of the gland to form lobules. The lobules are not completely separated, inasmuch as the medulla consists of a continuous inner core (Fig. 1). Trabeculae extend into the cortex of the thymus from the septa and capsule. The medulla of the thymus possesses numerous circular bodies called *thymic* or *Hassall's corpuscles* (**HC**). These are large concentric layers of eosinophilic matter which can easily be distingushed with low power (Fig. 1).

The main cellular constituents of the thymus are *(1)* lymphocytes (thymocytes), with characteristic small, round, dark-staining nuclei (**white circle**) and *(2)* epithelioid supporting cells, with large, elongated, indented, pale staining nuclei (**black circle**). Both of these can be seen in Figure 2, which is a high-power view of the junction between cortex and medulla.

The thymus gland remains as a large structure until the time of puberty. At this time, regressive changes occur which result in a significant reduction in the amount of thymic tissue. Comparison of Figure 1 with Figure 3 illustrates the changes that occur with age. The young thymus (Fig. 1) is highly cellular and contains a minimum of adipose tissue. On the other hand, in the older thymus (Fig. 3) much adipose tissue (**AT**) is present be-

KEY

AT, adipose tissue
BV, blood vessels
Cap, capsule
HC, Hassall's corpuscles
S, septa
white circle, nuclei of lymphocytes
black circle, nuclei of epithelioid cells
arrow, tangential cut through arterial wall
Fig. 1 (human), x 40; Fig. 2 (human), x 640; Fig. 3 (human), x 65.

tween the lobules. Moreover, even within the aggregations of lymphocytes there are fat cells.

Some blood vessels (**BV**) are seen in Figure 3. At one point a small artery (**arrow**) has been cut tangentially so that its lumen has been missed. The lightly stained, elongated, and oriented nuclei around the head of the arrow belong to the smooth muscle cells of the tunica media.

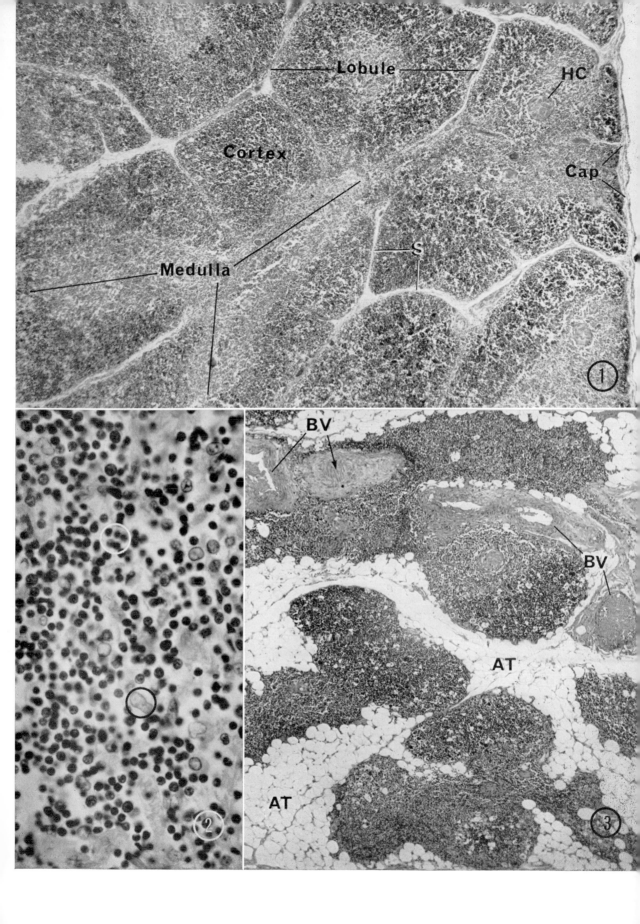

INTEGUMENT

THE INTEGUMENT, OR SKIN, consists of two major layers, the *epidermis* and the *dermis*. Under the dermis is a layer which contains large amounts of adipose tissue, the *hypodermis* (also called the tela subcutanea or superficial fascia). The skin serves a variety of functions, and variations in the character of the dermis and epidermis occur according to functional demands.

The epidermis consists of stratified squamous epithelium. The deepest layer of cells in the epidermis is called the basal layer. Cells from this layer migrate to the surface to replace those which are constantly being lost. As the cells move toward the surface they engage in the synthesis of an intracellular protein, called *keratin*. The cells ultimately become a keratinized mass. Collectively the keratinized cells constitute the *stratum corneum*. This serves as a thin but tough protective coat on the outer surface of the skin.

The epidermis gives rise to nails, hairs, sebaceous glands, and sweat glands. Sweat glands and hairs develop from the epidermal surface and grow into the underlying dermis. Very frequently they extend as far as the dermo-hypodermal junction or into the hypodermis itself. Sebaceous glands arise from developing hair follicles (a hair follicle is the epithelial sheath that surrounds the hair shaft) and remain associated with them. In a few places sebaceous glands exist without hair follicles, for example, at epidermo-mucosal junctions, however, the development of the sebaceous glands probably occurs in association with a hair follicle which subsequently disappears. Each hair follicle is also associated with a bundle of smooth muscle cells, the *arrector pili*. Hairs are not found on the palms of the hands and the soles of the feet, and these areas have no sebaceous glands. Sweat glands are, however, found in these two regions.

The dermis consists largely of dense irregular connective tissue. It contains nerve endings, blood vessels, and lymphatic vessels. Two kinds of nerve endings can be seen in routine H & E preparations: *Meissner's corpuscles* and *Pacinian* or *lamellated corpuscles*. Meissner's corpuscles are for tactile discrimination; they are immediately under the epidermis. Pacinian corpuscles are for deep pressure: they are deeply situated in the dermis and may also be in the hypodermis. Whereas Meissner's corpuscles are confined to the skin, Pacinian corpuscles are distributed more widely throughout the body.

Plate 35. SKIN I

A section from the skin of the face is shown in Figure 1. The epidermis (**Epi**) is the surface layer; the dermis (**Derm**) is the underlying connective tissue. Figure 1 provides general orientation regarding the location of sweat glands (**Sw**) and their ducts, (**D**), hair follicles (**HF**), sebaceous glands (**Seb**), and the arrector pili muscle (**AP**).

The epidermis (**Epi**) and dermis (**Derm**) from the anterior abdominal wall are shown at higher magnification in Figure 2. The epidermis is relatively thin. The deep part is called the *stratum germinativum* (**SG**). It is several cells thick; the nuclei of the cells are readily evident. As the cells from the basal layer of the stratum germinativum move toward the surface, they synthesize the intracellular protein, keratin. Just before the cells became keratinized, granules (keratohyaline granules) appear in the cytoplasm of the cells. These granules stain with hematoxylin, giving the cells a dark appearance. The layer of cells which contains the keratohyaline granules is referred to as the *stratum granulosum* (**SGr**). In places where the skin is not particularly thick, as in the anterior abdominal wall, this layer is not very striking. On the surface, the epidermis consists of a layer of keratinized cells, called the *stratum corneum* (**SC**). This layer looks more fibrous than cellular. The nuclei of the cells cannot be seen.

In contrast to the epidermal cells which are closely applied, the cells of the dermis are widely separated. The cytoplasm of these cells cannot be distinguished from the intercellular fibrous material, so that the dermis appears to consist of nuclei that are separated by fibers. Most of these fibers are collagenous, but elastic fibers are also present. Immediately under the epithelium, the dermis is less dense. This part of the dermis is called the *papillary layer* (**PL**). The deeper part of the dermis is less cellular, and contains more numerous and thicker bundles of collagenous fibers. This part of the dermis is called the *reticular layer* (**RL**). The elastic fibers are more coarse in the reticular layer than in the papillary layer (see Plate 7).

A section through the skin of the palmar

KEY

AP, arrector pili muscle
D, ducts
Derm, dermis
DP, dermal papillae
Epi, epidermis
HF, hair follicle
PL, papillary layer
RL, reticular layer
SC, stratum corneum
Seb, sebaceous gland
SG, stratum germinativum
SGr, stratum granulosum
SL, stratum lucidum
Sw, sweat gland
arrows, Meissners corpuscles
arrowheads, spiral portion of sweat ducts

Fig. 1 (human), x 65; Fig. 2 (human), x 120. Fig. 3 (human), x 65.

surface of the hand is shown in Figure 3. The epidermis (**Epi**) is especially thick and four layers can be recognized: the stratum germinativum (**SG**), the stratum granulosum (**SGr**), the stratum lucidum (**SL**), and the stratum corneum (**SC**). The stratum lucidum is present in epidermis only if the stratum corneum is exceptionally thick, as it is in the palms and soles. The epidermal-dermal junction is irregular, due to the presence of numerous connective tissue papillae (dermal papillae) (**DP**) which project into the undersurface of the epidermis. The **arrows** indicate structures just under the epidermis which are likely to be Meissners corpuscles. Although their identification is not clear at this magnification, the horizontal disposition of nuclei in these areas suggests that they are. Note that the papillary layer (**PL**) of the dermis is more cellular than the reticular layer (**RL**). Two ducts from sweat glands are shown as they enter the undersurface of the epidermis. The ducts are slightly curved (**D,** Fig. 1) as they travel through the dermis; they take a spiral course (**arrowheads,** Fig. 3) as they penetrate the epidermis.

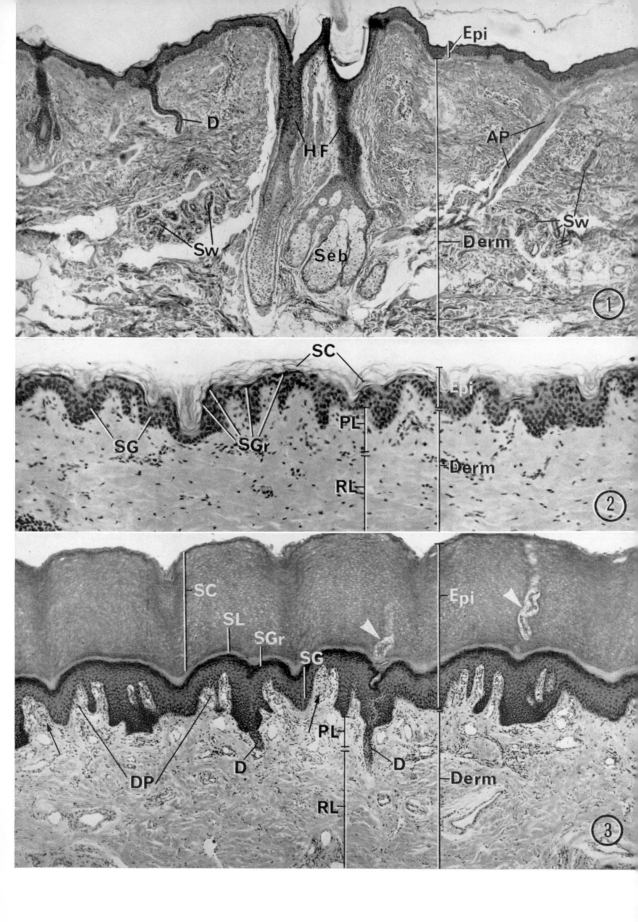

Plate 36. SKIN II

Two sebaceous glands opening into a hair follicle are shown in Figure 1. The sebaceous glands (**Seb**) appear as a thick cluster of cells that are closely applied to each other. The cytoplasm appears empty because it contains much lipid material which is lost during the preparation of the tissue. The cells at the periphery of the sebaceous gland are small and flat. They contain only a small amount of cytoplasm, and are capable of dividing. As the cells move away from the peripheral location, they begin to elaborate their product and the cytoplasm becomes filled with lipid. The synthetic activity continues until the cell is filled with the lipid product. At this point the nucleus becomes pyknotic (**arrows**), the cell is disrupted, and the oily product is discharged into the hair follicle (**HF**) and ultimately onto the skin surface. Because the cell is sacrificed during the secretion, sebaceous glands are classified as *holocrine glands.*

The follicle is in a resting stage and does not show the various layers that are evident in an active follicle. The hair shaft (**HS**) is in the center of the follicular tube. It stains very lightly.

Sweat glands develop from the epidermis. They are simple, coiled tubular glands. The secretory portion of the gland is a coiled tube deep in the dermis or in the upper part of the hypodermis. The duct portion travels through the dermis as a slightly curving tube, and as it penetrates the epidermis it spirals. A section through the terminal portion of a sweat gland (**Sw**) is shown in Figure 2. This is only one tube, but because it is coiled, it is cut in a number of places. The secretory portion of the gland consists of columnar cells (**inset**). The round nuclei at the basal part of the glandular epithelium belong to myoepithelial cells. The duct (**D**) portion of the gland is narrower; it consists of two layers of cuboidal cells. The duct cells stain more intensely than the cells of the secretory part of the gland. The lumen of the duct portion is evident in the **inset.** The field (Fig. 2) also includes some adipose tissue (**AT**).

Pacinian corpuscles (**PC**) are located deep in the dermis or in the outer portion of the

KEY

AT, adipose tissue
D, duct
HF, hair follicle
HS, hair shaft
MC, Meissners corpuscle
PC, Pacinian corpuscle
Seb, sebaceous gland
Sw, sweat gland
arrows, pyknotic nuclei

Fig. 1 (monkey), x 160; Fig. 2 (human), x 160; (insets), x 400; Fig. 3 (human), x 160; Fig 4 (human), x 640.

hypodermis. They are pressor receptors. In histological sections (Fig. 3), they resemble the cut face of an onion. Successive concentric layers of cells and delicate collagenous fibers account for the appearance. The nuclei of some of the extremely flat cells can be seen. The nerve component is located in the center.

Meissners corpuscles (**MC**) are located immediately under the epidermis. They are tactile receptors. In histological section (Fig. 4), they have an elongated shape. The internal structure consists of cells and supporting elements that are oriented at right angles to the long axis of the corpuscle. The corpuscle is separated from the epidermal cells by a small amount of connective tissue.

"Intercellular bridges" appear as the faint striations between the epidermal cells.

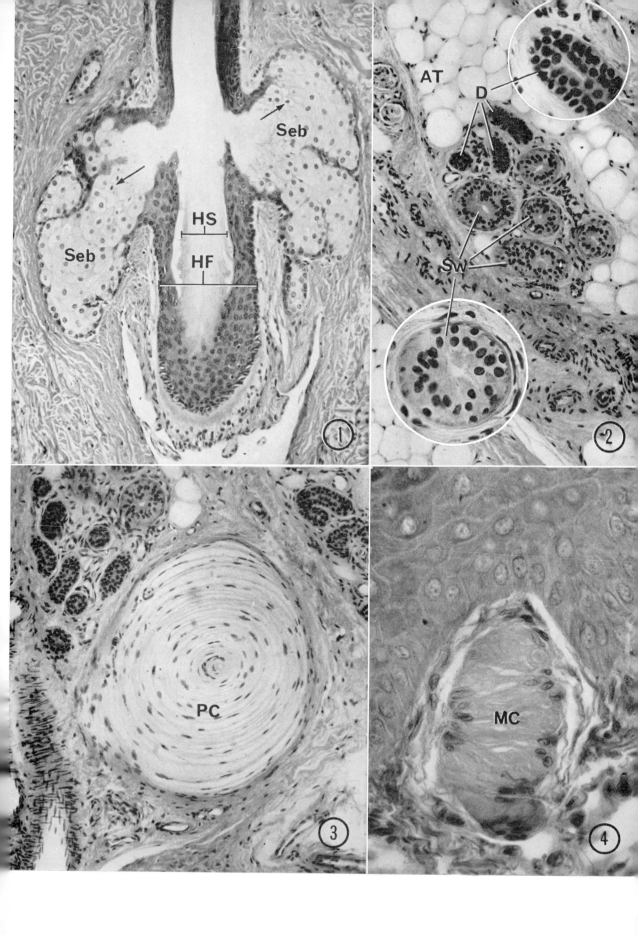

DIGESTIVE SYSTEM

THE DIGESTIVE SYSTEM consists of the alimentary canal and a number of glands associated with the canal. From the esophagus to the anus, the alimentary canal is a tube whose wall can be recognized as comprising four layers designated the mucosa, submucosa, muscularis externa, and serosa (or adventitia). The oral cavity and pharynx are not only engaged in the early aspects of alimentation, but also serve the respiratory system and consequently have special structural features which reflect these overlapping functions.

Of the four layers of the alimentary canal, the *mucosa* is the inner lining. It consists of an epithelial surface, a cellular connective tissue called the lamina propria, and a thin layer of smooth muscle, called the *muscularis mucosae*. From the stomach to the anal canal, the mucosa contains glands. The esophagus also has mucosal glands, but only at its upper and lower ends, not in the intermediate portion.

The *submucosa* is made up of irregular connective tissue. It serves as the major route for the larger blood vessels that are within the wall of the alimentary canal. In the esophagus and upper part of the duodenum, the submucosa contains glands. Autonomic ganglion cells are also present in the submucosa (*Meissner's plexus*).

The *muscularis externa* consists of smooth muscle, except in the upper part of the esophagus. The smooth muscle is arranged in layers. Between the layers of smooth muscle, especially in the intestine, the muscularis externa contains autonomic ganglion cells which are part of *Auerbach's* plexus. The upper part of the esophagus contains striated muscle; the middle region contains both smooth muscle and striated muscle; and the lower part contains smooth muscle.

The *serosa* (visceral peritoneum) consists of a layer of simple squamous epithelium (mesothelium) and a small amount of supporting connective tissue. The esophagus and bare areas of the alimentary tube do not possess a serosa. In these places, the outer layer consists of connective tissue and is called the *adventitia*.

A large number of glands are associated with the alimentary canal. They develop from the epithelial lining of the canal. Some of these (the gastric glands and intestinal glands) are confined to the mucosa; some extend into the submucosa (esophageal and duodenal glands); and some extend beyond the wall of the tube (the salivary glands and pancreas).

The mucosal glands are simply tubular invaginations from the surface epithelium into the underlying connective tissue. The submucosal and extramural glands develop into a branching system of ducts which have a ball-like arrangement of cells (the acini or alveoli) at their terminals. The duct system allows the secretions to reach the lumen of the alimentary canal. In addition to its acinar components the pancreas contains the islets of Langerhans, which are endocrine components.

The liver is also a gland that is related to the alimentary canal. It develops from the epithelial lining of the alimentary canal and retains a connection with the lumen via the hepatic duct and common bile duct. However, the liver is significantly different from the other glands in structural organization and function and will be dealt with specially. The gall bladder is a sac-like structure which stores and concentrates the bile (a liver product) until it is needed.

Plate 37. TONGUE I

The tongue is a muscular organ covered by mucous membrane. The mucous membrane consists of stratified squamous epithelium (**Ep**) resting on a loose connective tissue (**CT**). The undersurface of the tongue is relatively uncomplicated (Fig. 4); however, the dorsal surface is modified to form three types of papilla (Figs. 1–3): *filiform, fungiform,* and *vallate.* These are organized as follows: the vallate papillae form a V-shaped row which divides the tongue into a body and a root. The dorsal surface of the body, i.e., anterior to the vallate papillae, contains filiform and fungiform papillae. The filiform papillae (**Fil P**) are more numerous. These are bent conical elevations of the epithelium, with the point of the elevation directed posteriorly (Fig. 1). These papillae do not possess taste buds.

Fungiform papillae (**Fun P**) are scattered about as isolated, slightly rounded, and elevated structures situated between the filiform papillae. A large connective tissue core (primary connective tissue papilla) forms the center of the fungiform papilla, and smaller connective tissue papillae (secondary connective tissue papillae) project into the base of the surface epithelium (**arrowhead,** Fig. 2). Fungiform papillae contain one or more taste buds on their free surface. None is included in Figure 2, but at least five are shown in Figure 3. Taste buds extend throughout the whole thickness of the epithelium. This is not evident when the taste bud is cut obliquely, in which case the taste bud may appear as an oval or circular structure. The filiform papillae in Figure 2 look different from those in Figure 1 because they are cut in a different plane and the bent conical nature of the papilla is not evident.

The undersurface of the tongue is shown in Figure 4. The smooth surface of the stratified squamous epithelium (**Ep**) contrasts with the irregular surface of the dorsum of the tongue. Connective tissue (**CT**) is immediately deep to the epithelium, and deeper still is the striated muscle (**M**). The epithelial surface of the tongue is not usually keratinized.

The numerous connective tissue papillae

KEY

BV, blood vessel
CT, connective tissue
Ep, epithelium
Fil P, filiform papillae
Fun P, fungiform papilla
M, muscle
TB, taste buds
arrows, connective tissue papillae
arrowhead (Fig. 2), secondary connective tissue papilla
arrowheads (Fig. 3), taste buds
Figs. 1–4 (monkey), x 65.

that project into the base of the epithelium of the entire tongue give the epithelial-connective tissue junction an irregular profile. Often connective tissue papillae are cut obliquely and then appear as islands of connective tissue within the epithelial layer (**arrows,** Figs. 1–3). These should not be confused with taste buds which may also appear as light areas within the epithelium (**arrowheads,** Fig. 3). The epithelium that immediately surrounds the connective tissue "island" consists of basal cells. They stain differently from the cells which surround the taste bud.

The connective tissue extends as far as the muscle without change in character, and no submucosa is recognized. The muscle of the tongue is striated, and is unique in its organization in that the fibers travel in three planes. Therefore, most sections will show muscle fibers cut longitudinally, at right angles to each other, and in cross section. In Figure 4, fibers that are cut longitudinally and in cross section are shown.

The surface of the tongue behind the vallate papillae (namely, the root of the tongue) contains lingual tonsils (see page 76).

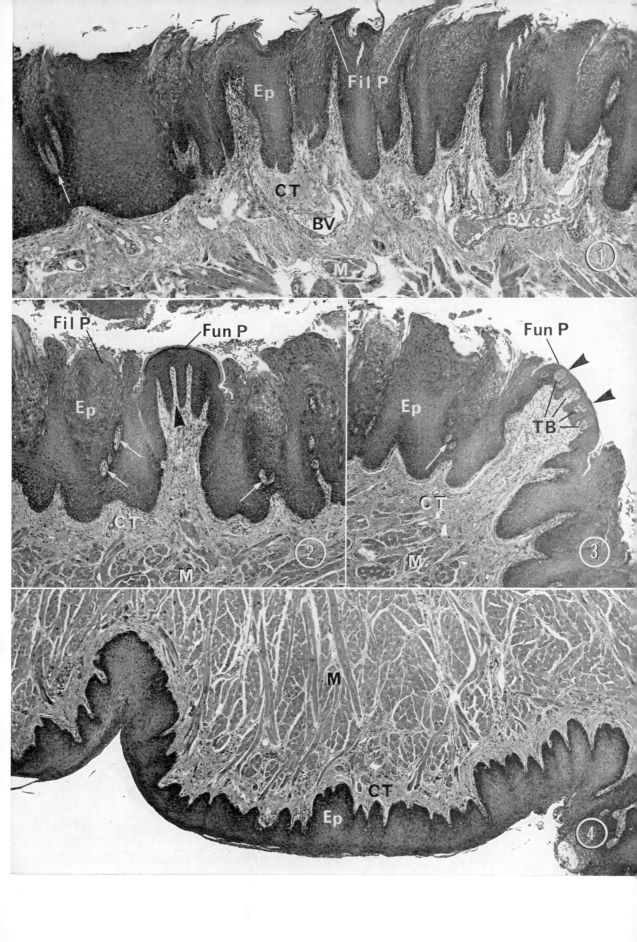

Plate 38. TONGUE II

The sides of the tongue contain a series of ridges that bear taste buds. When these ridges are cut at right angles to their long axis, they appear as a row of papillae (Fig. 1). These ridges, called *foliate papillae,* can immediately be distinguished from fungiform papillae because they appear in rows, whereas fungiform papillae appear alone. Moreover, numerous taste buds (**TB**) are present on adjacent walls of neighboring foliate papillae. In contrast, fungiform papillae have taste buds on the dorsal surface. The foliate papillae are covered by stratified squamous epithelium that is usually not, or only slightly, keratinized. The part of the epithelium (**Ep**) that is on the free surface of the foliate papillae is thick and has a number of secondary connective tissue papillae (**arrowheads**) projecting into its undersurface.

The connective tissue within and under the foliate papillae contains serous type glands (**Gl**), called von Ebner's glands, which open via ducts (**D**) into the cleft between neighboring papillae. Occasionally, the ducts are dilated (**D'**). The darker patches (**arrows**) within the connective tissue represent accumulations of round cells, which are probably lymphocytes. Foliate papillae are not conspicuous in the adult human tongue, but are more evident in the infant tongue.

Of the true papillae found on the dorsal surface of the tongue—filiform, fungiform, and vallate—the vallate are the largest. About seven to eleven of these form a "V" between the body and root of the tongue. The papillae are covered by stratified squamous epithelium which may be slightly keratinized. Each vallate papilla (Fig. 2) is surrounded by a trench or cleft. Numerous taste buds (**TB**) are on the lateral walls of the papillae; moreover, the tongue epithelium facing the papilla within the cleft may contain some taste buds. The dorsal surface of the papilla is rather smooth; however, numerous secondary connective tissue papillae (**arrowheads**) project into the underside of the epithelium. The deep trench surrounding the vallate papillae and the presence of taste buds on the sides rather than on the surface are features which distinguish val-

KEY

CT, connective tissue
D, ducts
D', dilated duct
Ep, epithelium
Gl, serous glands
TB, taste buds
arrows (Fig. 1), lymphocytes
arrow (Fig. 3), intercellular "bridges"
arrowheads (Figs. 1 and 2), secondary connective tissue papillae
arrowheads (Fig. 3), taste bud pore

Fig. 1 (monkey), x 40; Fig. 2 (monkey), x 65; Fig. 3 (monkey), x 640.

late from fungiform papillae.

The connective tissue near the vallate papillae contains many serous type glands (**Gl**), *von Ebner's glands,* which open via ducts (**D**) into the bottom of the trench.

The taste buds extend through the full thickness of the stratified squamous epithelium (Fig. 3) and open at the surface at a small pore (**arrowheads**). The cells of the taste bud are chiefly spindle shaped and oriented at a right angle to the surface. The nuclei of the cells are elongated and mainly in the basal two-thirds of the bud. Nerve fibers enter the epithelium and end in close contact with the cells of the taste bud, but they cannot be identified in routine H & E preparations. Several cell types are present in the taste bud; some are special receptor cells. Note the intercellular "bridges" between the cells in the stratified squamous epithelium (**arrow**).

In addition to von Ebner's glands, which are entirely of the serous type, the tongue contains mixed (serous and mucous) glands near the apex and mucous glands in the root (not illustrated).

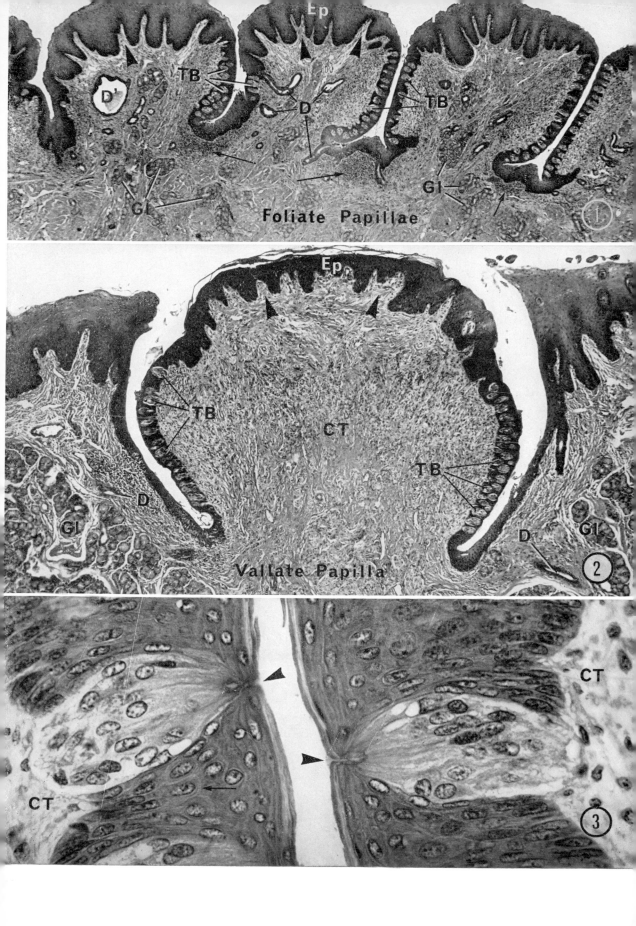

Foliate Papillae

Vallate Papilla

Plate 39. SOFT PALATE

The *soft palate* is the posterior part of the roof of the mouth. Instead of bone as in the *hard palate,* it contains striated muscle between the nasal and oral surfaces. During swallowing, the soft palate separates the nasopharynx from the oropharynx.

A section through the entire thickness of the soft palate is shown in Figure 1. From top to bottom, the following components can be recognized: *1*) the epithelial (**EP**) lining of the nasal surface (a small polyp (**P**) is connected by a stalk to the surface); *2*) the lamina propria (**LP**) of nasal mucosa; *3*) glands (**Gl**); *4*) striated muscle (**StM**); *5*) mucous glands (**MGl**); *6*) lamina propria (**LP**) of oral mucosa; and *7*) epithelial (**Ep**) lining of the oral surface.

The epithelium (**Ep**) lining the nasal surface consists of ciliated stratified columnar cells (Fig. 2). The ciliated columnar cells on the surface do not reach the basement membrane, but rest on deeper, cuboidal cells. Goblet cells (**GC**) are also present in this layer. The epithelium rests on a thick basement membrane (**BM**). The lamina propria (**LP**) is loose and cellular. It contains an aggregation of lymphocytes (**Lym**) and mixed sero-mucous glands. Some of the nuclei of the cells which make up these glands are oval in appearance (**arrows**), whereas others are flattened against the basal part of the cell. The glands may also invade the muscular layer (see Fig. 1).

Stratified columnar epithelium does not have a wide distribution. It is present where stratified squamous epithelium meets columnar or pseudostratified columnar epithelium as, for example, in the larynx, at the junction of the naso- and oropharynx, and on the upper surface of the soft palate.

The muscle of the soft palate is striated. Although striations are not evident at the magnification in Figure 1, it is possible on the basis of other characteristics (see page 106) to conclude that it is striated and not smooth. Connective tissue is between the muscle bundles.

The oral side of the soft palate contains numerous mucous glands. The nuclei of the mucous cells are pressed against the basal part

KEY

BM, basement membrane
D, duct
Ep, epithelium
GC, goblet cells
Gl, glands
LP, lamina propria
Lym, lymphocytes
MGl, mucous glands
P, polyp
StM, striated muscle
arrows (Fig. 2), oval nuclei of serous cells
arrows (Fig. 3), lymphocytes in epithelial layer
arrowheads, flat nuclei of mucous cells
asterisks, connective tissue papillae

Fig. 1 (monkey), x 40; Figs. 2 and 3 (monkey), x 160.

of the cell (**arrowheads**) thereby outlining the mucous alveoli. A duct (**D**) through which these glands empty their secretions onto the surface is seen in Figure 3.

The epithelium on the oral surface and posterior edge of the soft palate is stratified squamous. Numerous connective tissue papillae (**asterisks**) project into the undersurface of the epithelium. The dark staining of the deepest part of the epithelium is due in part to the cytoplasmic staining of the basal cells. New cells which will migrate to the surface are produced in this layer. As the cells approach the surface, the nuclei become flattened and oriented in a plane parallel to the surface. The presence of nuclei in the surface cells indicates that the epithelium is not keratinized.

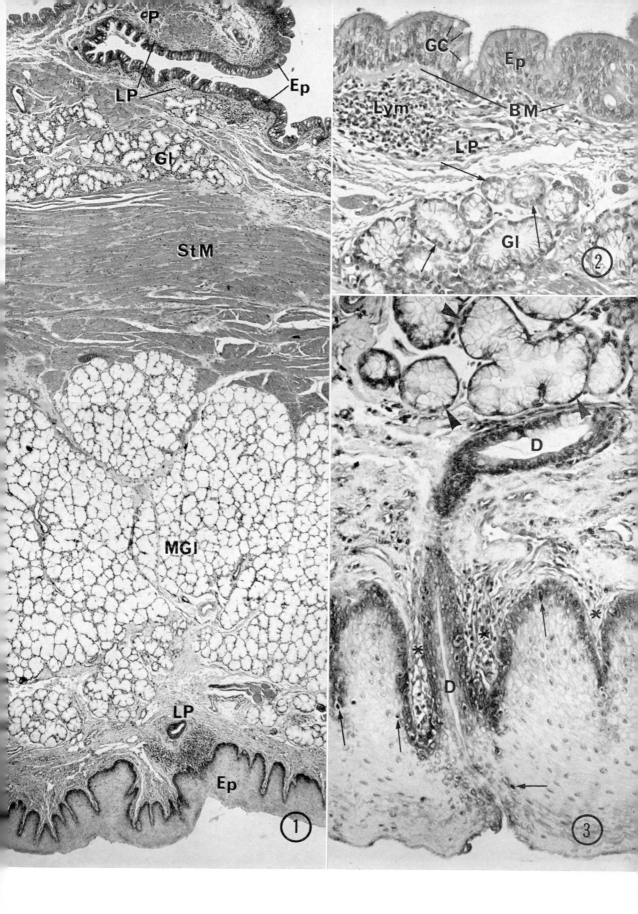

Plate 40. SALIVARY GLANDS 1

The salivary glands are compound (branched) tubulo-alveolar glands. Acini of salivary glands are made up of either serous cells (*serous acini*) or mucous cells (*mucous acini*). Serous acini can be distinguished from mucous acini in several ways. The cytoplasm of serous cells is clearly evident whereas the cytoplasmic part of the mucous cell regularly appears empty. This is because the mucus is usually lost during the preparation of routine H & E sections. In addition to cytoplasmic appearance, consideration of the shape and location of the nucleus may be of assistance in distinguishing between mucous and serous cells. The nuclei of mucous cells usually appear flattened and pressed against the base of the cell; the nuclei of serous cells, on the other hand, are more often oval or spherical and not pressed against the base of the cell. The most definitive way to distinguish between mucous and serous cells is to stain the mucus. This requires special methods.

The ducts of salivary glands are designated as *intercalary, secretory,* and *excretory.* The smallest ducts are the intercalary ducts. These are comprised of low cuboidal or flattened cells. They empty into larger ducts called secretory or striated ducts. These ducts are lined by columnar cells whose cytoplasm stains with eosin and contains basal striations. The largest ducts are the excretory ducts. They are usually surrounded by a large amount of connective tissue and they occupy an interlobular location.

The *submandibular glands* contain both serous and mucous acini (Fig. 1). In man the serous components predominate. The mucous acini (**MA**) appear as the light areas; the serous acini appear as the darker areas. The nuclei of the cells that constitute the serous acini occupy a peripheral location and suggest the extent of the acini. The duct (**ED**) that is surrounded by a large amount of connective tissue (**CT**) is an excretory duct. A large number of striated ducts (**SD**) are within the substance of the gland. These are smaller than the excretory duct but stand out because of the patent lumen. The nuclei of the duct cells appear as a ring around the lumen.

KEY

CT, connective tissue
ED, excretory duct
ID, intercalary duct
L, lumen
MA, mucous acinus
S, septa
SA, serous acinus
SD, striated duct
arrows, serous demilunes

Fig. 1 (human submandibular gland), x 65; Fig. 2 (human submandibular gland), x 160; (inset), x 400.

Connective tissue septa (**S**) are seen throughout the field.

Figure 2 shows the submandibular gland at higher magnification. A large striated duct (**SD**) occupies the center of the field. An intercalary duct (**ID**) is seen where it joins the striated duct. Serous (**SA**) and mucous acini are present throughout the field. Not all of the serous cells are organized as acini. Many of them form a cap on the mucous acini (**arrows**). These caps of serous cells are called *demilunes.* A demilune in relation to a mucous acinus is shown in the **inset.** Note how the nuclei of the mucous cells are flattened and are at the basal end of the cell; the nuclei of the serous cells are spherical. The lumen (**L**) of the mucous acinus is clearly evident.

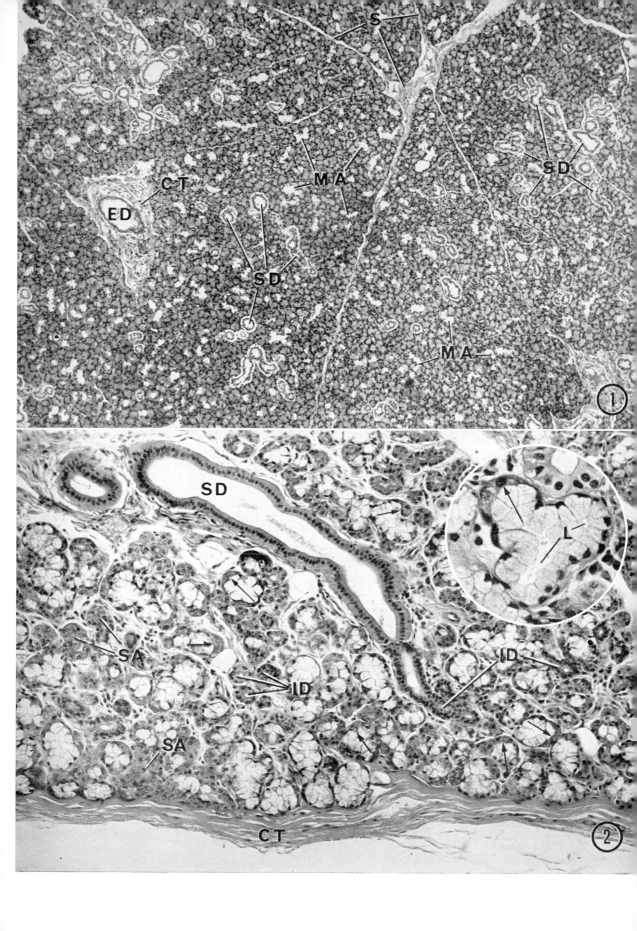

Plate 41. SALIVARY GLANDS II

The *sublingual glands* resemble the submandibular glands in that they contain both serous and mucous elements. However, in man, the *mucous acini* predominate. *Intercalary ducts* are not usually present, or if they are, they are extremely short and thus difficult to find. The sublingual gland is shown in Figure 1. The mucous acini are the most conspicuous components. They are the light groups of cells; the darker groups are *serous acini* (**SA**) or *demilunes* (**arrows**). Many of the mucous acini are not really a spherical arrangement of cells, but rather tubular channels of mucous cells. In this respect they differ from serous acini. A large duct (**ED**) is located in the center of the field, surrounded by connective tissue. The lining of the duct consists of low columnar epithelium.

The *parotid gland* in the human consists entirely of *serous acini* (Fig. 2). Intercalary (**ID**), striated (**SD**), and *excretory ducts* are present. The section was stained to reveal the granules that are present in serous cells. The septa (**S**) and stroma are also highlighted in this preparation. The striated ducts can be readily identified because they possess clearly evident, patent, lumens and a lining of columnar cells. The lumens of the acini are not conspicuous and the organization of the acini may not always be clear. However, in many cases the nuclei of the acinar cells appear to be disposed in a circular pattern thereby suggesting the extent of the acinus.

A higher magnification of the stromal connective tissue that borders several acini is shown in the inset. The nuclei are in the basal part of the cell; the lumens (**arrows**) are beyond the apex. Many of the cells contain secretory granules (the secretory granules of gland cells which produce digestive enzymes are called *zymogen granules*). Some of the flattened nuclei that appear to be at the junction of the connective tissue and the base of the serous cells are nuclei of myoepithelial cells. These cells are also present in the other salivary glands.

Fat cells are usually present in the connective tissue of the larger septa within the salivary glands. These appear empty in H & E

KEY

ED, excretory duct
ID, intercalary duct
S, septa
SA, serous acini
SD, striated duct
arrows (Fig. 1), serous demilunes
arrows (Fig. 2, inset), lumens of serous acini

Fig. 1 (human sublingual gland), x 160; Fig. 2 (human parotid gland), x 160, (inset), x 640.

sections because, like the mucus, lipid is lost during preparation of the tissue. It should be noted that mucus is lost during the time that the tissue is in aqueous solutions, whereas lipid is lost during the time that the tissue is in the lipid solvents.

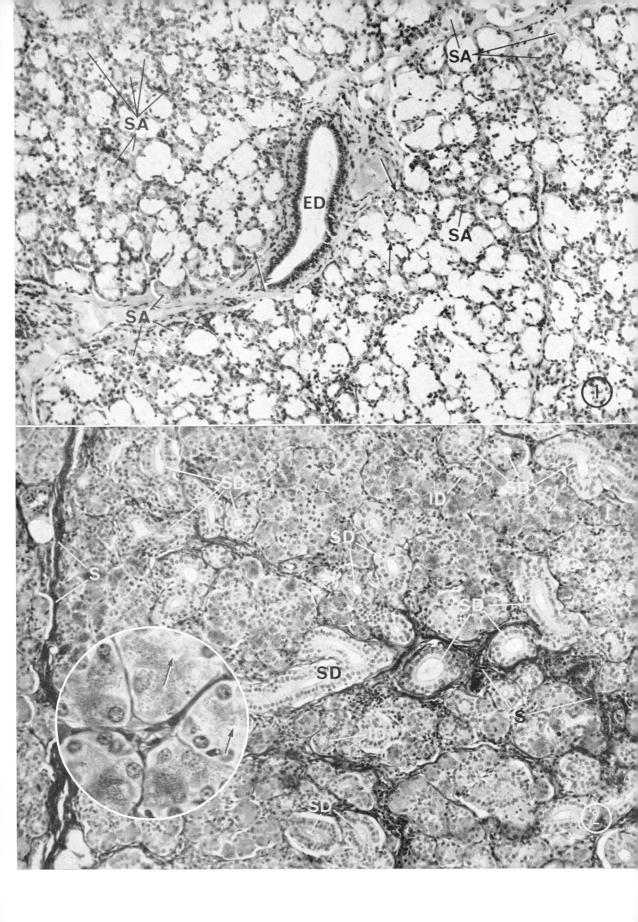

Plate 42. DEVELOPING TOOTH

During early fetal development, a plate of epithelium called the *dental lamina* grows into the underlying embryonic connective tissue (mesenchyme) from the oral epithelium. At regular intervals, where future teeth will be, the cells of the dental lamina proliferate and become the *enamel organs*.

The enamel organ (**EO**) appears as an expanded cell mass that has been invaginated by a connective tissue papilla, the *dental papilla* (**DP**) (Fig. 1). It is attached to the oral epithelium (**Ep**) by the dental lamina (**DL**). The junction between the enamel organ and the dental papilla assumes the shape of the future *dentino-enamel junction* before dentinogenesis or amelogenesis begins. The mesenchyme that surrounds the enamel organ and dental papilla forms a delicate fibrous sac called the *dental sac* (**DS**). This sac along with its contents is called the *tooth germ* (**TG**).

Figure 2 shows a tooth germ in which dentinogenesis and amelogenesis have just begun. The parts of the enamel organ are designated: the *inner enamel epithelium* (**A**) (these are called *ameloblasts* once they begin to form *enamel*), the *stratum intermedium* (**SI**), the *stellate reticulum* (**SR**), and the *outer enamel epithelium* (**OEE**). The dental papilla (**DP**) will become the future pulp cavity. At the periphery of the dental papilla (**DP**) are the columnar shaped *odontoblasts* (**O**) which produce *dentin* (**D**). The enamel (**E**) is deposited by ameloblasts on the surface of the previously formed dentin. Once amelogenesis begins the enamel organ becomes reduced in extent and the columnar ameloblasts are the most conspicuous cell type.

Figure 3 shows a tooth, stained with toluidine blue, at a later stage of development. The enamel (**E**) is unstained, however, the ameloblasts (**A**), dentin (**D**), and odontoblasts (**O**) stain intensely. The most recently formed enamel and dentin are at the bottom of the figure. A serial section of this region, stained with H & E, is examined at higher magnification in Figure 4. The sequence of events that are shown in Figure 4 (and in Fig. 2) are as follows: (1) cells of the enamel organ induce mesenchymal cells of the dental papilla to

KEY

A, ameloblasts
D, dentin
DL, dental lamina
DP, dental papilla
DS, dental sac
E, enamel
EO, enamel organ
Ep, oral epithelium
O, odontoblasts
OEE, outer enamel epithelium
Pd, predentin
SI, stratum intermedium
SR, stellate reticulum
TG, tooth germ

Fig. 1 (pig), x 16; Fig. 2 (dog), x 40; Fig. 3 (rat), x 65, (inset), x 160; Fig. 4 (rat), x 160, (inset), x 640.

become odontoblasts; (2) the odontoblasts begin to produce dentin; (3) when the ameloblasts are confronted with the dentin, they deposit enamel on the outer dentinal surface.

In the formation of dentin, an organic matrix containing collagenous fibers is produced by the odontoblasts. This calcifies to become dentin. The immediate product of the odontoblasts is called *predentin* (**Pd**). It stains less intensely than the dentin. The *odontoblastic process* (inset, Fig. 4) is contained in a *dental tubule* and both the process and its tubule extend through the entire thickness of the dentin.

In the early stages of amelogenesis, the ameloblasts secrete an organic matrix. Mineralization of this (as with the dentinal matrix) begins almost immediately. However, after the enamel reaches its full thickness, organic material is removed and the enamel continues to mineralize to a greater extent than occurs anywhere else in the body. Ameloblasts assume characteristics of absorptive cells (inset, Fig. 3) when they engage in the removal of the organic material.

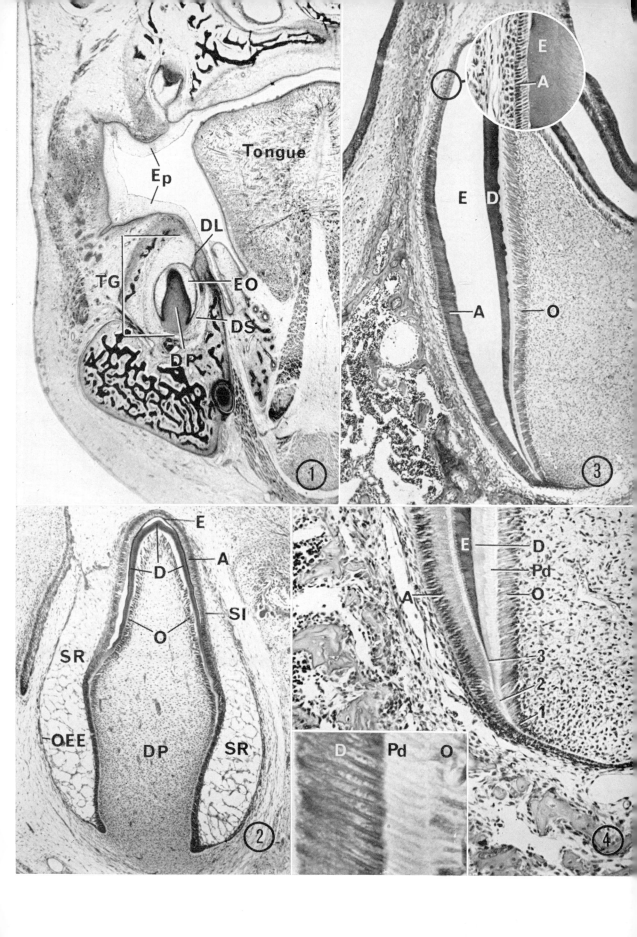

Plate 43. ESOPHAGUS

The *esophagus* serves chiefly to convey material from the pharynx to the stomach. These materials are moved rapidly from the region where the respiratory system shares its passages with the alimentary structures. In connection with this, it should be noted that the oral cavity and the upper part of the esophagus contain striated muscle within their walls.

The wall of the esophagus is shown in Figure 1. The *mucosa* (**Muc**) consists of *stratified squamous epithelium* (**Ep**) resting on the *lamina propria* (**LP**). The boundary between the epithelium and lamina propria is distinct and somewhat uneven due to the presence of numerous connective tissue papillae (**arrows**). The dark band at the epithelial-connective tissue junction is due largely to the cytoplasmic staining of the basal cells. This staining is related to the fact that new cells are produced in the basal layer. The cells constantly migrate from the basal layer to the surface and during this migration, the shape and orientation of the nuclei change. In the deeper layers the nuclei are spherical; in the more superficial layers the nuclei are elongated and oriented parallel to the surface. The fact that nuclei can be seen throughout the epithelial layer as far as the surface indicates that this epithelium is not keratinized.

Whereas the boundary between the epithelium and lamina propria is striking, the boundary between the *mucosa* and *submucosa* (**Subm**) is less well marked. The deepest part of the mucosa is the *muscularis mucosae* (**MM**) and this serves as the marker. The nuclei of the smooth muscle (**SM**) cells all appear spherical because the muscle cells have been cut in cross section (Fig. 2). The submucosa consists of irregular connective tissue with numerous blood vessels (**BV**). No glands are shown in the submucosa of Figure 1, but they are regularly present throughout this layer.

The *muscularis externa* (**ME**) in Figure 1 is striated (therefore a specimen from the upper part of the esophagus). Although the striations are not evident at this low magnification, reference to the inset and then to Figure 3 will substantiate this identification. The inset shows two kinds of longitudinally cut, ori-

KEY

Adv, adventitia
BV, blood vessels
Ep, stratified squamous epithelium
LP, lamina propria
M(Sm), smooth muscle
M(St), striated muscle
ME, muscularis externa
MM, muscularis mucosae
Muc, mucosa
SM, smooth muscle
Subm, submucosa
arrows, connective tissue papillae

Fig. 1 (monkey), x 65, (inset), x 65; Fig. 2 (monkey), x 160; Fig. 3 (monkey), x 640.

ented, fibrous type tissues. They stain differently, but of more significance is the arrangement and number of nuclei. In one case (Fig. 3), numerous elongated and oriented nuclei are scattered throughout; this is smooth muscle [**M(Sm)**]. In the other, fewer elongated nuclei are present, moreover, they are largely at the periphery of the bundles; this is striated muscle [**M(St)**], the cross striations are clearly evident, Re-examination of Figure 1 shows that it consists of muscle bundles which resemble the striated muscle of Figure 3 in terms of nuclear number, orientation and location. The inset and Figure 3 are from the middle of the esophagus where both smooth and striated muscle are present. The distal third of the esophagus contains only smooth muscle.

External to the muscularis externa is the *adventitia* (**Adv**).

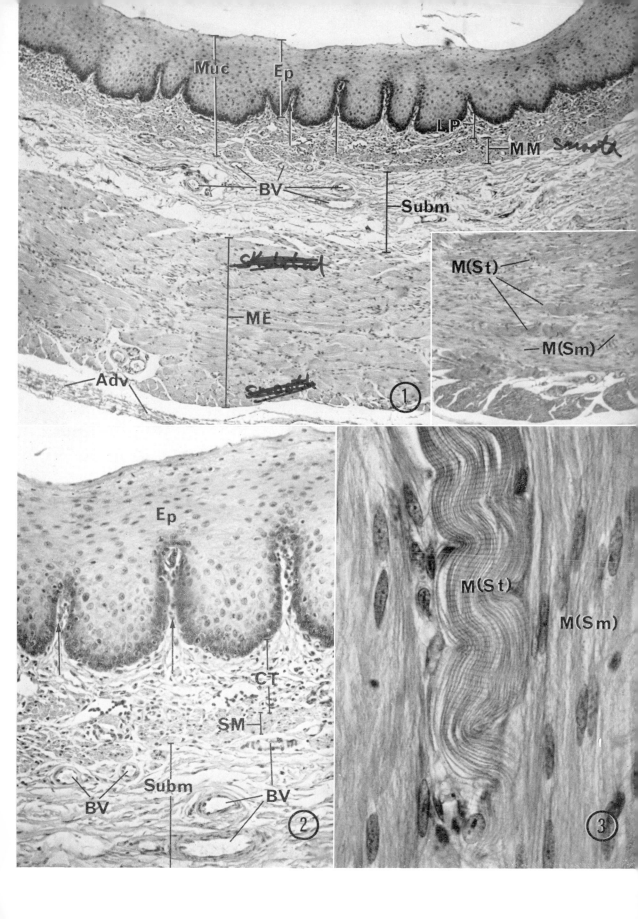

Muc
Ep
LP
MM *smooth*
BV
Subm
Skeletal
ME
Smooth
Adv
①

M(St)
M(Sm)

Ep
CT
SM
Subm
BV
BV
②

M(St)
M(Sm)
③

Plate 44. Esophagus and Cardia

The surface of the stomach contains numerous depressions called *gastric pits* (**P**) or *foveolae.* Glands open into the bottom of the pits. The glands that are in the immediate vicinity of the cardiac orifice are called *cardiac glands.* (The glands in the pyloric region are called *pyloric glands,* and those throughout the remainder of the gastric mucosa are called *fundic glands.*)

The junction between the esophagus and stomach is abrupt (Fig. 1). In the esophagus the mucosa is comprised of stratified squamous epithelium (**Ep**) resting on a lamina propria with numerous papillae (**arrows**). In the stomach, the mucosa contains a surface of columnar epithelium (**Ep**), and numerous tubular glands (**Gl**) in addition to a highly cellular lamina propria (**LP**) (Fig. 2). Just beyond the junction in Figure 1, the gastric mucosa is folded and the glands are cut in cross section. At the actual junction, however, the glands are cut along a longitudinal axis. This region (**rectangle**) is examined at higher magnification in Figure 2.

The epithelium of the gastric surface and pits is columnar. However, it is a special type of epithelium in that each cell produces mucus. In other mucous membranes, a mucous secretion is produced by goblet cells, which occupy the surface with other cells, or by mucous glands that are more deeply situated and empty their secretions via a duct, or by a combination of these two arrangements. In the stomach, the cytoplasm of each surface and pit cell (Figs. 2 and 3) contains a mucous cup distal to the nucleus, so that the entire surface epithelium, and that of the pits, forms a mucous sheet comprised of *mucous surface cells* (**MSC**). The nucleus of each mucous surface cell is surrounded by non-mucous cytoplasmic material. In contrast, the nuclei of mucous gland cells (see below) appear to be in direct contact with the mucus.

The fundus of the gland (part furthest removed from the opening) also contains mucous cells (**MGC**) (Fig. 4), which discharge their product via a duct (**D**). The mucus appears to fill the entire cytoplasmic part of the cell, and the nucleus is pushed to the basal part,

KEY

AT, adipose tissue
D, duct
Ep, epithelium
Gl, glands
LN, lymph nodule
LP, lamina propria
MGC, mucous gland cells
MM, muscularis mucosae
MSC, mucous surface cells
P, gastric pits
arrows, connective tissue papillae
arrowheads, chief cells of fundic glands

Fig. 1 (monkey), x 40; Fig. 2 (monkey), x 160; Fig. 3 (monkey), x 640; Fig. 4 (monkey), x 640.

seemingly in direct contact with the mucous component of the cytoplasm. The part of the cell that was formerly occupied by mucus appears clear because the mucus is lost during preparation of routine H & E sections. Cardiac glands are not very extensive. The **arrowheads** indicate where the darkly staining chief cells of fundic glands can be seen (Fig. 1).

The round cells at the bottom of Figure 2, in the vicinity of the muscularis mucosae (**MM**), are mostly lymphocytes from the periphery of a lymph nodule (**LN**) that is just inside the stomach (Fig. 1). The light network in the submucosa is adipose tissue (**AT**).

Cardiac glands are easy to confuse with pyloric glands. For a consideration of this problem, see page 112.

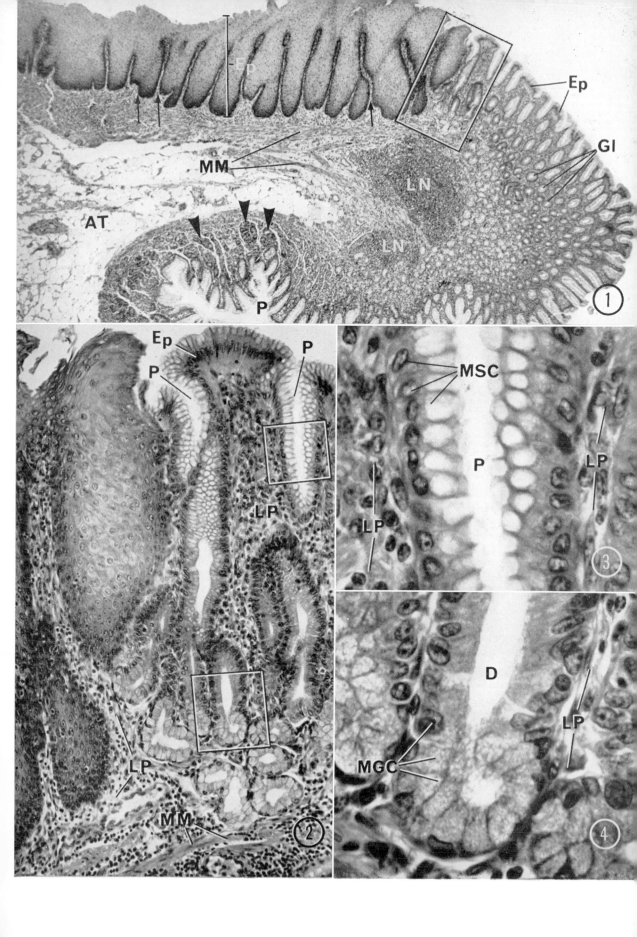

Plate 45. STOMACH, FUNDIC REGION

The entire thickness of the stomach wall is shown in Figure 1. This is from the *fundic region* and is typical of most of the stomach except for the cardiac and pyloric regions. The *mucosa* (**Muc**), *submucosa* (**subm**), *muscularis externa* (**ME**), and *serosa* (**S**) are indicated. The inner surface of the stomach is divided into areas that are designated mamillated areas. These areas are separated from neighboring mamillated areas by grooves (**asterisks**).

The surface of the gastric mucosa, including that of the *gastric pits* (**P**), is lined by a continuous sheet of mucous surface cells (Fig. 2). The *fundic glands* (**GL**) extend from the bottom of the pits to the muscularis mucosae (**MM**). They are relatively straight tubular glands, except at their fundic region (the part furthest from the opening), where they become coiled. The glands are so numerous that they appear to make up almost the entire mucosa. In the mid-region of the mucosa the glands are tightly packed and the lamina propria (**LP**) appears as thin cellular strands that are squeezed between the glands. The lamina propria is more conspicuous under the surface epithelium and pit epithelium, and in the vicinity of the muscularis mucosae.

Several kinds of cells are present in the fundic glands. In the fundic region (Fig. 3), the main cell type is the *chief cell* (**CC**). The nuclei of chief cells are characteristically in the basal part of the cell and surrounded by cytoplasm that stains with hematoxylin. Chief cells synthesize digestive enzymes. *Parietal cells* (**PC**) are also present in fundic glands. The cytoplasm of these cells stains intensely with eosin. These cells are located between the chief cells, but they are usually recessed from the lumen. Near the mid-portion of the mucosa, the parietal cells become more numerous and their presence in larger numbers accounts for the lighter appearance of this region. Parietal cells secrete hydrochloric acid. *Mucous neck cells* are near the opening of the glands into the pits. They are located between the parietal cells. These cells produce a mucous material that differs from that which is produced by the surface cells. *Argentaffine*

KEY

CC, chief cells
Gan C, ganglion cell
GL, fundic glands
LP, lamina propria
LV, lymphatic vessel
ME, muscularis externa
MM, muscularis mucosae
Muc, mucosa
P, gastric pits
PC, parietal cells
S, serosa
Subm, submucosa
asterisks, grooves between mamillated areas
Fig. 1 (monkey), x 100; Fig. 2 (monkey), x 160; Fig. 3 (monkey), x 640.

cells are also present in the gastric glands, but special methods are required for their demonstration.

The submucosa consists of relatively dense connective tissue (Fig. 1). The muscularis externa (**ME**) is comprised of smooth muscle. It is described as being disposed into three layers: an inner oblique, a middle circular and an outer longitudinal. However, these are difficult to discern. The serosa (**S**) consists of a layer of *mesothelium* resting on a small amount of connective tissue. A lymphatic vessel (**LV**) is in the serosa. The stomach wall contains nerve cells that are arranged in the same manner as in the intestinal canal (see page 120).

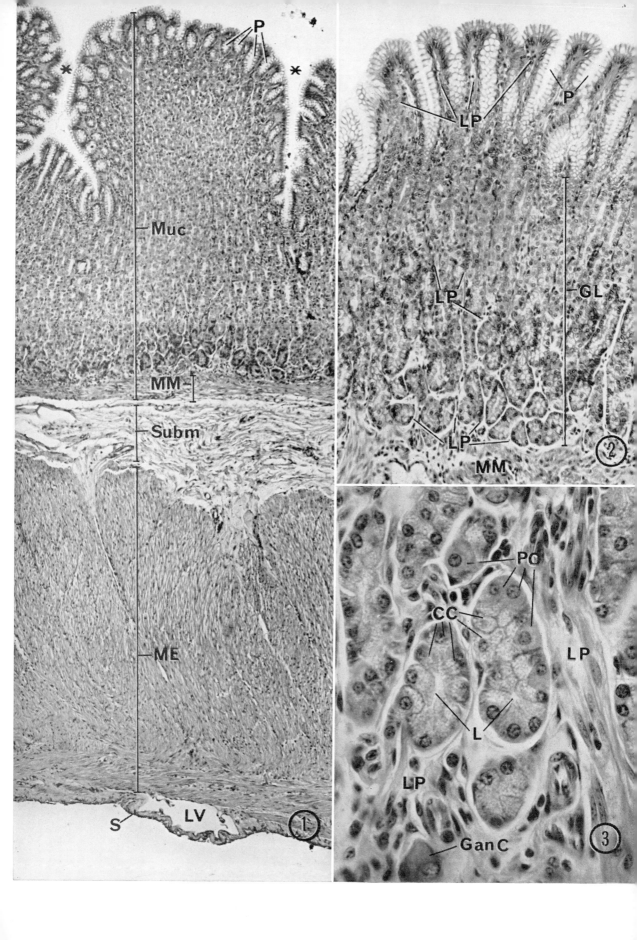

Figure 1: P, Muc, MM, Subm, ME, S, LV

Figure 2: LP, P, GL, MM

Figure 3: PO, CC, LP, L, Gan C

Plate 46. Stomach, Pyloric Region

The part of the stomach leading to the duodenum is called the *pyloric region.* The glands (**Gl**) in this region are shown in Figure 1. They are rather straight, and it is difficult to determine where the pits end and the glands begin. Glands are shown opening into gastric pits (**arrows**) in the upper part of Figure 1.

The fundic region of the pyloric glands (part farthest from the opening) is coiled and may appear oval or spherical when sectioned, even if the remainder of the gland has been cut longitudinally. Between the glands is the cellular lamina propria (**LP**). The deepest part of the mucosa is the muscularis mucosae (**MM**). Under this is the submucosa; it contains an artery (**A**) and vein (**V**). The smooth muscle cells of the muscularis externa (**ME**) have been cut in cross section.

The **upper rectangle** of Figure 1 is examined at higher magnification in Figure 2. As stated before (page 108), the columnar cells (**Ep**) that line the surface and pits of the stomach possess a mucous cup (**MC**) distal to the nucleus (**N**). The nucleus is surrounded by nonmucous cytoplasmic material (**BC**), and collectively the cells form a mucous sheet. A lymphocyte (**L**) has wandered into the epithelial layer from the lamina propria (**LP**).

The area within the **lower rectangle** is illustrated at higher magnification in Figure 3 and shows the fundic region of the pyloric glands. One gland has been cut in cross section (**asterisk**). The cells are polarized in the manner that is typical of cells that secrete onto a surface or into a lumen. The cytoplasm borders the lumen, and the nuclei are in the basal part of the cell. These are *mucous gland cells.* They differ in appearance from *mucous surface cells* in that the nuclei (of mucous gland cells) appear to be in direct contact with mucous material of the cytoplasm.

Pyloric and cardiac glands can be readily distinguished from fundic glands because fundic glands possess different cell types (chief and parietal) that are conspicuous in routine H & E sections. However, pyloric glands are difficult to distinguish from cardiac glands. Several pointers may be of assistance in dis-

KEY

A, artery
BC, basal cytoplasm of mucous surface cells
Ep, epithelium
Gl, pyloric glands
L, lymphocyte
LP, lamina propria
MC, mucous cup
MM, muscularis mucosae
N, nuclei of mucous surface cells
V, vein
arrows, gastric pits
Fig. 1 (human), x 160; Figs 2 and 3 (human), x 640.

tinguishing between these two. Obviously, if part of the esophagus is included in the specimen, the gastric component in its immediate vicinity is the cardiac region; if part of the duodenum is included in the specimen, the gastric component is the pyloric region. To some extent, distinguishing between pyloric and cardiac glands is based on familiarity and intangible impressions. The pyloric pits are usually described as being deeper than the cardiac pits, however, this difference may not be evident in every case. An additional feature that may be of use is: the cardiac glands appear to be more coiled and dilated in their fundic regions, whereas the pyloric glands appear to be less coiled and less dilated.

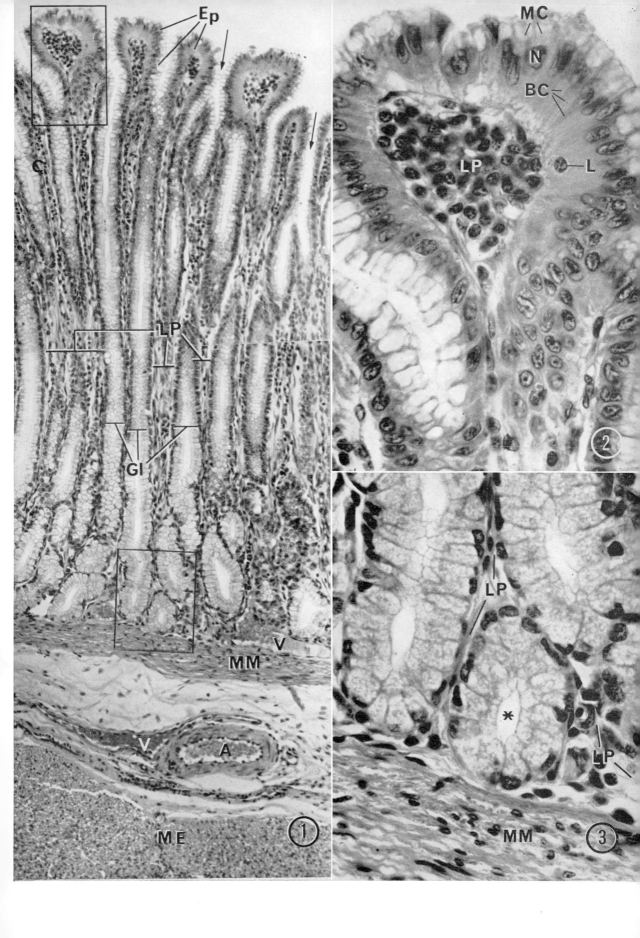

Plate 47. SMALL INTESTINE

The small intestine is a tube, about twenty feet long, that extends from the stomach to the large intestine. It is divided into three parts: *duodenum, jejunum,* and *ileum.* There is, however, no sharp dividing line between these three regions.

The inner surface of the small intestine contains permanent circular folds *(plicae circulares, valvulae conniventes, valves of Kerckring),* which form ridges that are roughly at right angles to the long axis of the tube. Therefore, in a longitudinal section of the intestine (Fig. 1), these folds appear as a series of regular elevations (**PC**). However, they also travel in longitudinal directions for short distances and therefore, even in cross sections (Fig. 2) the plicae may resemble those that are seen in longitudinal sections. The plicae circulares begin in the duodenum; they are tallest and most numerous in the jejunum (Fig. 1) and become shorter and less numerous in the ileum.

Isolated nodules of lymphoid tissue are located in the proximal end of the intestinal canal. More distally they appear in increasingly larger aggregates, so that in the ileum (Fig. 2) aggregates of lymph nodules (**LN**) called *Peyers patches,* are regularly found. These nodules are located opposite the mesenteric attachment. Note the break in the muscular layer (**arrowhead**) where blood vessels are traveling between the mesentery (**M**) and the submucosa.

Figure 3 shows an area comparable to that within the **rectangle** in Figure 1; it includes a plica. In routine H & E sections the four layers of the intestinal wall are distinguished as follows: The *mucosa* (**Muc**) is the inner layer which appears dark, because of the large numbers of epithelial cells and the numerous cells of the lamina propria. The mucosa contains both *villi* (**V**) and *intestinal glands* (**IG**). The glands are also called *crypts of Lieberkühn.*

The submucosa (**Subm**) is the light-staining layer under the mucosa. It forms the core of the plica and contains large blood vessels (**BV**). The muscularis externa (**ME**) is external to the submucosa; it is disposed into two dis-

tinct layers: an inner circular and an outer longitudinal layer. The serosa (**S**) is the light-staining region external to the muscularis externa.

The area within the **rectangle** in Figure 2 is examined at higher magnification in Figure 1 of Plate 50; a region comparable to that within the **large rectangle** (Fig. 3) is examined in Plate 48; a region comparable to the **small rectangle** (Fig. 3) is examined in Figure 3 of Plate 50.

The duodenum can be distinguished from the jejunum and ileum because it contains glands in the submucosa. (They may not be in the distal part of the duodenum.) The jejunum and ileum are not distinguished by any clear cut differences, but rather by relative differences. The jejunum is described as possessing a greater number of plicae circulares than the ileum; the ileum has large numbers of lymph nodules, many of which are aggregated.

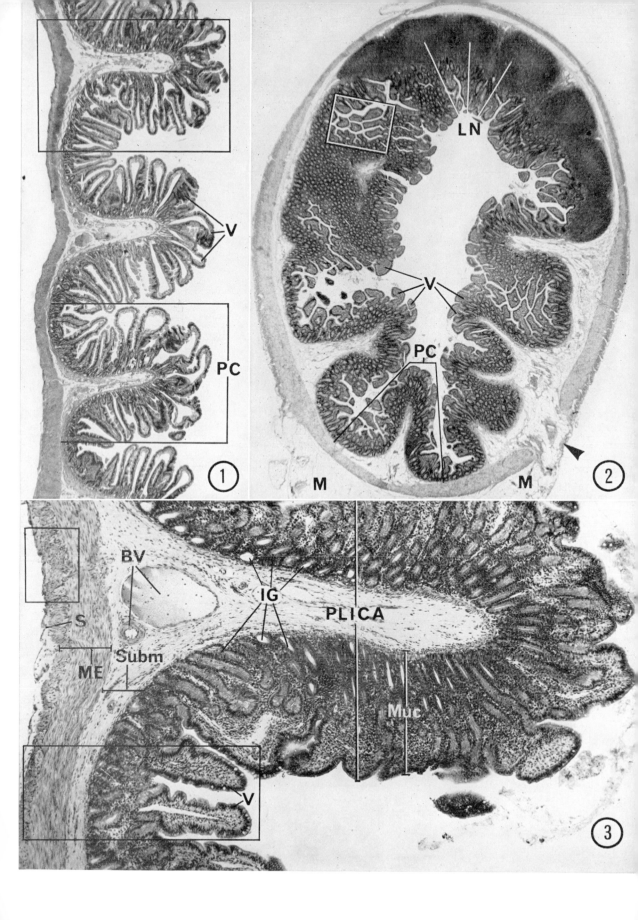

1

V

PC

2

LN

V

PC

M   M

3

BV

IG

PLICA

S

Subm

ME

Muc

V

Plate 48. Duodenum

The *duodenum* is the shortest part of the small intestine, measuring about 10 to 12 inches in man. It is adherent to the posterior abdominal wall in the human and, therefore, nonmobile; it receives the contents from the stomach, pancreas, liver and gall bladder; and it contains glands in the submucosa.

Figure 1 shows a segment of the duodenal wall that is comparable to the large rectangle in Figure 3 of the preceding plate, i.e., a plica circulares is not included. The mucosa, submucosa (**Subm**) and muscularis externa (**ME**) are shown (the serosa has been broken away). The mucosa occupies the upper part of the field. The villi project above the surface into the lumen of the duodenum; the glands "dip" into the supporting connective tissue. A **broken line** indicates the boundary between the villi and the glands.

Two kinds of cells are present on the surface of the villi (Fig. 2): columnar *absorptive cells* (**Ep**) and *goblet cells* (**GC**). The nuclei of the absorptive cells are elongate and at the basal region of the cells. The absorptive cells of the small intestine possess a *striated border* (see Plate 49). The spherical nuclei (**arrows**) belong to lymphocytes which have migrated into the epithelial layer.

The lamina propria (**LP**) makes up the core of the villus. It contains large numbers of round cells. Most of these are lymphocytes. The lamina propria of the villus also contains smooth muscle cells (**SM**). Contraction of these cells accounts, in part, for the variation in height of neighboring villi. Villi also contain lacteals and blood vessels, but they are not evident in Figures 1 and 2.

The fundic regions of the intestinal glands *(crypts of Lieberkühn)* are shown in the upper part of Figure 3. These glands (**IG**) are relatively straight. Note the highly cellular nature of the lamina propria (**LP**) which surrounds the glands. *A more complete consideration of villi and intestinal glands is to be found in the two succeeding plates.*

The submucosa consists of irregular connective tissue. It differs from submucosa of other parts of the small intestine because it contains glands (Fig. 3), called *Brunner's glands* (**BG**).

KEY

BG, Brunner's glands
BV, blood vessels
D, duct
Ep, epithelium
GC, goblet cells
IG, intestinal glands
LP, lamina propria
ME, muscularis externa
MM, muscularis mucosae
SM, smooth muscle
Subm, submucosa
arrows, nuclei of lymphocytes
broken line, boundary between villi and glands
Fig. 1 (dog), x 65; Figs. 2 and 3 (dog), x 160.

These are branched tubular or branched tubulo-alveolar glands whose secretory components consist of columnar epithelium. A duct (**D**) through which these glands open into the lumen of the duodenum is shown (Figs. 1 and 3) penetrating the *muscularis mucosae* (**MM**).

The two layers of the *muscularis externa* (**ME**) are shown in Figure 1. The inner circular layer is cut in cross section; the outer longitudinal layer is cut longitudinally. Therefore, this is a longitudinal cut through the duodenum.

The pancreatic duct and common bile duct enter the duodenum via a common opening called the *ampulla of Vater* (not shown). In some individuals there is an accessory pancreatic duct which also opens into the duodenum.

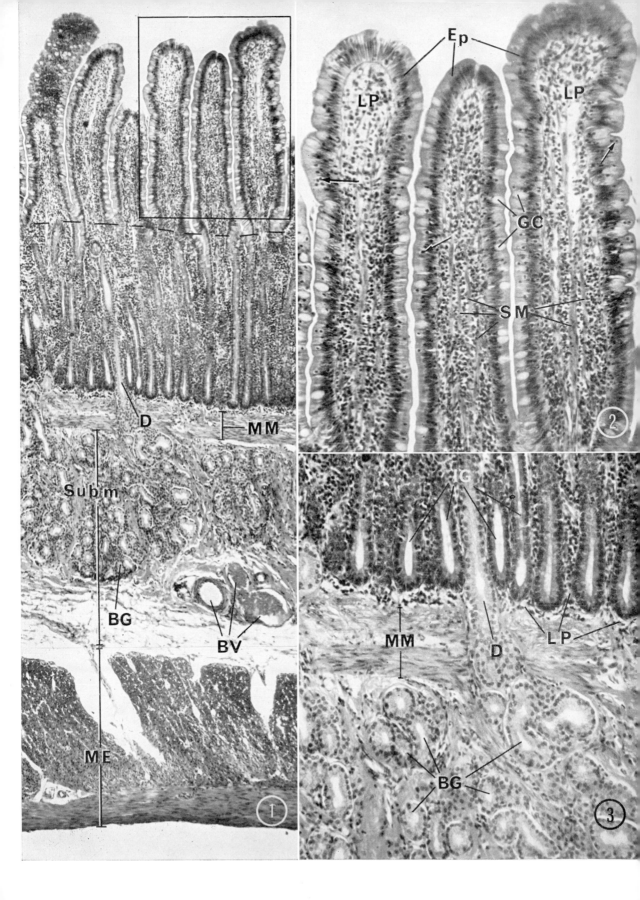

Plate 49. Villi

Villi are found only in the small intestine. They are fingerlike projections into the lumen, and are one of the modifications of the small intestine which serve to increase the amount of surface that is available for absorptive activity.

A villus is a mucosal projection (Fig. 1). Its core consists of a highly cellular lamina propria (**LP**); its surface consists of columnar absorptive cells (**Ep**) and goblet cells (**GC**). Each villus contains a centrally located lacteal (**L**). This is a lymphatic capillary which begins in the villus. In this specimen, the lacteals are widely dilated. In addition to the lacteal, the lamina propria of the villus contains small blood vessels and smooth muscle cells.

The lacteals (**L**) are lined by extremely flat endothelial cells (Fig. 2). The nuclei of these cells appear as the elongated, dark-staining profiles [**E(N)**] directly at the surface. At each nuclear extremity, one can see the attenuated cytoplasm [**E(C)**] which constitutes most of the wall of the lacteal. The other elongated nucleus [**SM(N)**], close to the surface, does not belong to an endothelial cell since its cytoplasm does not occupy a surface location. Its location and shape, in comparison to the other cells of the lamina propria, indicate that it is a smooth muscle cell. Nuclei of *plasma cells* (**PC**) can be seen. Other cells are difficult to identify although some of those with the vesiculated, elongated, or irregular shaped nuclei are likely to be fibrocytes.

The columnar absorptive cells contain a striated border (**SB**). Electron micrographs indicate that the striated border is due to the presence of closely packed, straight *microvilli* all of which are about the same height. The cells rest on a basement membrane (**BM**), which is evident in this illustration as a thin line, although it is not usually seen in H & E preparations. The cells are somewhat separated near the basement membrane and this enables one to identify the cell boundaries. However, the cell boundaries are also evident (**arrows**) near the surface where the cells are not separated. The nuclei of the absorptive cells all have essentially the same shape, orientation, and staining characteristics, and even

KEY

BM, basement membrane
E(C), cytoplasm of endothelial cell
E(N), nucleus of endothelial cell
Ep, epithelium
GC, goblet cells
L, lacteal
LP, lamina propria
Lym, lymphocytes
PC, plasma cells
SB, striated border
SM(C), smooth muscle cytoplasm
SM(N), smooth muscle nucleus
arrowheads, nuclei of goblet cell
arrows, boundaries of epithelial cells

Fig. 1 (monkey), x 160; Fig. 2 (monkey), x 640.

if the cytoplasmic boundaries were not evident, the nuclei would be an indication of the shape and orientation of the cells.

A number of round, intensely staining nuclei are scattered throughout different levels of the epithelial layer. These are nuclei of lymphocytes (**Lym**). The remaining nuclei (**arrowheads**) belong to goblet cells, which are located at different levels of the epithelial layer, just basal to the mucous cup. The mucous cup of the goblet cells shows some pale staining material. Most, if not all, of the mucus is lost during preparation of routine sections. If mucus is retained, it stains intensely.

It should be noted that villi may differ in appearance according to plane of section, cellularity of lamina propria, degree of lacteal dilatation, etc.

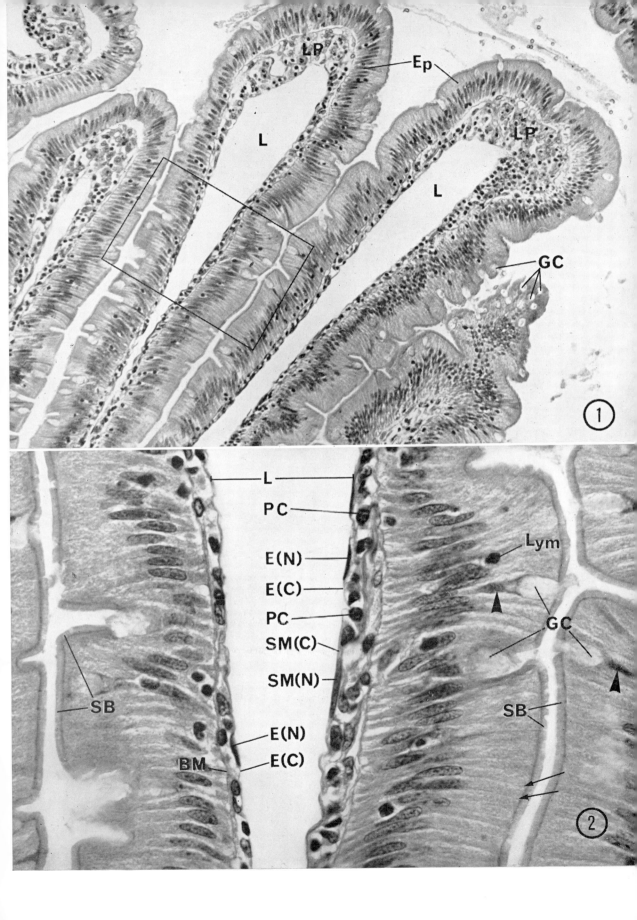

Plate 50. INTESTINAL GLANDS AND MUSCULARIS EXTERNA

Figure 1 is a higher magnification of the area within the **rectangle** of Figure 2, Plate 47. *Villi* (**V**) and *intestinal glands* (**IG**) are shown. Both of these have been cut in cross section. Since villi are finger-like projections into the lumen, they appear as islands of tissue surrounded by a space, the intestinal lumen. Each island has a central core of connective tissue, the lamina propria (**LP**), and an epithelial surface (**Ep**). Goblet cells (**GC**) appear as the light oval or spherical profiles in the epithelial layer. A lacteal (**L**) is shown in one of the villi.

The glands are invaginations into the underlying connective tissue. Because they are cut in cross section they appear as a central lumen bounded by columnar cells. The glands are surrounded by the numerous connective tissue cells of the lamina propria. Since the intestinal glands are rather straight tubular glands, they present essentially similar profiles.

The deeper regions of two intestinal glands are shown at greater magnification in Figure 2. As indicated above, each is surrounded by the cellular connective tissue that constitutes the lamina propria (**LP**) and each has a central lumen (**asterisk**). Examination of the gland cells shows that the cytoplasm contains large (eosinophilic) granules. The granules are secretory granules related to intestinal enzymes and the cells which contain these granules are called *Paneth* cells (**PC**). The epithelium of the intestinal glands also contains *argentaffine cells*. Special methods are needed to demonstrate these cells. Argentaffine cells are associated with the secretion of serotonin.

The muscularis externa and serosa (**S**) are illustrated in Figure 3. This region is comparable to the **small rectangle** in Figure 3, Plate 47. The inner circular layer [**SM(C)**] and the outer longitudinal layer [**SM(L)**] are separated by a parasympathetic ganglion. This is part of *Auerbach's plexus*. Several *ganglion cells* (**Gan C**) with large spherical nuclei are evident. The smaller nuclei belong to supporting cells. Parasympathetic ganglion cells are also present in the submucosa as components of *Meissner's plexus*. However, these are less numerous, and therefore more difficult to find.

KEY

Ep, epithelium
GC, goblet cells
Gan C, ganglion cells
IG, intestinal glands
L, lacteal
LP, lamina propria
M, mesothelium
PC, Paneth cells
S, serosa
SM(C), circular layer of smooth muscle
SM(L), longitudinal layer of smooth muscle
V, villi
asterisk, lumen of intestinal glands
Fig. 1 (monkey), x 160; Fig 2 (human), x 640; Fig. 3 (monkey), x 640.

The serosa (**S**) consists of simple squamous epithelium, mesothelium (**M**), which rests on delicate fibrous connective tissue.

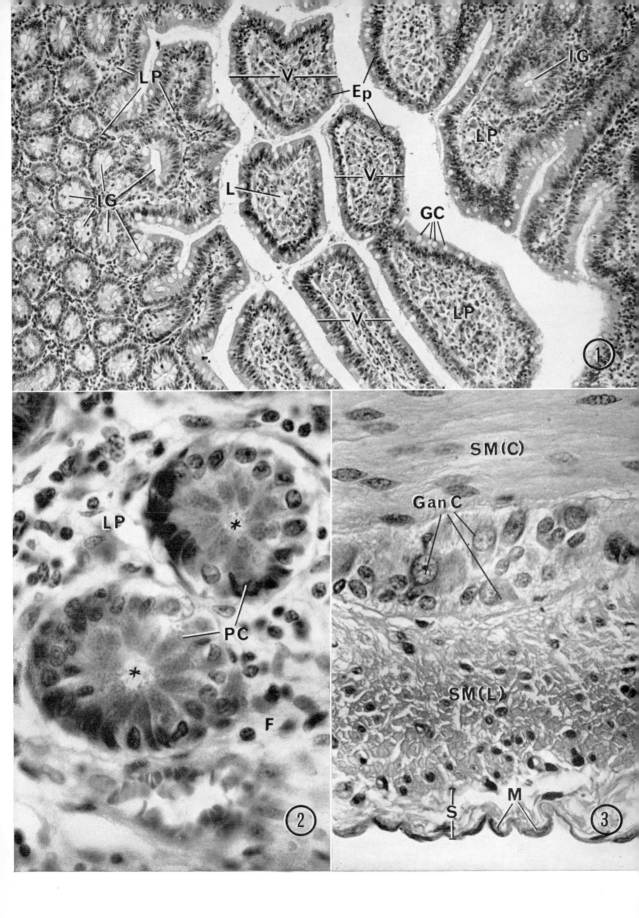

Plate 51. APPENDIX AND LARGE INTESTINE

Appendix. The appendix is a fingerlike process that is suspended from the cecum. Its wall is characterized by the presence of large numbers of lymphocytes which are organized as nodules. These are chiefly in the submucosa, but may break into the mucosa. The appendix has no villi or plicae circulares.

The wall of the appendix is illustrated in Figure 1. The *lumen* (**L**), *mucosa* (**Muc**), *submucosa* (**Subm**), *muscularis externa* (**ME**) and *serosa* (**S**) are shown. The mucosa contains straight tubular glands (**Gl**) which extend as far as the muscularis mucosae (**MM**) (Fig. 2), and are surrounded by a highly cellular lamina propria (**LP**). Most of the cells of the lamina propria are lymphocytes, however, fibrocytes, eosinophils, and other round cells are also present. Lymphocytes (**Lym**) may be so numerous in the mucosa and submucosa that they obscure the muscularis mucosae. The glands (*crypts of Lieberkühn*) contain large numbers of goblet cells, and in their fundic region may contain *Paneth cells* and *argentaffine cells.*

The submucosa (**Subm**) consists of a rather dense irregular connective tissue. Some adipose tissue (**AT**) and two aggregations of lymphocytes (**Lym**) are shown. Although the fibrous nature of the submucosa is readily evident in Figure 1, the amount of lymphatic tissue may be sufficiently great to obscure the fibrous material.

The muscularis externa (**ME**) is comprised of an inner circular layer and an outer longitudinal layer of smooth muscle. External to the muscularis externa is the serosa (**S**).

Large intestine. The wall of the large intestine (colon) contains the same layers that are found in the stomach and small intestine. However, the large intestine has no villi or plicae circulares. The mucosa (**Muc**) contains straight tubular glands (crypts of Lieberkühn) that extend throughout the entire thickness as far as the muscularis mucosae (see Plate 52). The glands, as in the appendix, contain large numbers of goblet cells. However, Paneth cells and argentaffine cells are rarely found.

The submucosa (**Subm**) consists of a rather dense irregular connective tissue. Adipose tis-

KEY

AP, Auerbach's plexus
AT, adipose tissue
Gl, glands
L, lumen
LP, lamina propria
LV, lymphatic vessel
Lym, lymphocytes
ME, muscularis externa
MM, muscularis mucosae
Muc, mucosa
S, serosa
SM(C), circular layer of smooth muscle
SM(L), longitudinal layer of smooth muscle
Subm, submucosa

Fig. 1 (human), x 40; Fig. 2 (human), x 160; Fig. 3 (monkey), x 65.

sue (**AT**) and blood vessels can be seen in this layer. The muscularis externa (**ME**) consists of an inner circular layer [**SM(C)**] and an outer longitudinal layer [**SM(L)**]. The smooth muscle cells of the outer layer are grouped into three separate, longitudinal bundles (taenia coli), one of which is shown in Figure 3. The regular arrangement of muscle cells helps to distinguish the muscularis externa from the irregular arrangement of fibers that constitute the submucosa. The light areas between the two muscular layers contain components of Auerbach's plexus (**AP**).

The serosa consists of a thin layer of connective tissue that is surfaced by a single layer of squamous epithelium (mesothelium). The space (**LV**) in the serosa is not an artifact, it is a lymphatic vessel. This cannot be established at the low magnification of Figure 3, but was determined by examination of this slide and its serial neighbors at higher magnification.

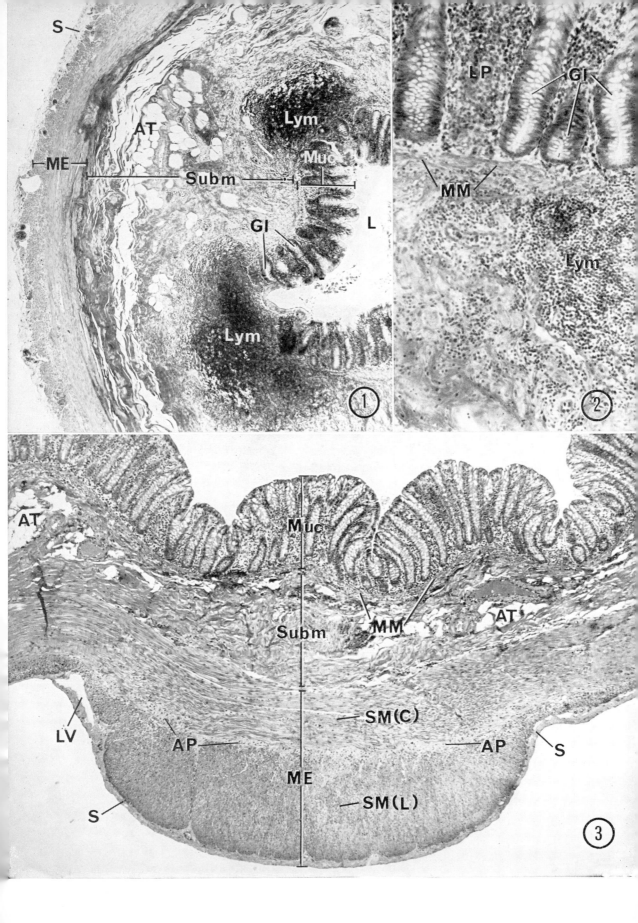

Plate 52. Mucosa of Large Intestine

The mucosa (**Muc**) and some submucosa of the large intestine are shown in Figure 1. The junction between the two is indicated by the muscularis mucosae (**MM**). A large number of lymphocytes are in the submucosa of this specimen. They are so numerous that at one point (**asterisk**) they obscure the muscularis mucosae and become continuous with the cellular lamina propria (**LP**) of the mucosa. These lymphocytes are at the periphery of a lymph nodule.

The mucosa of the large intestine contains straight tubular glands, crypts of Lieberkühn. These extend as far as the muscularis mucosae. When a gland is cut longitudinally (**arrow**) it appears as an invagination of the surface epithelium (**Ep**). When the glands are cut in cross section (Fig. 2) they present circular profiles with a central lumen.

The crypts of the large intestine can be readily recognized because the lumens of the glands are invariably patent. This is evident not only in Figures 1, 2, and 3, but is generally true.

The cross-sectioned glands in Figure 2 are surrounded by the highly cellular lamina propria (**LP**). Immediately surrounding the glands are elongated, flattened nuclei (**arrowheads**). Cytoplasmic material can be seen extending from the extremities of these nuclei. This cytoplasm is extremely attenuated, moreover, it is very close to the base of the epithelial cells (**Ep**) and it could be confused with a basement membrane if it were not related to a nucleus. Electron micrographs of cells with elongated nuclei that are related to tubular glands in this fashion indicate that they are smooth muscle cells.

The surface cells of the mucosa are largely columnar absorbing cells. They possess a striated border which is less prominent than that of the small intestine, but nevertheless readily seen (**arrows**) in well prepared specimens (**inset**, Fig. 1). Goblet cells (**GC**) are very numerous within the gland, but Paneth cells and argentaffine cells are rarely found. Although the epithelial cells (**Ep**) in the fundic region of the glands (Fig. 3) do not appear very different from those that are closer to the

KEY

Ep, epithelium
GC, goblet cells
LP, lamina propria
Lym, lymphocytes
MM, muscularis mucosae
Muc, mucosa
arrow, longitudinally cut intestinal gland
arrows (inset), striated border
arrowheads, nuclei of peritubular smooth muscle cells
asterisk, numerous lymphocytes obscuring the muscularis mucosae
Fig. 1 (human), x 160; Figs. 2 and 3 (monkey), x 640.

surface, they are regarded as being less differentiated. They give rise to new cells which will migrate to the surface to replace the cells that are constantly being desquamated.

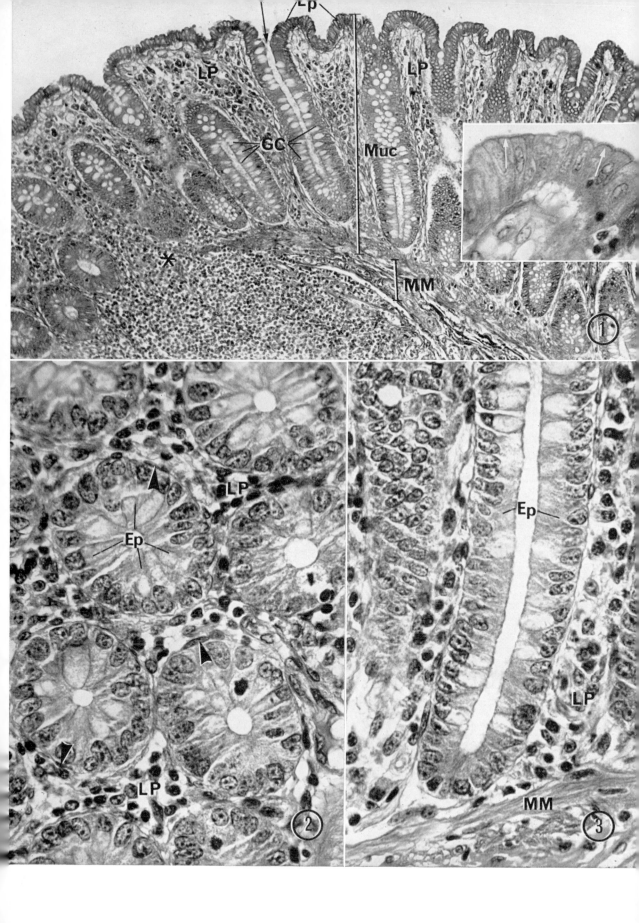

Plate 53. LIVER I

The liver consists of large numbers of functional units called *lobules.* These are roughly cylindrical in shape with a venous channel, the *central vein,* traveling through its long axis. Irregular interconnecting sheets or plates of hepatic cells radiate outward from the central vein and constitute the parenchyma. Sinusoidal capillaries (*sinusoids*) separate the sheets of hepatic cells and empty into the central veins. In the human, the lobules are poorly delineated from their neighbors, and it is often difficult to determine where one lobule ends and the next begins.

In a low power view of a liver section (Fig. 1), large numbers of hepatic cells appear to be uniformly disposed throughout the whole specimen. The plates of hepatic cells are one cell thick, but when sectioned, appear as interconnecting cords one or more cells thick according to the plane of section. The sinusoids appear as the light areas between the cords of cells. In addition to the sinusoids, three groups of blood vessels are present: *1*) *central veins* (**CV**), 2) tributaries of *hepatic veins* (**HV**, Fig. 2), and 3) components of the *portal canal* (**PC**), namely, the branches of the *hepatic arteries* (**HA**) and *portal vein* (**PV**), which accompany the *hepatic ducts* (**HD**).

The central veins are larger than sinusoids. They are, in fact, the most distal radicles of the hepatic veins. Central veins travel alone, and have extremely thin walls. Several sinusoids can be seen emptying into the central veins of Figure 1 (**arrows**). Central veins empty into hepatic veins.

Figure 2 shows two hepatic veins (**HV**). The larger one is surrounded by a considerable amount of connective tissue. However, this connective tissue does not contain any other vessel of comparable size. This is a diagnostic characteristic of hepatic veins, i.e., a large vessel traveling alone. The smaller vein is surrounded by correspondingly less connective tissue.

A portal canal is examined at higher magnification in Figure 3. The hepatic artery, portal vein, and hepatic duct constitute a *portal triad.* The lumen of the portal vein (**PV**) is much larger than the lumen of the

KEY

CV, central veins
HA, hepatic artery
HD, hepatic duct
HV, hepatic veins
PC, portal canal
PV, portal vein
arrows, sinusoids entering central vein

Fig. 1 (human), x 65; Fig. 2 (monkey) x 65; Fig. 3 (monkey), x 160.

accompanying hepatic artery (**HA**), although the thickness of the walls is about the same. Both of these are readily distinguished from the hepatic duct (**HD**) which has a wall of columnar epithelium. Another portal canal is seen in Figure 1.

At this point it is well to re-examine Figure 1 in order to define the boundaries of a liver lobule. A lobule is readily identified when it is cut in cross section, and one has been delineated by the **broken lines.** The central vein, as its name implies, is centrally located. The hepatic cells and sinusoids appear to radiate outward from the central vein to the periphery of the lobule. Connective tissue and components of portal canals may be between adjacent lobules, however, very often, neighboring lobules are not separated by these structures and in these cases, the cords of hepatic cells seem to travel from one lobule to another.

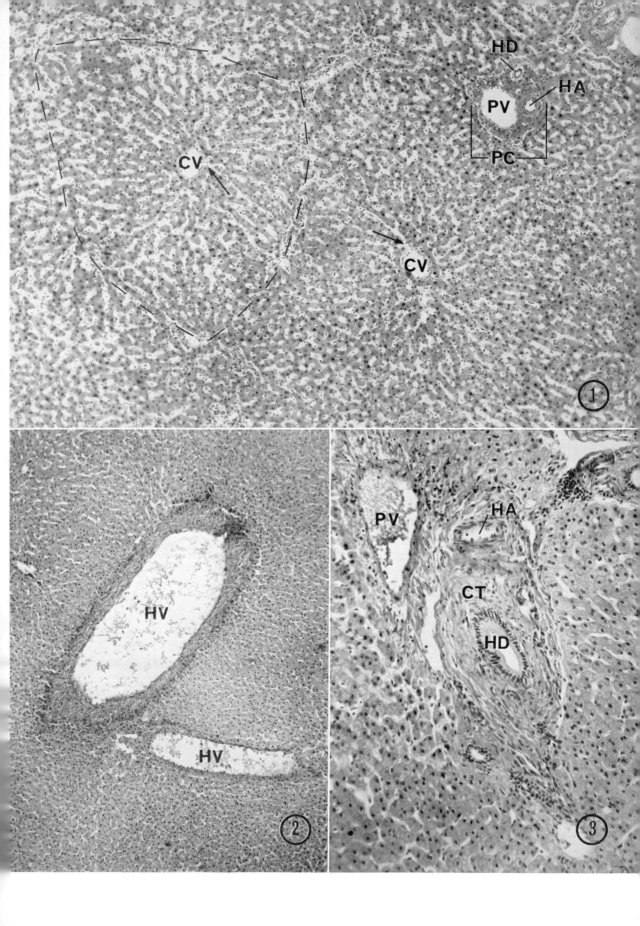

Plate 54. LIVER II

Hepatic cells are cuboidal cells that are arranged as interconnecting sheets one cell wide. In sections, these sheets or plates of cells appear as irregular interconnecting cords one or more cells wide according to the plane of section (Fig. 1). The nuclei of hepatic cells are characteristically large and spherical. They usually stain somewhat less intensely than the smaller nuclei of other cells in the liver and not infrequently, two nuclei are found in the same cell (**asterisks**). The boundaries between adjacent cells are not always evident, although they can be seen in Figures 1 and 2. Hepatic cells contain a fairly large amount of cytoplasm and this is filled with various organelles and, in the adequately fed individual, with glycogen. However, special preparations are needed to demonstrate these features.

The area inside the rectangle in Figure 1 is shown at high magnification in Figure 2. Small, channel-like spaces called *bile canaliculi* are located between the cells. They appear as small oval structures between adjacent cells (**brackets**). Actually these are places where adjacent cell membranes are separated to form a conduit. Small hepatic ducts (**HD**) are also evident in Figures 1 and 2. They consist of cuboidal cells; the small lumen can be distinguished in Figure 2. The bile canaliculi collect bile from the hepatic cells and convey it to the hepatic ducts. The ducts enter the interlobular connective tissue where they accompany a hepatic artery and a portal vein as a portal triad. Whereas the hepatic artery and portal vein carry blood to the liver, the hepatic ducts carry bile away from the liver.

The sinusoids are lined by phagocytic cells called *Kupffer* cells. When particulate material is injected into the bloodstream, these cells phagocytize this material and thereby remove it from the blood. Kupffer cells have irregularly shaped, often elongated nuclei and variable amounts of cytoplasm. The nuclei often appear to project into the lumen of the sinusoids. A small space, the *space of Disse,* is situated between the sinusoidal wall and the hepatic cells. This space is not usually seen in well preserved specimens.

KEY

HD, hepatic duct
asterisks, binucleate cells
arrows, unstained nuclei of Kupffer cells
brackets, bile canaliculi

Fig. 1 (monkey), x 640; Fig. 2 (monkey), x 1240; Fig. 3 (rat) x 640.

Figure 3 is an unstained section of a liver from an animal that was injected with trypan blue. The trypan blue was phagocytized by the Kupffer cells and can be seen as it fills the cytoplasm and partly surrounds the clear, unstained nuclei (**arrows**).

The hepatic artery and portal vein conduct blood to the liver. The blood of the portal vein is from the alimentary canal, pancreas, and spleen; by this arrangement materials that are absorbed from the alimentary canal can be acted on by the liver before they enter the systemic circulation. The liver not only modifies and removes portal blood constituents, but it also participates in maintaining certain blood components of the systemic circulation at appropriate levels. Branches of the portal vein and hepatic artery both open into the sinusoids. Blood then enters the central veins and leaves the liver via the hepatic veins.

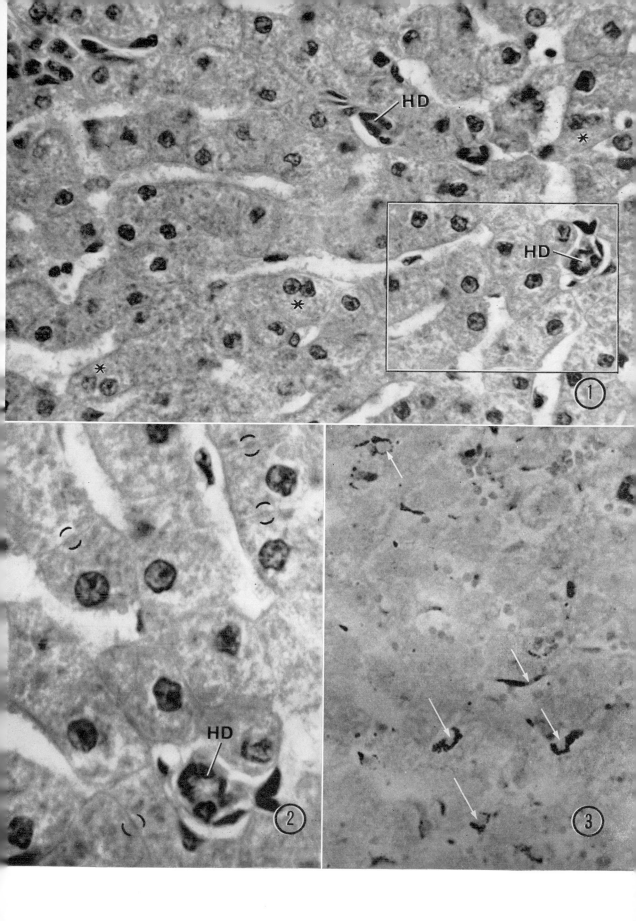

Plate 55. GALL BLADDER

The gall bladder is a hollow pear-shaped organ which concentrates and stores the bile. Its wall (**Fig.** 1) is comprised of a *mucosa* (**Muc**), *muscularis* (**Mus**), and an *adventitia* (**Adv**), or, on its free surface, a serosa. The mucosa (**Fig.** 2) consists of a simple columnar epithelium (**Ep**) resting on loose, irregular, connective tissue (**CT**); the muscularis consists of interlacing bundles of smooth muscle (**SM**); the adventitia (**Fig.** 1) consists of irregular connective tissue and contains a considerable amount of adipose tissue (**AT**), and blood vessels (**BV**).

The mucosa is thrown into numerous folds when the muscularis is contracted. This is the usual histological appearance of the gall bladder unless, of course, steps are taken to fix and preserve it in the distended state. Occasionally the section cuts through a recess in a fold and the recess may then resemble a gland (**X**). The mucosa however does not possess glands except in the neck.

The epithelial lining (**Ep**) of the gall bladder consists of absorptive cells. They have certain characteristics which may assist the student in identifying the gall bladder and distinguishing it from other organs. Only one cell type is present in the epithelial layer (**Fig.** 3). These are tall columnar cells; the nuclei are in the basal portion of the cell. The cells possess a delicate *striated border* (**arrows**). However, this is not always evident in routine H & E sections. The cytoplasm stains rather evenly with eosin. This is in keeping with its absorptive function and is in contrast to the staining of cells that are engaged in the secretion of proteinaceous material. Such cells possess basophilic material within their cytoplasm, moreover, the cytoplasm of protein secreting cells may stain unevenly due to the presence of Golgi material, and secretory granules.

The muscle cells can be recognized largely by their organization (**Fig.** 2). Note that groups of elongated nuclei are oriented in generally the same direction. In many places, the nuclei appear as slight thickenings in an eosinophilic fiber (the smooth muscle cytoplasm). This is a particularly strong diag-

KEY

Adv, adventitia
AT, adipose tissue
BV, blood vessels
CT, connective tissue
Ep, epithelium
Muc, mucosa
Mus, muscularis
SM, smooth muscle
X, mucosal recess
arrows, striated border

Fig. 1 (monkey), x 75; Fig. 2 (monkey), x 185; Fig. 3 (monkey), x 720.

nostic feature of smooth muscle. In this preparation the cytoplasm of the muscle cells stains a slightly different shade from the connective tissue and further facilitates its recognition.

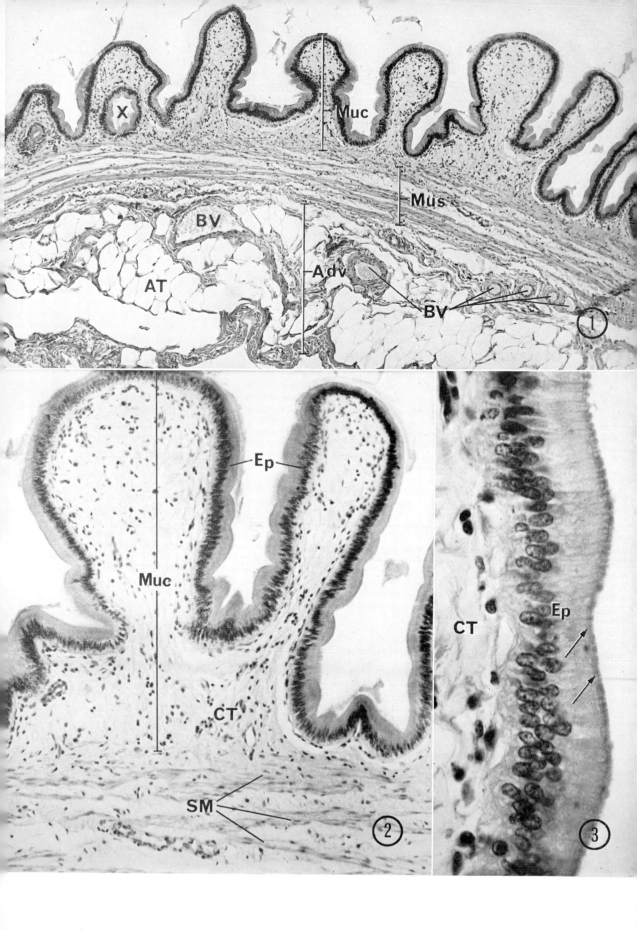

Plate 56. PANCREAS

The *pancreas* is a compound tubulo-alveolar gland. In addition to the exocrine components, it also contains *islets of Langerhans* which are endocrine components. A section through the pancreas is shown in Figure 1. It shows three islets of Langerhans (**IL**), a large duct (**D**), some smaller ducts (**arrows**) and throughout most of the field, the acinar components (**A**). A ganglion cell (**arrowhead**) is in the lower left of the figure.

The acini, or alveoli, consist of serous type cells. Characteristically the nuclei occupy a basal location within the cell. The basal part of the cell also contains some basophilic cytoplasm which stains intensely with hematoxylin. The serous alveoli appear as spherical or elongated aggregates of cells. The islets, on the other hand, appear as larger aggregates of cells. The nuclei of the island cells do not show any particular arrangement and the cytoplasm stains less intensely than the cytoplasm of the acinar components. Therefore, the islets usually appear as large islands of lightly stained cells among the darker alveoli.

The large duct (**D**) in the center of the field is surrounded by a moderately large amount of connective tissue (**CT**). It consists of columnar cells which surround a distinct lumen. The smaller ducts (**arrows**) can be recognized by the arrangement of the nuclei and the fact that the cytoplasm stains less intensely than the cytoplasm of the acinar cells. If the duct is collapsed or cut tangentially, it may simply appear as a row of nuclei.

Figure 2 shows an islet of Langerhans at higher magnification. Three types of cells can be demonstrated in special preparations, *A* or *alpha cells, B* or *beta cells,* and *D cells.* However, the different cell types cannot be distinguished with assurance in routine H & E sections.

Surrounding the islets in Figure 2 are the acini of the pancreas. The cells which make up the acini contain a large amount of basophilic cytoplasm. The acini also contain a small cell with pale staining cytoplasm. These are the *centro-acinar cells* (**arrowheads**). They occupy a central position within the acinus and are the beginning of the duct. Although

---

KEY

A, acini
CT, connective tissue
D, duct
GC, ganglion cell
IL, islets of Langerhans
arrows, small ducts
arrowhead (Fig. 1), ganglion cell
arrowheads (Fig. 2), centro-acinar cells
Fig. 1 (monkey), x 160; Fig. 2 (monkey), x 640.

---

these cells occupy a central position in the acini, they frequently appear to have a peripheral position due to the plane of section.

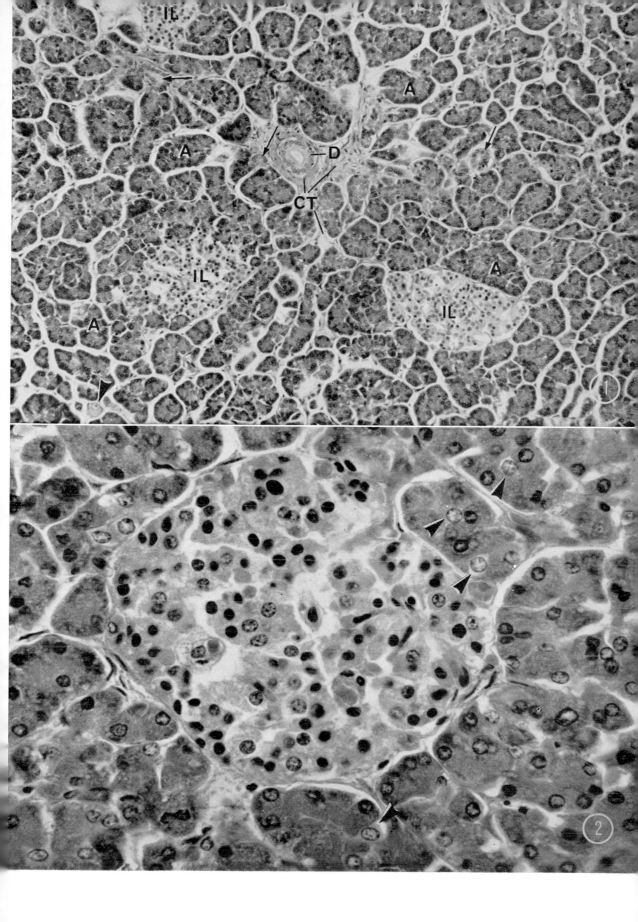

RESPIRATORY SYSTEM

THE RESPIRATORY SYSTEM consists of the lungs and the respiratory passages that lead to and from the lungs. The respiratory passages include the nose (and sometimes mouth), naso- and oropharynx, larynx, trachea and the two bronchi. Each bronchus enters a lung and continues to branch into smaller passages with increasingly thinner walls. These intrapulmonary branchings are called the bronchial tree. Blood vessels also enter the lungs with the bronchi; the blood vessels branch, and come into intimate contact with the terminal units of the bronchial tree, called the *alveoli*. This intimate relationship between pulmonary capillaries and alveolar air spaces is the structural basis for the main function of the respiratory system, namely, gas exchange within the lungs. This relationship is strikingly illustrated in the histological appearance of a lung section.

For most of its length, the respiratory passages are covered by a mucous film. This is produced by glands within the wall of the respiratory passages and by single celled glands (*goblet cells*) within the surface epithelium. Although the mucus serves several functions, such as trapping inspired particulate matter, moistening the air, and keeping the underlying tissues moist, it must be regularly removed. For this purpose, cilia are present on the surface of most of the cells that line the respiratory passages and upper part of the bronchial tree. It should be noted that cilia extend more distally into the bronchial tree than the mucus-producing glands.

The main function of the respiratory passages is to serve as an air conduit, and the structure of the walls reflects this function. Cartilage is present within the walls of the respiratory passages and the proximal part of the bronchial tree. The cartilage is arranged so that the passageways remain patent.

Parts of the respiratory system also serve other functions. For example, the olfactory mucosa serves as a receptor for smell, and the larynx serves in phonation. In both of these, advantage is taken of the air movement that is a consequence of respiration.

Plate 57. OLFACTORY MUCOSA

The *olfactory mucosa* is located in the roof and adjacent upper walls of the nasal cavity. It consists of a pseudostratified columnar epithelium which rests on a supporting connective tissue (Fig. 1).

The olfactory epithelium contains three cell types: *receptor cells, sustentacular cells,* and *basal cells.* The surface is modified by the presence of cilia and other specializations. It is not possible to identify the various cell types on the basis of cytologic characteristics in H & E preparations. However, on the basis of location of the nuclei, some estimate is possible. A "cytoplasmic zone" without nuclei immediately under the surface (Fig. 2) can be distinguished from a "nuclear zone." The nuclei of sustentacular cells (**Sus**) are located in the most superficial part of the nuclear zone, immediately adjacent to the cytoplasmic zone. The nuclei of the basal cells (**Bas**) are located in the deepest part of the nuclear zone, immediately adjacent to the connective tissue. The broadest part of the nuclear zone contains the nuclei of the receptor cells (**Rec**).

A receptor cell is a bipolar type of neuron which retains a surface location. It contains a distal process that extends from the nucleus to the surface, and at the surface it possesses a cytoplasmic vesicle, called the *olfactory vesicle,* that extends between the cilia. The olfactory vesicle is not always evident in H & E preparations and is not clear in Figure 2. The proximal part of the receptor cell extends toward the basal region of the olfactory layer. Here it continues as a slender axon which, along with the axons of other receptor cells, forms non-myelinated nerve bundles (**N**) that proceed through the connective tissue, through the cribriform plate, and into the cranial cavity. The axons of the receptor cells are extremely slender and appear as dots in cross section through the nerve. Nuclei of supporting cells are also evident within the nerve bundles.

The basal cells have only a small amount of cytoplasm. It remains near the nucleus and does not reach the surface. The sustentacular cells extend through the entire thickness of the epithelium. These cells do not contain cilia.

KEY

A, artery
Bas, basal cell nuclei
Gl, Bowman's glands
Lym, lymphatic vessel
N, nerve bundle
Rec, receptor cell nuclei
Sus, sustentacular cell nuclei
V, vein
Fig. 1 (cat), x 160; Fig. 2 (cat), x 640.

The connective tissue of the olfactory mucosa contains not only numerous bundles of the olfactory nerves, but also special glands called *Bowman's glands* (**Gl**). These glands contain a pigment that stains intensely with hematoxylin. Ducts from the glands carry secretions to the mucosal surface. A number of these are seen just as they are about to penetrate the epithelium. Numerous blood vessels are present in the connective tissue. The empty vessels with a flat epithelial lining are lymphatic vessels (**Lym**). They can be distinguished from arteries (**A**) and veins (**V**) because their walls are extremely thin, and also because they contain no blood cells. Although the absence of blood cells does not justify an identification of lymphatic vessels, the absence of cells in extremely thin-walled vessels is diagnostic, especially if all of the other vessels contain blood cells.

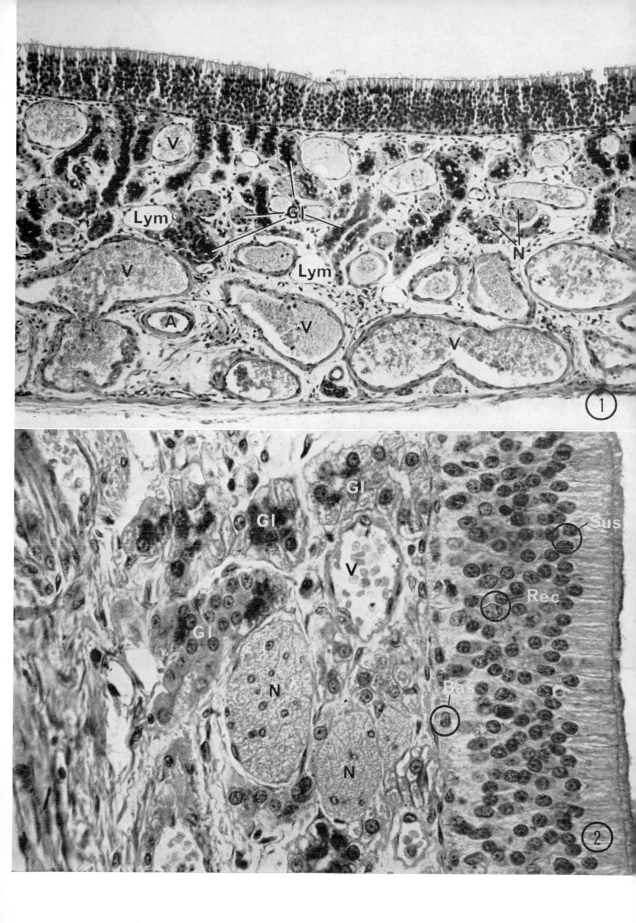

Plate 58. TRACHEA AND BRONCHUS

The trachea extends from the larynx to about the middle of the thorax, where it divides into two bronchi. Its primary function is to serve as a conduit for air. The lumen of the trachea is held open by a series of C-shaped hyaline cartilages which form the framework of the wall. Posteriorly, cartilage is lacking whereas smooth muscle and fibroelastic tissue are present.

The wall of the trachea consists of the following layers (see Fig. 1): From the inside (luminal surface) there is a *mucosa* (**Muc**), *submucosa* (**Submuc**), *cartilaginous layer* (**Cart**), and an *adventitia* (**Adv**).

The **rectangle** in Figure 1 outlines the area shown in Figure 2 at higher magnification. The mucosa consists of ciliated pseudostratified columnar epithelium (**Ep**) resting on a highly elastic lamina propria (**LP**). A division between the mucosa and submucosa is not evident in H & E sections, but the boundary (**double-headed arrow**) is marked by the presence of an elastic layer that is revealed with special stains. Seromucous glands (**Gl**) and their ducts are present in the submucosa (Fig. 2). Glands are also present in the posterior part of the trachea where there is no cartilage; here they often extend through the muscle layer into the adventitia.

Three cell types are present in the tracheal epithelium: *basal cells, ciliated columnar cells,* and *goblet cells* (Fig. 3). Basal cells, at the base of the epithelial layer, can be recognized by their spherical, densely staining nuclei (**N Bas**), which are close to the basement membrane. These cells contain little cytoplasm.

The ciliated columnar cells extend from the basement membrane to the surface. The nuclei of these columnar cells (**N Col**) are generally oval and tend to be located in the mid-region of the cell. Moreover, they are somewhat larger and paler staining than the basal cell nuclei. At their free surface, these cells contain numerous cilia which, together, give the surface a brush-like appearance. At the base of the cilia one sees a dense line. This is due to the linear aggregation of structures referred to as *basal bodies* that are connected to the proximal end of each cilium.

KEY

Adv, adventitia
Cart, cartilaginous layer
Ep, epithelium
Gl, glands
Gob, goblet cell
LP, lamina propria
Muc, mucosa
N Bas, nuclei of basal cells
N Col, nuclei of columnar cells
SM, smooth muscle
Submuc, submucosa
double-headed arrow (Fig. 2), approximate boundary between mucosa and submucosa
arrows (Fig. 3), nuclei of goblet cells

Fig. 1 (dog), x 65; Fig. 2 (dog), x 160; Fig. 3 (monkey), x 640; Fig. 4 (dog), x 40.

Interspersed between the ciliated cells are mucus-secreting goblet cells (**Gob**). The cell appears empty because the mucus is lost during tissue preparation. Characteristically, the flattened nuclei are at the base of the mucous cup (**arrows**).

Although basement membranes are not ordinarily seen in H & E preparations, one is regularly seen under the epithelium in the human trachea. It is conspicuous because of its thickness.

The trachea divides into two *bronchi,* one of which goes into each lung. The bronchi branch several times, decrease somewhat in diameter, and undergo certain structural changes (Fig. 4). The large C-shaped cartilages are now replaced by smaller plates (**Cart**) which completely surround the bronchus. The elastic layer is replaced by smooth muscle (**SM**) which now appears at the boundary between the mucosa and submucosa. The mucosa remains essentially the same, except for the presence of smooth muscle. The description of ciliated pseudostratified columnar epithelium given above also applies to the epithelium of the bronchi.

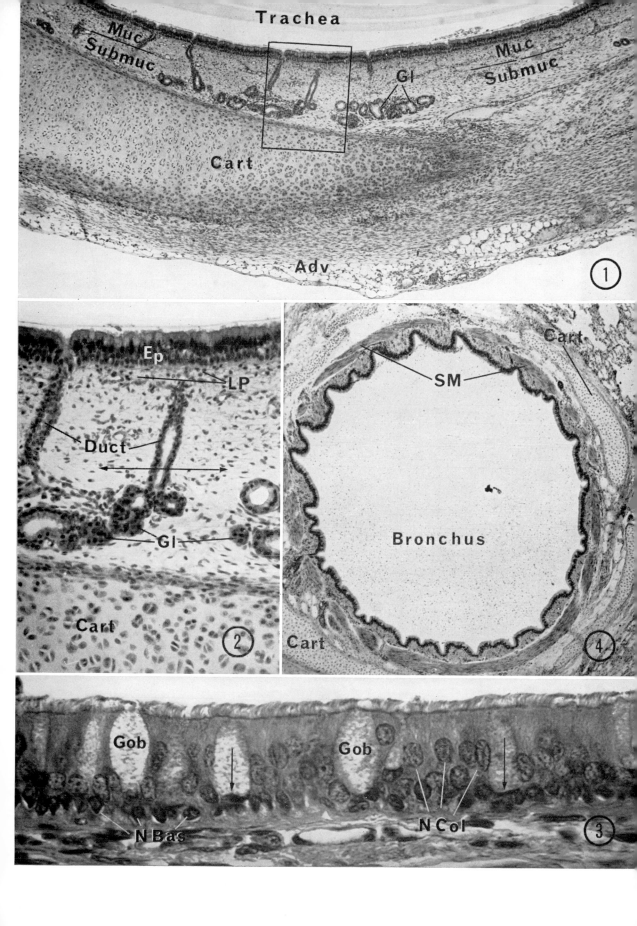

Plate 59. Bronchus and Bronchiole

Each bronchus enters a lung at a site called the hilus. The hilus also serves as the portal for the pulmonary artery and veins, bronchial artery, nerves, and lymphatic vessels. Sections that include the larger respiratory passages often show these structures. Figure 1 is a segment of the wall of a bronchus. The cartilage is not included in the illustration. This section shows the ciliated pseudostratified columnar epithelium (**Ep**) cut obliquely. The goblet cells appear as the clear spherical structures. Under the epithelium, in the lamina propria, are a number of round cells, mostly lymphocytes (**Lym**). In the bronchus, smooth muscle (**SM**) marks the boundary between the mucosa and submucosa, in contrast to the trachea where no boundary is evident. Below the smooth muscle is dense connective tissue (**CT**) and glands (**Gl**) of the submucosa. The submucosa also contains a collection of "ganglion cells" (**Gan C**). These are parasympathetic ganglia, and are recognized by their large cell bodies which contain an extremely large, spherical, pale staining nucleus.

As the respiratory tube proceeds more distally, certain elements are lost and the tube is now called a bronchiole rather than a bronchus. In a *bronchiole* the cartilage is no longer present; the seromucous glands of the submucosa disappear; goblet cells are reduced in number or entirely missing, and the epithelium becomes simple columnar, but is still ciliated. On the other hand, the smooth muscle remains and forms a conspicuous component of the wall. Elastic tissue is also a conspicuous feature of the wall but, again, requires special elastic tissue stains for its demonstration.

It should be emphasized that the changes from bronchus to bronchiole are gradual and some elements remain somewhat longer than others; therefore, one may encounter a respiratory tube showing features of both, such as that shown in Figure 2. A small amount of cartilage (**Cart**) is still present in this instance. However, it should be noted that the glands have disappeared and the smooth muscle (**SM**) constitutes a major component of the wall.

KEY

BV, blood vessel
Cart, cartilage
CT, connective tissue
Ep, epithelium
Gan C, ganglion cells
Gl, glands
Lym, lymphocytes
SM, smooth muscle
arrows, alveoli in wall of respiratory bronchiole

Fig. 1 (monkey), x 160; Fig. 2 (monkey), x 65; Fig. 3 (monkey), x 640; Fig. 4 (monkey), x 40.

The epithelium of a bronchiole is shown in Figure 3. This is simple columnar ciliated epithelium. At the base of the cilia are the basal bodies which appear as a dark line.

Figure 4 shows the alterations that occur as the respiratory tube is followed more distally. Evidently a branching has recently occurred; the larger part of the tube is on the left, whereas, on the right, the knife has cut the passage at two places. Above the respiratory passage is an accompanying blood vessel (**BV**) and an aggregation of lymphocytes (**Lym**). Alveolar spaces are seen in the remainder of the section. The respiratory passage, moving across the field to the right, loses more and more of its elements until the wall loses its continuity and is partly made up of *alveoli* (**arrows**). At this point, the tube is called a *respiratory bronchiole* because gas exchange occurs through the alveolar part of the wall. Proximal to this point the bronchiole is called a *terminal bronchiole*. Air exchange does not occur through the wall of the terminal bronchiole, or through the more proximal parts of the respiratory tree.

140

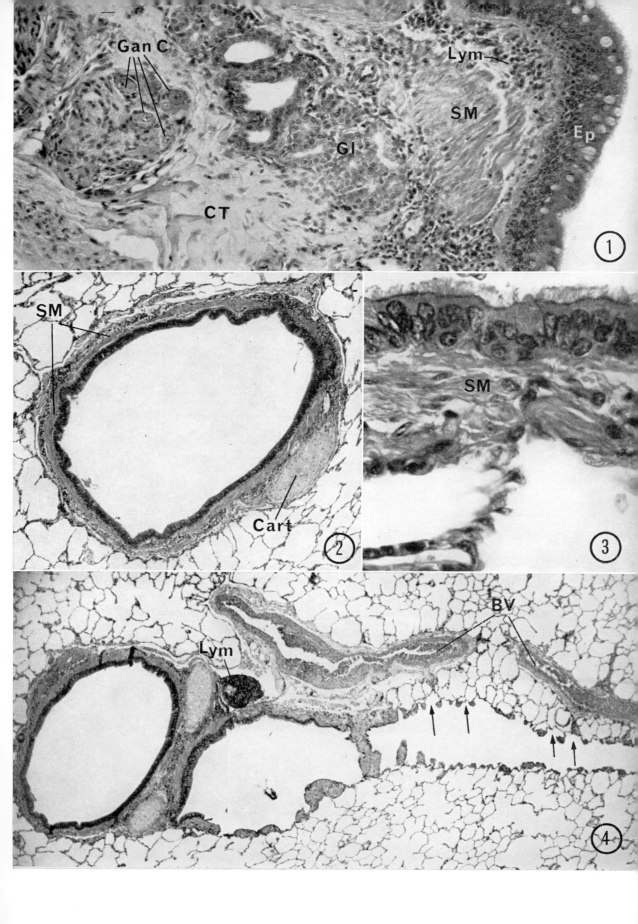

Plate 60. Respiratory Bronchiole, Alveolar Duct, Alveolar Sac, and Alveolus

The illustrations on the accompanying plate show those parts of the bronchial tree through which air exchange occurs with the blood stream; namely, the *respiratory bronchiole, alveolar duct, alveolar sac,* and *alveolus.* "Alveolar air" is contained within these spaces.

The respiratory bronchiole (Fig. 1) retains some of the characteristics of a terminal bronchiole since part of the wall, like that of the terminal bronchiole, is thick. However, as stated in the previous page, in addition to the thick segments which contain smooth muscle, alveolar sacs (**arrows**) also form part of the wall. Even at low power, the thick muscle-containing segments of the wall can easily be distinguished from the alveolar pockets. The muscle (**SM**) is easily recognized where it has been cut in a longitudinal fashion (Fig. 1). However, it is difficult to recognize when only small areas of the thick segments appear in the section. Surrounding the respiratory bronchiole in the remainder of the figure are the alveolar air spaces of the lung.

The area within the **rectangle** in Figure 1 is shown in Figure 2 at higher magnification. This permits a more detailed examination of the wall of the respiratory bronchiole. The surface of the respiratory bronchiole consists of cuboidal epithelium (**Ep**), and this rests on a very small amount of connective tissue. It should be noted that these epithelial cells are extremely small. The main component under the epithelial lining is the smooth muscle. However, as indicated above, it is sometimes difficult to recognize.

When the respiratory bronchiole (**RB**) loses its thick components, it opens into the terminal part of the bronchial tree (Fig. 3), namely, the alveolar duct, alveolar sacs, and alveoli. The most distal component of the respiratory tube is the alveolus (**A**). Groups of alveoli clustered together and sharing a common opening are referred to as alveolar sacs (**AS**). Alveoli that form a tube are referred to as alveolar ducts (**AD**).

The alveolar wall consists of a layer of extremely flattened cells in close contact with

KEY

A, alveolus
AD, alveolar duct
AS, alveolar sac
Ep, epithelium
RB, respiratory brochiole
RBC, red blood cell
SM, smooth muscle
WBC, white blood cell
arrows, alveolar sacs

Fig. 1 (monkey), x 65; Fig. 2 (monkey), x 160; Fig. 3 (monkey), x 65; Fig. 4 (monkey), x 640; Fig. 5 (monkey), x 960.

a capillary and a delicate connective tissue framework (Figs. 4 and 5). Actually, the respiratory epithelium of adjacent alveoli share capillaries and connective tissue so that the wall between neighboring alveoli consists of respiratory epithelium (extremely flattened squamous cells) on each air surface, separated by a capillary.

It should be evident that one cannot readily identify the cells which constitute the alveolar wall due to the extreme attenuation of the cytoplasmic portion of the cells. The alveolar wall also contains macrophages which may contain phagocytized material and which are then called *dust cells.* Although it is difficult to distinguish respiratory epithelium, capillary endothelium, and connective tissue cells from one another, the capillary lumen can usually be identified by the presence of blood cells. Several red blood cells (**RBC**) and a white blood cell (**WBC**) can be recognized within the capillaries of the alveolar wall.

Psed
↓
Bronchiole   Coll
Resp Bron(Cubord

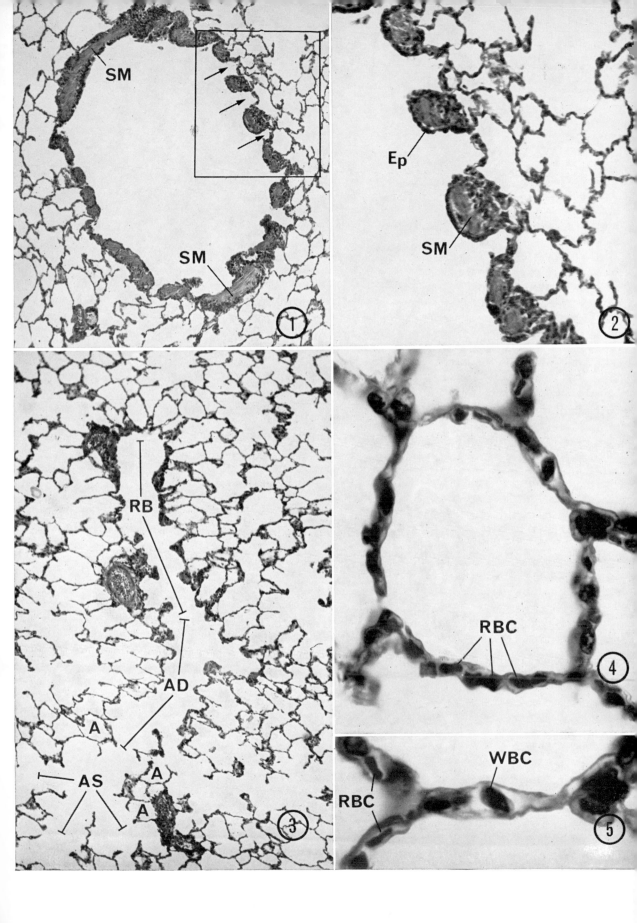

URINARY SYSTEM

THE URINARY SYSTEM consists of the paired kidneys and ureters, the urinary bladder and the urethra.

The functional unit of the kidney is the *nephron*. It consists of a tuft of capillaries, the *glomerulus,* and a *renal tubule*. The tubule begins as an expanded bulb, called the *renal capsule* or *Bowman's capsule*. This is in close association with the glomerulus and together, the glomerulus and the renal capsule form a filtering apparatus called the *Malpighian corpuscle*. The remaining parts of the renal tubule are designated, in order: the *proximal convoluted tubule, Henle's loop,* the *distal convoluted tubule* and the *arched collecting tubule*. Henle's loop can be further subdivided into a proximal thick segment (or the thick descending limb), the thin segment which usually includes the loop itself, and the distal thick segment (or the thick ascending limb). The distal thick segment may form the loop instead of the thin segment. The arched collecting tubule enters a common *collecting* tubule that serves a number of nephrons.

The collecting tubules pour their contents into funnel-shaped structures called *minor calyces,* and these, in turn, open into larger calyces (*major calyces*) which finally open into the largest chamber, the *renal pelvis*.

Because of the way in which nephrons are arranged, when a cut surface of the kidney is examined, the outer part of the kidney (the cortex) looks different from the inner part (the medulla). An entire nephron cannot be seen in a single section due to its tortuosity. It is nevertheless well to know that parts of the nephron are in the cortex, and parts are in the medulla. The Malpighian corpuscle, proximal convoluted tubule, distal convoluted tubule, and arched collecting tubule, are in the cortex. The loop of Henle and the collecting tubules are in the medulla; these are grouped to form conical-shaped structures which are called renal pyramids.

The arrangement of blood vessels in the kidney is unique. The capillaries that form the glomerulus have an *afferent arteriole* coming into them and *efferent arteriole* leaving them (instead of an arteriole coming in and a venule leaving). The efferent arteriole breaks up into a second capillary network (the *peritubular capillaries*) which is in close relationship to the renal tubules.

Plate 61. Kidney I

The cortex of the kidney is shown at low power in Figure 1. The most striking feature of the kidney cortex is the presence of numerous *renal corpuscles* (**RC**). They appear as the spherical bodies surrounded by a small clear space. Surrounding the renal corpuscles are the *proximal* and *distal convoluted tubules*. These present a variety of profiles in sections, most of which appear oval or spherical. However, because of their convolutions, it is also possible to find some whose profile resembles a U, J, or even an S. The renal corpuscles (**RC**), convoluted tubules (unlabeled) and larger blood vessels (**BV**) make up the part of cortex that is referred to as the *cortical labyrinth* (**CL**).

In Figure 1, the cortical labyrinths are separated by groups of tubules oriented in the same direction. These tubules, collectively, are referred to as the medullary rays (**MR**). Each tubule follows a rather straight course traveling to and from the medulla (actually the pyramids). When the medullary rays are cut longitudinally, the tubules present elongated profiles as they do in Figure 1.

The cortex of the kidney is also shown in Figure 2 at low power, but the plane of section is at a right angle to that of Figure 1, and the medullary rays (**MR**) are thus cut in cross section. In this case, the tubules of the medullary rays appear oval or spherical, but the convoluted tubules and renal corpuscles of the cortical labyrinth appear as they do in Figure 1. A random gathering of yarn to form a ball, when sectioned, would present the same kind of profiles regardless of the plane of section; a package of cigarettes, on the other hand, will appear as circular profiles if cut in cross section, or as elongated profiles if cut longitudinally. For these reasons, the convoluted tubules present the same type of profiles in Figures 1 and 2, whereas the medullary rays present different profiles, depending on the plane of section. The appearance of the medullary rays can therefore give some indication regarding the plane of section. The closeness of the medullary rays and the large-sized blood vessels indicate that this section is close to the medulla.

KEY

BV, blood vessel
CL, cortical labyrinth
MR, medullary ray
RC, renal corpuscle
arrow (inset), vascular pole
Fig. 1 (human), x 40; Fig. 2 (human), x 40; (inset), x 160.

The bulk of the kidney consists of parenchymal material, namely, the tubules, and only a small amount of stroma is present. The stroma consists of reticular fibers that surround the various parenchymal elements. Figure 2 is a silver preparation designed to illustrate the stroma. The reticular stroma appears as the black material that surrounds the tubules and the renal corpuscle (**RC**) (**inset**). The place where the blood vessels enter the renal corpuscle (the *vascular pole*) is indicated by an **arrow**.

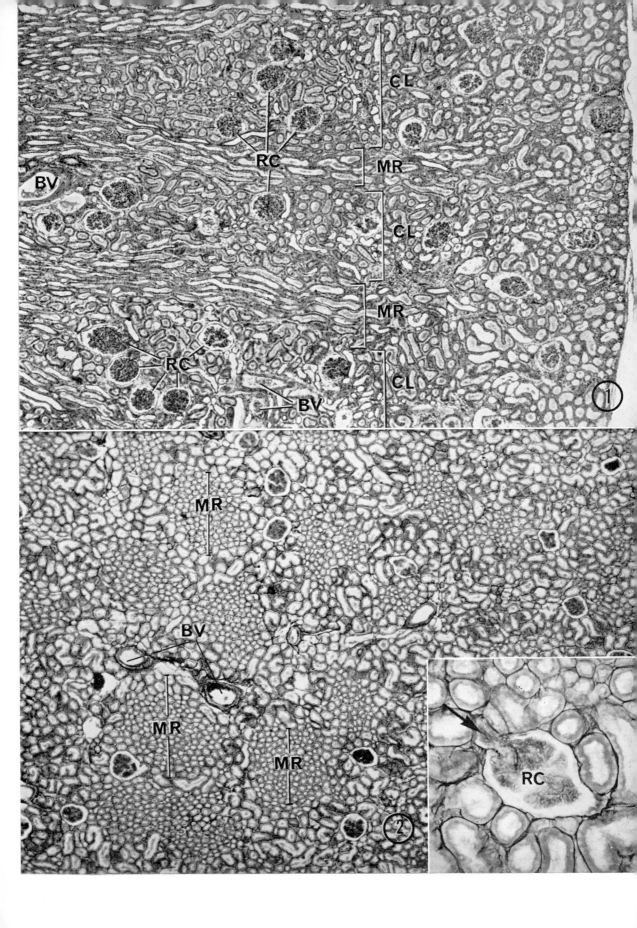

Plate 62. KIDNEY II

The components of the cortical laybrinth are shown in Figure 1. A renal corpuscle is in the center of the field, and both the urinary and vascular poles are included in the section. The junction between the parietal layer of Bowman's capsule and the proximal convoluted tubule is clearly seen at the urinary pole (**arrowheads**); a distal convoluted tubule (**D′**) is adjacent to the blood vessels at the vascular pole. The side of this tubule that is in direct proximity to the blood vessels contains a greater number of nuclei and is slightly thicker than the opposite side; this is the *macula densa* (**MD**). The cortical labyrinth also contains the cut profiles of kidney tubules and blood vessels (**BV**).

Proximal convoluted tubules are distinguished from distal convoluted tubules in a number of ways: *1*) The proximal tubule is more than twice as long as the distal tubule, consequently, the majority of tubules in a given area will be proximal. *2*) Proximal tubules have a slightly larger outside diameter than distal tubules, although the lumen may be smaller. *3*) Proximal tubules have a distinct *brush border,* whereas the distal tubules have smaller surface projections and typically possess a cleaner, sharper luminal surface. (The brush border of the proximal tubules may be broken or even lost during preparation). *4*) The lumen of the proximal convoluted tubule is often star-shaped; this is less often the case with distal tubules. *5*) Fewer nuclei appear in cross section of a proximal convoluted tubule than in distal tubules. *6*) Both proximal and distal tubules possess *basal striations,* but they are more prominent in proximal tubules.

Consider the two tubules marked 1 and 2 in Figure 1. In each, the luminal diameters are about the same. However, tubule 1 has a smaller outside diameter and shows about 16 nuclei, it is a distal tubule; tubule 2 has a larger outside diameter and shows only about 12 nuclei, it is a proximal tubule. In Figure 2 notice the brush border (**arrows**) of the proximal tubules (**P**) and the relatively sharp surface of the distal convoluted tubule (**D**). Peritubular capillaries (**Cap**) can be seen

KEY

BC, Bowman's capsule
BV, blood vessel
C, collecting tubule
Cap, peritubular capillary
D and **D′,** distal convoluted tubules
MD, macula densa
P, proximal convoluted tubules
arrows (Fig. 2), brush border
arrows (Fig. 3), glomerular capillaries
arrowheads (Fig. 1), urinary pole
arrowheads (Figs. 2 and 3), basal striations

Fig. 1 (human), x 165; Fig. 2 (guinea pig), x 500; Fig. 3 (guinea pig), x 500.

between the tubules.

A precipitate is present in the lumen of the proximal convoluted tubules that are shown in Figure 1. While this may enable one to quickly recognize proximal tubules in this specimen, it should be pointed out and emphasized that this is not a regular feature (see Figs. 2 and 3) and identification on this basis is tenuous.

Collecting tubules and arched collecting tubules (**C**) consist of cuboidal cells. A boundary can usually be seen between the cells, however, these boundaries are not always striking. Arched collecting tubule and collecting tubule cells do not possess basal striations. However, striations (**arrowheads**) can be seen in the cytoplasm of the distal and proximal convoluted tubules.

A renal corpuscle and its vascular pole are shown at higher magnification in Figure 3. Surrounding the corpuscle is the parietal layer of Bowman's capsule (**BC**). It consists of flat, squamous cells. Some red blood cells can be seen within the capillaries (**arrows**) that make up the glomerulus.

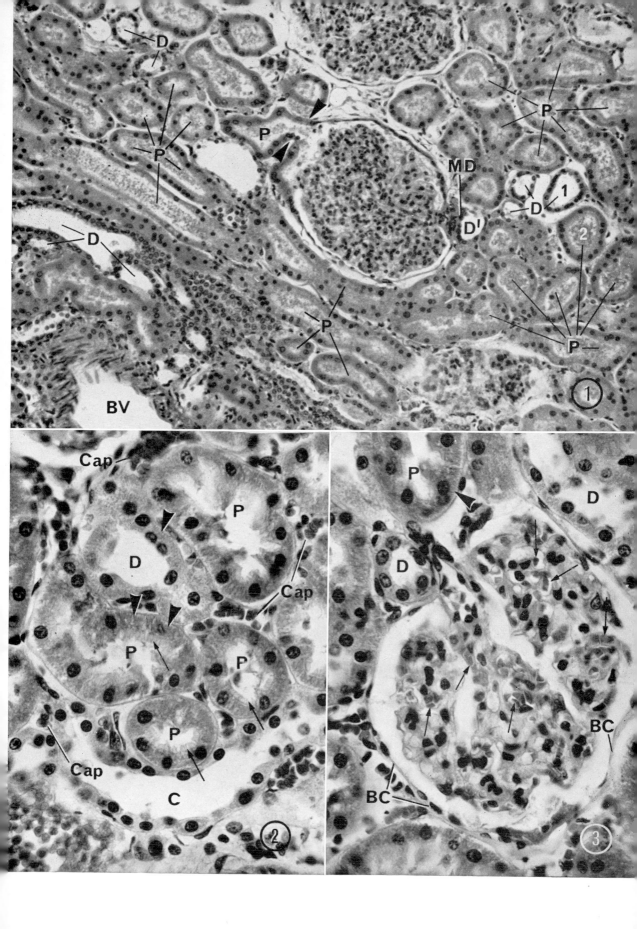

Plate 63. KIDNEY III

The apex of a *pyramid* projecting into a *calyx* (**Ca**) is shown in Figure 1. Cortical material is on both sides of the illustration and can be recognized by the presence of renal corpuscles and the convoluted tubules. Adipose tissue (**AT**) surrounds the calyx, and in the adipose tissue are branches of the renal artery (**A**) and vein (**V**). The space occupied by the adipose tissue, the large blood vessels, and the calyces are referred to as the *renal sinus*. It is just inside the opening (hilus) on the medial side of the kidney.

The pyramid and calyx are shown in Figures 2 and 3 at higher magnification. Figure 2 shows the pyramid and wall of the calyx in cross section. Therefore, the collecting tubules (**C**) appear circular. They are comprised of cuboidal or columnar cells and are distinguished because the boundaries between the cells are evident. It should be recalled that the boundaries between other cells of the kidney tubules are not distinct in H & E preparations. The smaller thin-walled tubules that are present in the pyramid in addition to the collecting tubules are either thin segments of Henle's loop or capillaries. It is not always a simple matter to distinguish between these. As a general statement, cells that make up the thin segments have spherical nuclei which bulge into the lumen; endothelial nuclei, on the other hand, are flat. If the capillaries contain red blood cells, the task of distinguishing between the two is simplified significantly.

The outer surface of the pyramid (**arrows**) is made up of a single layer of cuboidal or columnar cells which resemble cells of collecting ducts, inasmuch as the boundaries between the cells are evident.

Figure 3 shows essentially the same structures as shown in Figure 2, except that the collecting tubule (**C**) is cut longitudinally. Note the similarity between cells of the collecting tubule and cells that line the surface of the pyramid (**arrows**).

The surface of the calyx [**Ca(S)**] consists of *transitional epithelium* (**TE**) (Figs. 2 and 3). This epithelium is stratified and appears thicker than the simple epithelium on the surface of the pyramid. Transitional epithe-

KEY

A, renal artery
AT, adipose tissue
C, collecting tubule
Ca, calyx
Ca(S), surface of calyx
SM, smooth muscle
TE, transitional epithelium
V, renal vein
arrows, surface of pyramids

Fig. 1 (guinea pig), x 40; Fig. 2 (guinea pig), x 160; Fig. 3 (guinea pig), x 640

lium will be examined in more detail in the following two plates.

Collagenous fibers are present in the connective tissue under the transitional epithelium of the calyx (Fig. 3). The wall of the calyces also contain smooth muscle. In Figure 1, near the bottom, the wall of the calyx has been cut tangentially. The lumen and epithelium have been missed, but the smooth muscle (**SM**) is included.

150

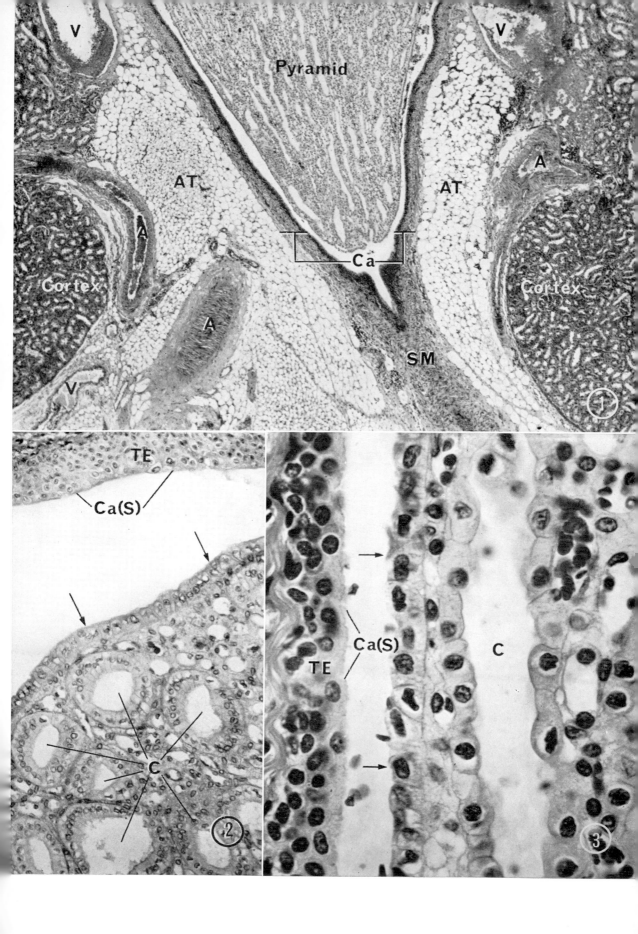

Plate 64. Ureter

The ureters conduct urine from the kidneys to the urinary bladder. These tubes do not simply serve as a route whereby urine flows to the urinary bladder by gravity, but they contribute to the flow of urine by means of regular peristaltic contractions. The wall of the ureters consists of a lining of transitional epithelium, smooth muscle, and supporting connective tissue. These components are organized as a *mucosa* (**Muc**), *muscularis* (**Mus**) and *adventitia* (**Adv**) and are illustrated in Figure 1. The lumen is characteristically star-shaped.

The wall of the ureter is examined at higher magnification in Figure 2. One can immediately recognize the lining of the inner surface which appears distinct and sharply delineated from the remainder of the wall. The inner, sharply delineated part, in direct contact with the lumen, is the transitional epithelium (**Ep**). The remainder of the wall is made up of connective tissue (**CT**) and smooth muscle. The latter can be recognized as the darker staining, slightly oriented layer with connective tissue on both sides of it. The section also shows some blood vessels and adipose tissue **AT**).

The transitional epithelium (**Ep**) and its supporting connective tissue (**CT**) constitute the mucosa (**Muc**). *Transitional epithelium is considered on page 154.* A distinct submucosa is not present, although the term is sometimes applied to the connective tissue that is closest to the muscle.

The muscularis (**Mus**) consists of smooth muscle. It is arranged as an inner longitudinal layer [Sm(**L**)], a middle circular layer [SM(**C**)], and an outer longitudinal layer [SM(**L**)]. The outer longitudinal layer is present only at the lower end of the ureter. In a cross section through the ureter, the inner and outer smooth muscle layers will also be cut in cross section, whereas the circular middle layer of muscle cells will be cut longitudinally. This is as they appear in Figure 2. The elongated and oriented nuclei of the middle layer are easy to recognize, but the inner and outer layers of muscle cells are a little more difficult to identify. They appear as the spherical or

KEY

A, artery
Adv, adventitia
AT, adipose tissue
BV, blood vessels
CT, connective tissue
Ep, transitional epithelium
Muc, mucosa
Mus, muscularis
SM(C), circular layer of smooth muscle
SM(L), longitudinal layers of smooth muscle
V, vein

Fig. 1 (monkey), x 80; Fig. 2 (monkey), x 165.

oval structures, some of which contain a smaller dark staining nucleus. The connective tissue external to the smooth muscle is referred to as the adventitia (**Adv**).

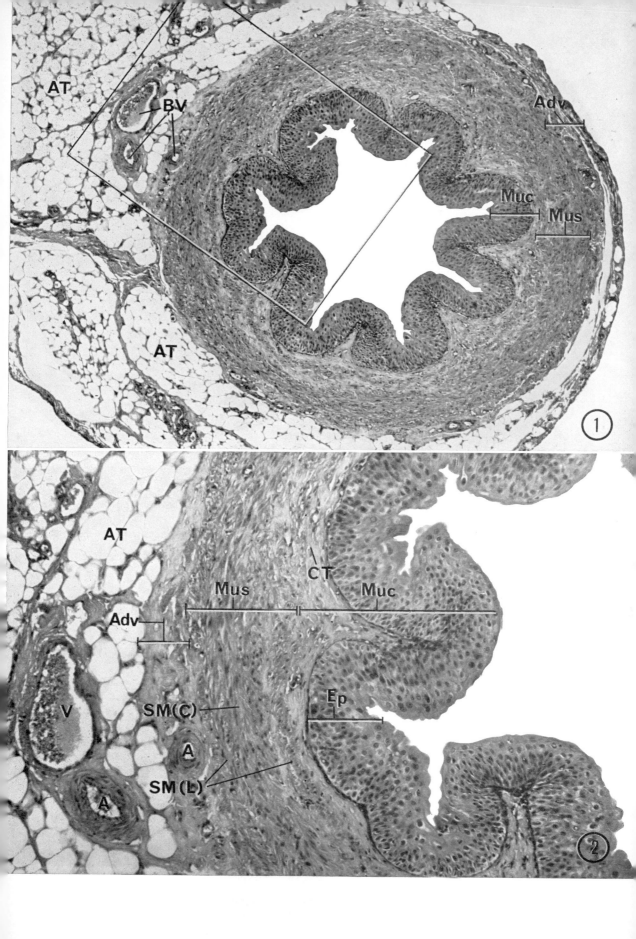

Plate 65. URINARY BLADDER

The urinary bladder receives urine from the two ureters and stores it until it is discharged via the urethra. Its structure reflects these functions. It possesses a lining of transitional epithelium which adapts to changes in bladder volume, and the wall contains bundles of smooth muscle which function in discharging the urine.

The full thickness of the urinary bladder is illustrated in Figure 1. It shows the *mucosa* (**Muc**), the *muscularis* (**Mus**), and the *serosa* (**S**). The mucosa consists of transitional epithelium (**EP**) and its supporting connective tissue (**CT**). A distinct submucosa is not present, although as with the ureter, the connective tissue closest to the muscle is sometimes referred to as a submucosa. The muscularis consists of smooth muscle which is arranged in three layers: an inner longitudinal [**SM(L)**], middle circular [**SM(C)**], and outer longitudinal layer [**SM(L)**]. The smooth muscle stains more intensely than the connective tissue. On the basis of organization, the bundles of smooth muscle cells can be recognized because they are surrounded by connective tissue (**CT**). This relationship is especially evident when the smooth muscle is cut obliquely or in cross section. When the smooth muscle is cut longitudinally, the relationship is less evident, but then the elongated profiles of the smooth muscle cell nuclei serve as a diagnostic feature. Moreover, even at this low magnification, one can see some of the nuclei in an intracellular location. Another extremely useful criterion for distinguishing smooth muscle from connective tissue in Figure 1 is that the number of nuclei in a given area of smooth muscle (**white circle**) is greater than the number of nuclei in a comparable area of connective tissue (**black circle**).

A serosa is present on the upper surface of the bladder; it consists of a layer of simple squamous epithelium (mesothelium) which rests on a small amount of supporting connective tissue. Elsewhere, the outer layer of the wall consists of a fibrous adventitia.

The **rectangles** in Figures 1 and 2 indicate areas that are examined at higher magnifica-

KEY

CT, connective tissue
EP, epithelium
Lym, lymphocytes
Muc, mucosa
Mus, muscularis
S, serosa
SM(C), circular layer of smooth muscle
SM(L), longitudinal layer of smooth muscle
arrows, binucleate cells

Fig. 1 (monkey), x 65; Fig. 2 (monkey), x 160; Fig. 3 (monkey), x 640.

tion in Figures 2 and 3, respectively, to show the transitional epithelium. In the contracted state the epithelium (**EP**) is characterized by the presence of dome-shaped cells on the free surface and large numbers of pear-shaped cells immediately under the surface cells. The cells at the surface are large and occasionally have two nuclei (**arrows**). Deeper cells, on the other hand, are smaller. Because of the absence of connective tissue papillae, the epithelial-connective tissue junction is rather even. An aggregation of lymphocytes (**Lym**) is immediately under the epithelial surface. This is not an unusual observation.

The thickness of the transitional epithelium depends on the degree of bladder (or ureteral) distention. In the empty ureter or bladder, it appears to be about five cells deep. However, when they are distended, it appears to have a thickness of only two or three cells.

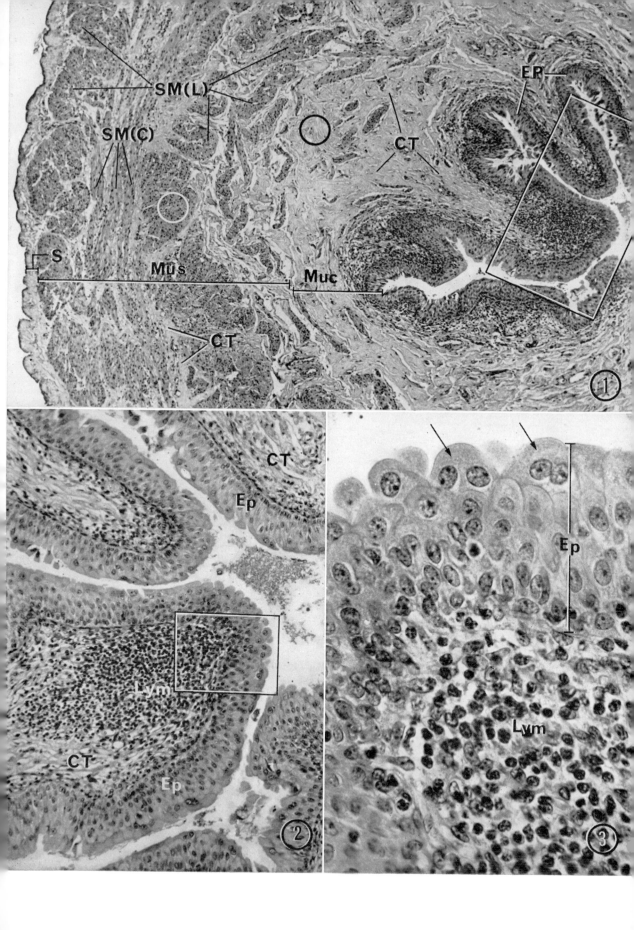

MALE REPRODUCTIVE SYSTEM

THE MALE REPRODUCTIVE SYSTEM consists of two testes, the duct system leading from them, the penis, and the accessory glands. The testes produce both *spermatozoa* and *hormones*. The spermatozoa are produced by an extensively coiled system of tubules called the *seminiferous tubules*. In the human, spermatogenesis begins at about the time of puberty. In order for this to occur, it is necessary for the testes to have descended into the scrotum. The hormones are produced by cells called *interstitial cells of Leydig*. They are located in the interstices between the seminiferous tubules.

The duct system includes: the *straight tubules* and *rete testes,* which are within the testes; the *efferent ductules,* which leave the testes; the *ductus epididymis,* a long coiled tubule within the epididymis, which is within the scrotum and closely applied to the testis; the *ductus deferens,* which leaves the scrotal sac, enters the body cavity through the inguinal canal, and continues into the pelvis; the *ejaculatory duct,* which pierces the prostrate gland; and the *urethra,* which finally courses through the penis. The urethra serves both the urinary system and the reproductive system as a terminal duct.

The accessory glands are the *seminal vesicles,* the *prostrate gland,* and the two small *bulbourethral glands*. The seminal vesicles empty into the ductus deferens where it becomes the ejaculatory duct. The prostate gland surrounds the first part of the urethra and opens into it; the bulbourethral glands empty into the membranous part of the urethra. All of these glands add their secretions to those of the seminiferous tubules, and the total mixture, containing spermatozoa, is referred to as semen.

The manner whereby materials are moved through the above tubular and duct systems is not entirely clear. In some places, a thick layer of smooth muscle within the wall is obviously implicated. Cilia may also serve in this capacity. However, it should be noted that the amount of smooth muscle within the walls varies, and part of the duct system, (straight tubules and rete testis) has no muscle whatsoever.

Plate 66. TESTIS I

The *seminiferous* tubules are extremely tortuous and in a section of the testis each tubule may be cut in many places (Fig. 1). Circular and oval profiles are the predominant forms; however, due to the tortuosity, "C," "U," or "S" shaped profiles are also regularly seen. The lumens (L) of the tubules in a mature testis are conspicuous.

The framework of the testis consists of a capsule, called the tunica albuginea (TA), and septa (S), which divide the testis into compartments. A more delicate connective tissue stroma (arrow) extends into the compartments and surrounds the seminiferous tubules (Fig. 2). Small blood vessels (BV) are contained in the stroma (Fig. 3). Not infrequently, clusters of cells without a lumen (X), which represent tangential sections through a seminiferous tubule, are seen (Fig. 2). These should not be confused with Leydig cells (see Plate 67).

It should be noted that the tubules do not all have the same appearance (Fig. 2). This is due to the fact that spermatogenesis occurs in waves along the length of the tubule, and all of the stages may not be evident in a particular part of a tubule at a particular time. For example, some of the cells in tubule A have already differentiated into spermatozoa, the heads of which can be seen as the small intensely staining oval bodies at the luminal surface. However, this stage of differentiation has not been reached in tubule B and spermatozoa are not yet evident.

Two distinctly different kinds of cells are present in the wall of the tubule (Fig. 3), cells of the spermatogenic series and *sustentacular,* or *Sertoli cells.* The sustentacular cells differ from cells of the spermatogenic series in appearance and are considerably fewer in number. Whereas the cells of the spermatogenic series have spherical nuclei, the nuclei of Sertoli cells (SC) are usually oval. Moreover, they are pale staining and radially oriented. The cytoplasm of Sertoli cells extends from the periphery of the tubule to the lumen, but the full extent cannot be seen in H & E sections.

Spermatogenesis begins at the periphery of

KEY

BV, blood vessel
L, lumen of seminiferous tubule
PS, primary spermatocytes
S, connective tissue septum
SC, Sertoli cells
Sg, spermatogonia
St, spermatids
Sz, spermatozoa
TA, tunica albuginea
arrow, connective tissue stroma
A, B, X, see text
Fig. 1 (monkey), x 65; Fig. 2 (monkey), x 160;
 Fig. 3 (monkey), x 640.

the tubule, and later stages are represented closer to the lumen. At the periphery of the tubule are the *spermatogonia* (Sg), or primitive germ cells, about 12 μ in diameter. These differentiate into *primary spermatocytes.* Primary spermatocytes (PS) are about 17-19 μ in diameter, and lie next to spermatogonia, on the luminal side. The nuclei typically show chromatin that is in the process of organizing into chromosomal forms. This process appears to take a significant period of time, and for this reason, primary spermatocytes are readily seen in sections. Primary spermatocytes divide and form *secondary spermatocytes.* These divide quickly and for this reason are not often seen in sections; they are smaller than primary spermatocytes. Secondary spermatocytes divide into *spermatids* (St). Spermatids are about 9 μ in diameter, and are usually found in groups near the lumen of the tubule. Spermatids differentiate into *spermatozoa.* Spermatozoa (Sz) have small, dark-staining ovoid heads. If spermatozoa are present, the heads are located at the border of the lumen, in contact with Sertoli cell cytoplasm; the tails extend into the lumen. The relationship of spermatozoa to Sertoli cell cytoplasm may not be evident in routine sections.

The seminiferous tubules are surrounded by a basement membrane and external to this are found cells with a flat elongated nucleus. Ultrastructural studies show that some of these nuclei belong to smooth muscle cells.

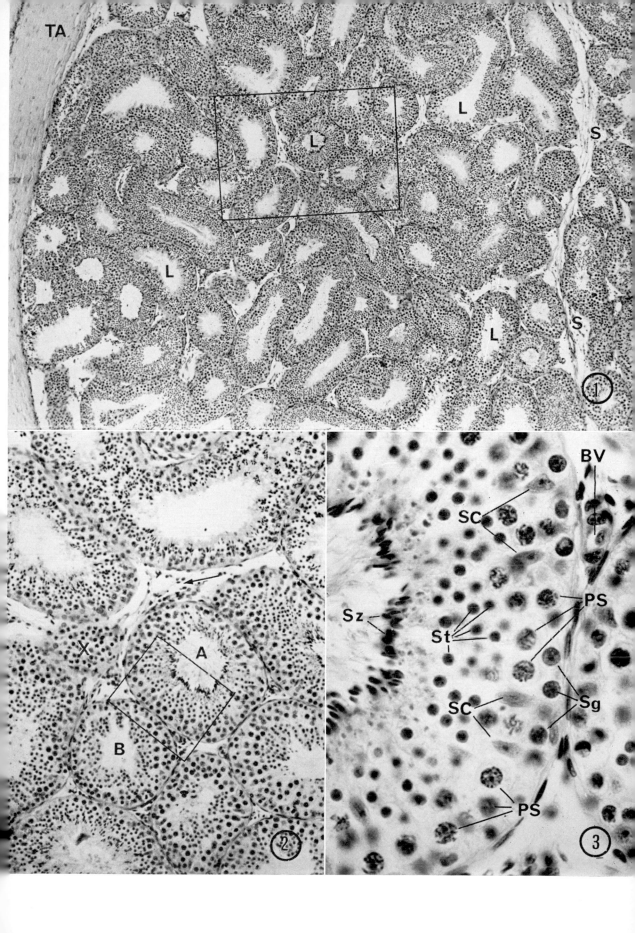

Plate 67. TESTIS II

The variety of cell types that are indicative of spermatogenesis in the mature seminiferous tubules are not present in the testes before puberty (Fig. 1) or in the undescended testis. In fact, the "tubules" are actually solid cords of cells. In these cords, a cell which resembles Sertoli cells predominates. These are the future Sertoli cells. The cords also contain a second cell type, the *primordial spermatogenic cell*. These cells have a centrally placed, spherical nucleus. The cytoplasm takes little stain and appears as a light ring around the nucleus. This gives the cell a distinctive appearance in histological sections (**arrows**). Generally, these cells are found at the periphery of the cord, although some may be more centrally placed.

Interstitial cells of Leydig (**L**) are more evident in the immature testes and can be seen between the cords even at low magnification (Fig. 1). Leydig cells are ovoid or polygonal in shape (Fig. 2), and usually closely grouped so that adjacent cells are in contact with each other. The nucleus of the Leydig cell is spherical; the cytoplasm may appear vacuolated and empty due to the large amount of lipid which is lost during the tissue preparation. In the human, rod-shaped crystalloids may be seen within the cytoplasm. Despite the fact that these cells are mesodermal in origin and lie in a connective tissue stroma they possess certain epithelial characteristics. They have large nuclei in which the chromatin appears stranded and clumped; they have a relatively large amount of cytoplasm, the boundaries of which are readily seen in histological sections, and some of the cells contact each other without intervening fibrous material. For these reasons, these cells are referred to as epithelial-like, or epithelioid. Leydig cells produce testosterone and other steroid hormones.

In addition to the Leydig cells, the space between the cords contains a delicate connective tissue stroma (**CT**). Some blood vessels (**BV**) may be seen within this stroma. A delicate connective tissue septum (**S**) is also shown (Fig. 1), and typically the larger blood vessels are associated with the septum.

KEY

BV, blood vessels
CT, connective tissue
Ep, epithelium
L, Leydig cells
RT, rete testis
S, connective tissue septum
arrows, primordial spermatogenic cells

Fig. 1 (monkey), x 160; Fig. 2 (monkey), x 640; Fig. 3 (human), x 40; (inset), x 640.

Straight tubules and rete testes. In the posterior of the testis, the connective tissue of the tunica albuginea extends more deeply into the organ (Fig. 3). This inward extension of connective tissue is called the *mediastinum testis*. It contains a network of anastomosing channels called the *rete testis* (**RT**). The epithelium (**Ep,** inset) that lines these channels is generally cuboidal. However, there is some degree of variation and not infrequently, in some areas, the lining cells may be columnar or they may even be squamous. The epithelial cells have a single cilium, however, this is difficult to see in routine H & E sections. The seminiferous tubules open into these channels, by way of the *straight tubules*. The junction between the seminiferous tubules and the straight tubules is abrupt. Straight tubules have the same structure as the rete testis. Both straight tubules and rete testes are in fact epithelial-lined, interconnecting spaces in connective tissue. No special organization of the connective tissue can be seen, nor is smooth muscle present.

160

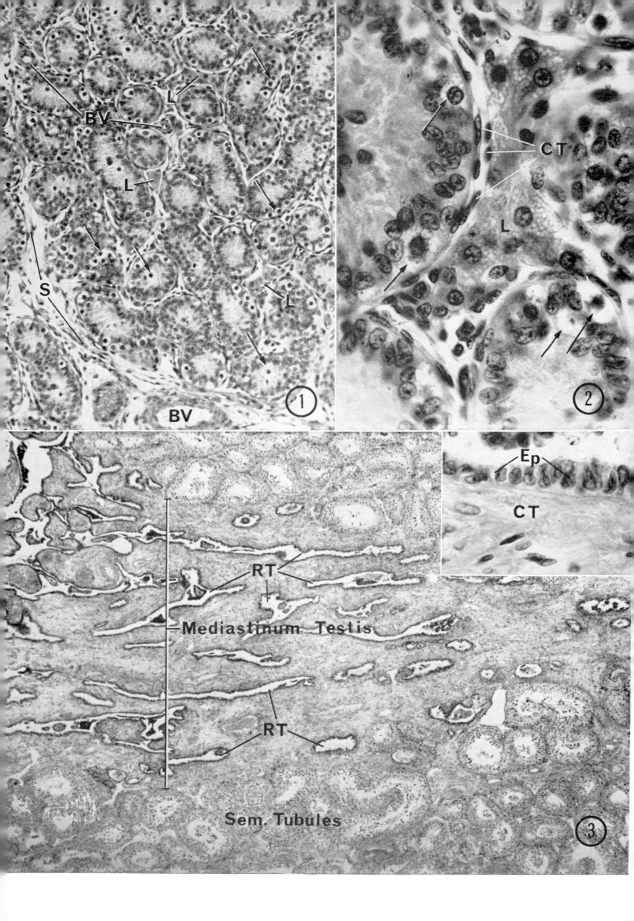

Plate 68. EFFERENT DUCTULES AND EPIDIDYMIS

Efferent ductules. About eight to twelve efferent ductules leave the testis and serve as channels from the rete testis to the epididymis. The epithelium (**Ep**) that lines the efferent ductules is pseudostratified columnar. It is distinctive in that tall columnar cells alternate with cuboidal cells giving the lumenal surface a more uneven or undulating appearance than the basal surface (Fig. 1). Some of the cells possess cilia. In addition to the columnar and cuboidal cells, basal cells are present and for this reason the epithelium is designated pseudostratified columnar.

The efferent ductules are surrounded by a thin layer of circularly arranged smooth muscle cells (**SM**). The muscle is close to the epithelial surface, being separated from it by only a small amount of connective tissue. Some small blood vessels (**BV**) are shown in the wall of the efferent ductules and also in the surrounding connective tissue (**CT**).

Epididymis. The epididymis, by virtue of its shape, is divided into a *head, body,* and *tail*. It contains a convoluted tube called the *ductus epididymis*, into which the efferent ductules open.

A section through the epididymis cuts through the duct in a number of places. The epithelium (**Ep**) which lines the duct contains two types of cells, tall columnar cells and basal cells (**inset**). Because of this, the epithelium is designated pseudostratified columnar. The free surface of the columnar cells contains *stereocilia* (**arrows**) which can be seen even with low magnification. These are extremely long, branching microvilli which evidently adhere to each other during the preparation of the tissue to form the long tapering structures that are seen with the light microscope.

The duct is surrounded by circularly arranged smooth muscle (**SM**) cells which can be recognized by their elongated and oriented nuclei. The difference in staining between muscle and connective tissue also enables one to distinguish these two from each other. The connective tissue (**CT**) has no special organization.

The duct of the epididymis is readily dis-

KEY

BV, blood vessel
CT, connective tissue
Ep, epithelium
SM, smooth muscle
arrows, stereocilia

Fig. 1 (human), x 160; Fig. 2 (human), x 78; (inset), x 640.

tinguished from the efferent ductules because the lumenal surface of the epithelium is more even than the lumenal surface of the efferent ductule, and for many stretches, the lumenal surface and the basal surface of the epithelial cells are parallel. As noted above, this is not so with the efferent ductules, where the lumenal surface is typically more uneven than the basal surface of the epithelium. In the epididymis, the nuclei of the columnar cells are typically elongated and located in the basal part of the cell. They are readily distinguished from the spherical nuclei of the basal cells. In the efferent ductules, the nuclei of the different cell types are not always easily identified.

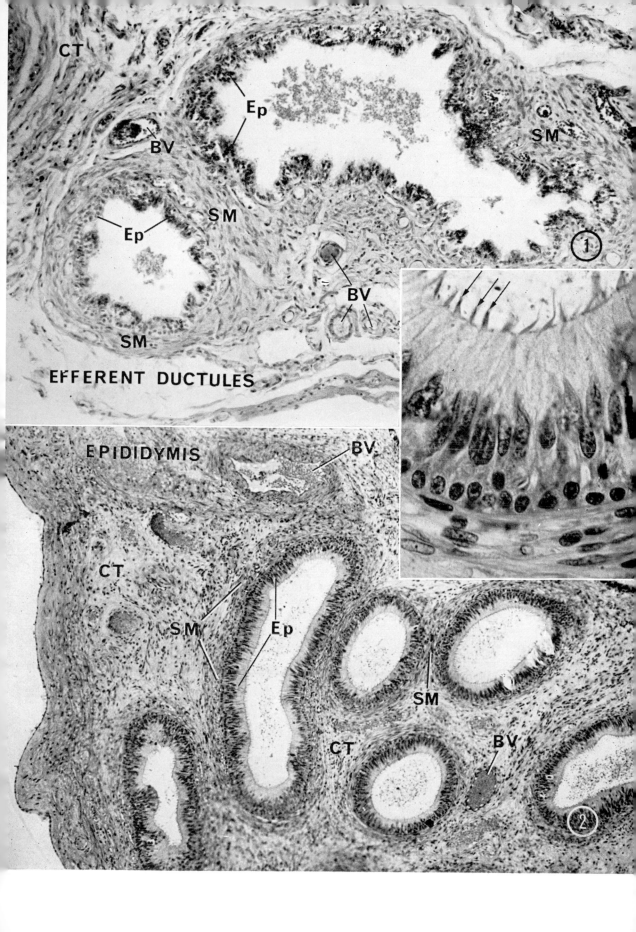

EFFERENT DUCTULES

EPIDIDYMIS

Plate 69. DUCTUS DEFERENS AND SEMINAL VESICLE

Ductus deferens. The ductus deferens continues from the duct of the epididymis. It leaves the scrotum and passes through the inguinal canal as a component of the spermatic cord. At the deep inguinal ring it continues into the pelvis, and behind the urinary bladder it joins with the seminal vesicle to form the ejaculatory duct. The ejaculatory duct then pierces the prostrate gland and opens into the urethra.

A cross section through the ductus deferens is shown in Figure 1. The wall is extremely thick, due mostly to the presence of a large amount of smooth muscle. The muscle contracts when the tissue is removed, causing longitudinal folds of the mucosa to form. For this reason, the lumen usually appears somewhat star-shaped in cross section.

The epithelial lining (**Ep**) of the ductus deferens consists of pseudostratified columnar epithelium which may contain stereocilia (Fig. 2). It resembles the epithelium of the epididymis. The elongated nuclei of the columnar cells are readily distinguished from the spherical nuclei (**arrow**) of the basal cells. (Spherical nuclei are easy to recognize if they are sufficiently numerous in an epithelial layer; they always appear spherical regardless of the plane of section. Elongated nuclei have variable appearances according to the plane of section.) The epithelium rests on a loose connective tissue (**CT**) which extends as far as the smooth muscle, and no submucosa is described.

The smooth muscle of the ductus deferens (Figs. 1 and 2) is arranged as a thick outer longitudinal layer [**SM(L)**], a thick middle circular layer [**SM(C)**], and a thinner inner longitudinal layer [**SM(L)**]. Blood vessels (**BV**) and nerves are in the connective tissue that surrounds the ductus deferens. A nerve bundle (**N**) is present just below the ductus deferens.

Seminal vesicle. The seminal vesicles are small elongated sacs that are folded upon themselves, and, in a section, the lumen may be cut in several places (Fig. 3).

The *mucosa* of the seminal vesicles is characterized by being extensively folded or ridged. The ridges vary in size; they branch

KEY

BV, blood vessels
CT, connective tissue
Ep, epithelium
N, nerve
SM, smooth muscle
SM(C), circular layer of smooth muscle
SM(L), longitudinal layer of smooth muscle
arrow (Fig. 2), basal cells
arrows (Fig. 3), arches formed by large mucosal folds
arrowheads, villus-like appearance of mucosal folds

Fig. 1 (human), x 42; Fig. 2 (human), x 160; Fig. 3 (human), x 16; Fig. 4 (human), x 160.

and interconnect with each other. The larger ridges may form recesses which contain smaller ridges, and when these are cut obliquely, they appear as mucosal arches which enclose the smaller folds (**arrows**). When the plane of section is normal to the surface, the mucosal ridges appear as villi (**arrowheads**). The lower part of Figure 3 shows where the mucosa was cut tangential to the surface, but close to the base of the mucosal folds. Note how interconnecting folds appear as alveoli when cut in this manner.

The mucosa consists of a layer of pseudostratified columnar epithelium resting on a sparse but cellular connective tissue (**CT**) (Fig. 4). The basal cells are not particularly numerous and are difficult to identify.

The mucosa rests on a thick layer of smooth muscle (**SM**). The smooth muscle is described as consisting of a middle circular layer and an outer longitudinal layer, but these are difficult to identify. The difference in staining between the smooth muscle and connective tissue in this preparation makes it easy to distinguish these two components.

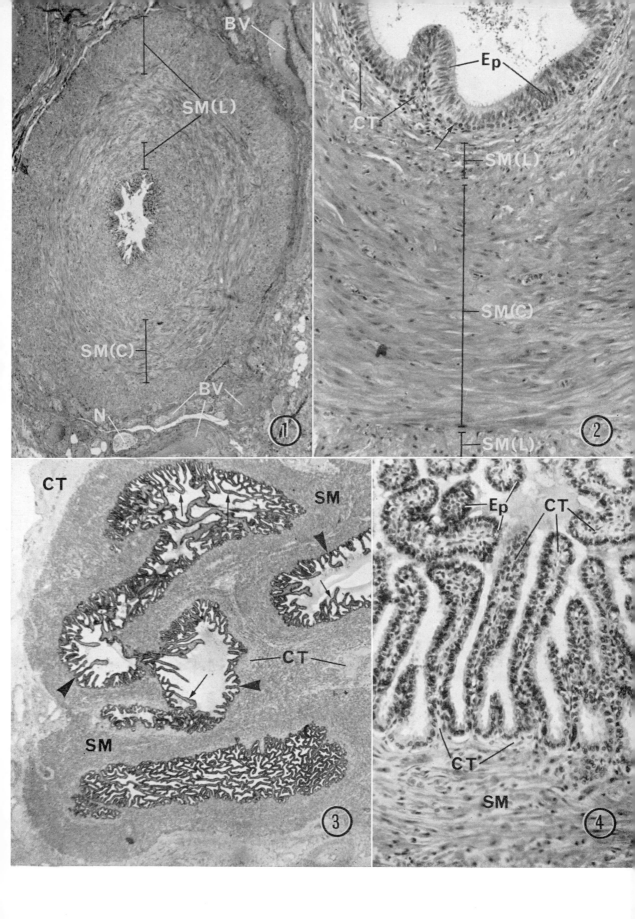

Plate 70. PROSTATE GLAND

The *prostate* gland surrounds the first part of the urethra (prostatic urethra). It consists of about 40 tubulo-alveolar glands that are contained in a fibroelastic stroma. The stroma is characterized by the presence of numerous small bundles of smooth muscle so that it can also be described as a fibromuscular stroma. Surrounding the gland is a fibroelastic capsule which also contains small bundles of smooth muscle. Ducts from the gland empty into the prostatic portion of the urethra.

A section of the prostate gland is shown in Figure 1. The capsule (**Cap**) is in the upper part of the field, the glandular components are in the lower part. The tube-alveoli of the prostate gland vary greatly in form as evidenced in the illustration. They may appear as tubes, as alveoli, as alveoli with branches, or as tubes with branches. They may appear distended, or they may be collapsed. Frequently, in older individuals, precipitates (*prostatic concretions*) (**PC**) are present in the lumens. These stain with eosin and may have a concentric lamellar appearance. With time, they may become impregnated with calcium salts.

The area enclosed within the **large rectangle** (Fig. 1), is shown at higher magnification in Figure 2, and shows some characteristic features of the tube-alveoli. In many places the epithelium bulges into the lumen; and sometimes the top of an epithelial fold is cut to give the impression of an island of cells in a lumen (**arrows**). Large numbers of closely packed nuclei are seen when a fold is cut obliquely or crosswise (**arrowheads**). This is one of the characteristic features of the prostate gland epithelium.

Figure 3 shows the epithelial cells at higher magnification. The epithelium consists mainly of columnar cells, although basal cells are also present. For this reason, the epithelium is classified as pseudostratified columnar. The columnar cells are described as containing secretion granules and lipid droplets, but these are not always evident. Many cells possess apical cytoplasmic protrusions (**arrows**) which seemingly break off into the lumen.

The various tube-alveoli are surrounded by

KEY

BV, blood vessels
Cap, capsule
N, nerve bundle
PC, prostatic concretion
SM, smooth muscle
SM(L), smooth muscle, longitudinal section
SM(X), smooth muscle, cross section
arrows (Fig. 2), epithelial "islands"
arrows (Fig. 3), apical cytoplasmic protrusions
arrowheads, nuclear clusters

Fig. 1 (human), x 40; Fig. 2 (human), x 145; Fig. 3 (human), x 640; Fig. 4 (human), x 160.

a fibroelastic stroma containing smooth muscle (fibromuscular stroma). The smooth muscle is not organized in a way which suggests that it belongs to any single tube or alveolus, as in the epididymis, but rather appears to be randomly dispersed in the stroma. In Figure 1, the staining of the muscle differs from the staining of the connective tissue. The muscle appears as the elongated dark fibers or as dark oval bodies (**SM**), in either case surrounded by a more extensive continuous phase of lighter staining connective tissue. Some bundles of smooth muscle are also to be seen in the capsule. The **upper rectangle** in Figure 1 is examined at higher magnification in Figure 4. This shows the smooth muscle cut in longitudinal [**SM(L)**] and cross section [**SM(X)**], and also reveals the presence of a nerve bundle (**N**). The nerve bundle stains very much like the connective tissue, but can be recognized because it has a perineurial sheath surrounding it.

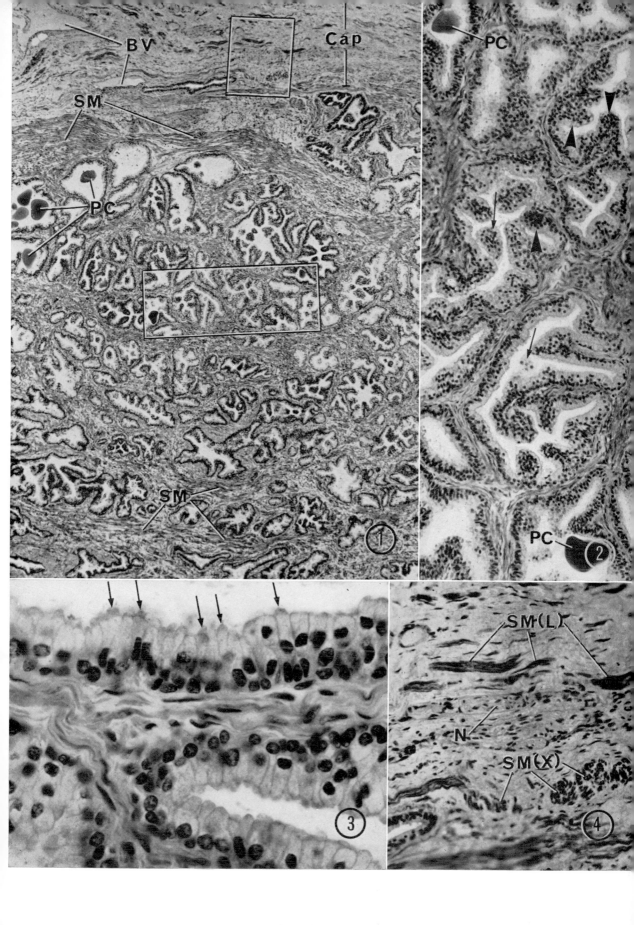

FEMALE REPRODUCTIVE SYSTEM

THE FEMALE REPRODUCTIVE SYSTEM consists of the ovaries and a system of related ducts, the external genitalia, and the mammary glands. Under the influence of the pituitary gland the ovaries undergo cycles of activity. Like the testes, the ovaries are cytogenic glands inasmuch as they produce the ova; they are also endocrine glands since they produce estrogen during one part of the ovarian cycle, and progesterone during another part.

The ovarian hormones have very profound and widespread effects throughout the body at the time of puberty. They bring about the development of the female secondary sex characteristics and the full development of the reproductive ducts and genitalia. In the mature female, ovarian hormones bring about marked cyclical changes in the female duct system, especially in the uterus.

Although the uterus does serve certain duct functions, it is especially adapted to serve as the organ in which the fetus develops, and at the end of gestation it expels the fetus.

During pregnancy, the ovarian hormones are involved in bringing about the alterations in the mammary gland that lead to its becoming a lactating organ.

Plate 71. Ovary I

The general topography of a young, but sexually mature, ovary is shown in Figure 1 at low power. The surface consists of a layer of epithelial cells, but these are not clearly revealed at this magnification. Immediately under the surface epithelium is a layer of rather uniform thickness called the *tunica albuginea* (**TA**). This is connective tissue which is continuous with the stroma of the ovary; however, it is distinguished from the stroma in that it is less cellular and more fibrous. Deep to the tunica albuginea and surrounded by a highly cellular connective tissue stroma are numerous spherical structures of uniform size, called the primary follicles.

The outer part of the ovary has a slightly different appearance from the inner part. The terms *cortex* (**C**) and *medulla* (**M**) are applied to the outer and inner parts, respectively. The medulla consists mainly of stroma. It is continuous with the hilus (not shown) and contains the larger blood vessels. The stroma of the medulla, especially near the hilus, contains some smooth muscle. At regular intervals, under the influence of pituitary hormones, some of the primary follicles begin to undergo changes that lead to the development of a mature ovum. These changes include a proliferation of cells and total enlargement of the follicle. During this process the developing follicles move into the medullary region. Therefore, it is not uncommon to see follicles in various stages of development or regression in the medullary region. At least two developing follicles (**arrows**) and two regressing (*atretic*) follicles (**arrowheads**) are present in the medulla (Fig. 1). The **large rectangle**, which includes one of each kind of follicle, is examined at higher magnification in Plate 72.

The surface of the ovary is shown in Figure 2. It consists of simple cuboidal epithelium and is referred to as *germinal epithelium* (**GE**). This epithelium has no striking surface specializations or cytoplasmic constituents that can be seen in routine sections. It is continuous with the *peritoneum* at the *mesovarium*. Whereas the peritoneum with its surface of squamous cells has a slick

KEY

C, cortex
FC, follicle cells
GE, germinal epithelium
M, medulla
N, oocyte nuclei
TA, tunica albuginea
X, oocyte with nuclei not shown
arrows, developing follicles
arrowheads, atretic follicles

Fig. 1 (monkey) x 65; Figs. 2 and 3 (monkey), x 640.

glistening appearance, the ovary with its surface of cuboidal cells has a dull appearance. The connective tissue under the epithelium is the tunica albuginea (**TA**) and just beyond this, parts of two primary follicles are shown.

The primary follicles within the **small rectangle** of Figure 1 are shown in Figure 3 at higher magnification. During fetal development cords of cells grow into the ovarian stroma from the germinal epithelium. These cords separate from the surface, break up into small cell nests, and become primary follicles. Each primary follicle consists of a large *oocyte* which is completely surrounded by a single layer of flattened *follicle cells* (**FC**). These cells form a complete investment of the oocyte. The nucleus (**N**) of the oocyte is large, but may not be included in the plane of section. Therefore, some oocytes (**X**) appear to be without a nucleus. Figure 3 also shows some characteristics of the cellular stroma. The stromal cells are spindle shaped; they should not be confused with smooth muscle cells.

At the time of birth, all of the primary follicles that will be available to the individual are already present in the cortex of the ovary. Moreover, in the newborn ovary, some of the follicles may show signs of development due to the influence of maternal hormones which may pass through the placenta. Therefore, the ovary of a newborn may resemble the young mature ovary that is illustrated in Figure 1.

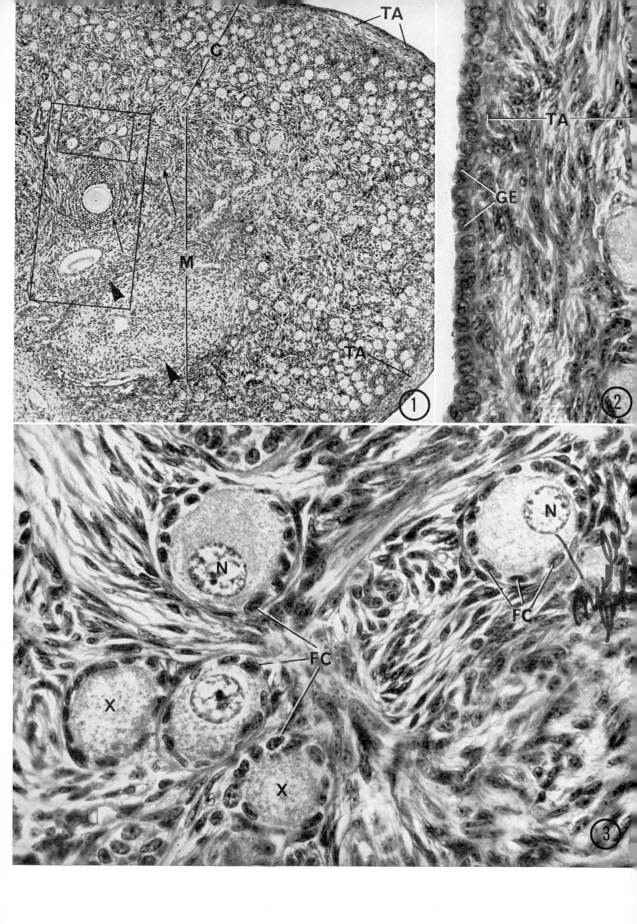

Plate 72. OVARY II

At the onset of sexual maturity in the female, the pituitary gland elaborates a hormone (*follicle stimulating hormone, FSH*) which is associated with the development of primary follicles into mature follicles. Under the influence of FSH, the single layer of investing follicle cells proliferates. As a result of this proliferation, a thick layer of follicle cells surrounds the oocyte. The oocyte and its nucleus also enlarge, and a homogeneous layer, called the *zona pellucida,* forms between the oocyte and the follicle cells. A follicle undergoing these changes is shown in Figure 1. This figure shows the area within the larger **rectangle** in Figure 1 of Plate 71 at higher magnification. Note the large number of follicle cells (**FC**) which now surround the enlarged oocyte. These cells developed from an original single layer of flattened cells. Note also the zona pellucida (**ZP**), which appears as the ring around the oocyte.

The follicle cells continue to proliferate and form a rather large ovoid cellular mass with the ovum on one side. Small fluid-filled spaces appear between the follicle cells; these ultimately become an extremely large single cavity called the *antrum* or *follicular cavity.* A growing follicle in which these changes have occurred is shown in Figure 2. The ovum is located at one end in a mound of cells called the *cumulus oophorus* (**CO**). The remaining follicle cells that surround the cavity (**Cav**) are now referred to as the *membrana granulosa* (**MG**) or as *granulosa cells.* A precipitate of the follicular fluid is within the cavity.

A higher magnification of the cumulus oophorus (Fig. 3) shows that the cells immediately in contact with the oocyte have a columnar shape. The apical cytoplasm of these columnar cells is just discernible (**arrow**). They are in correct relation to the oocyte only at the top. A distinct zona pellucida (**ZP**) can be seen immediately around the ovum. When the ovum is discharged, these cells and some others from the cumulus remain adherent to the oocyte and are called the *corona radiata.*

The connective tissue surrounding the follicle also undergoes some changes and is

KEY

AF, atretic follicle
Cav, follicular cavity
CO, cumulus oophorus
FC, follicle cells
MG, membrana granulosa
TE, theca externa
TI, theca interna
ZP, zona pellucida
arrow, apical cytoplasm of cells surrounding oocyte

Fig. 1 (monkey), x 640; Fig. 2 (monkey), x 65; Fig. 3 (monkey), x 160.

subsequently referred to as the *theca.* Numerous small blood vessels are present in the part of the theca that is immediately adjacent to the follicle cells, called the *theca interna* (**TI**). Some of the cells in this layer have round nuclei, are close to their neighbors, and may be described as being epithelioid. The outer part of the theca is more fibrous and is called the theca externa (**TE**). In contrast to the theca interna, the cells of the theca externa have nuclei that are more flattened; however, the boundary between the theca interna and theca externa is not sharp.

Although a number of follicles begin on this series of developmental changes, usually only one, the *Graafian follicle,* reaches maturity and will discharge an ovum. The others undergo regressive changes and degenerate. Therefore, a section of an ovary typically includes a number of regressing or *atretic follicles* (**AF**) (Figs. 1 and 2). In a regressing follicle, the oocyte degenerates. In addition, the theca cells proliferate and invade the granulosa cells so that, in some respects, a regressing follicle resembles a developing corpus luteum. However, the zona pellucida persists for some time in the atretic follicle, and when included in the section (**ZP**, Fig. 1), enables one to distinguish it from a corpus luteum. In these cases, the remains of the zona pellucida appears as an irregular homogeneous crescent or ring in a clear space that was formerly occupied by the degenerated oocyte. Ultimately, stromal elements replace the cellular elements.

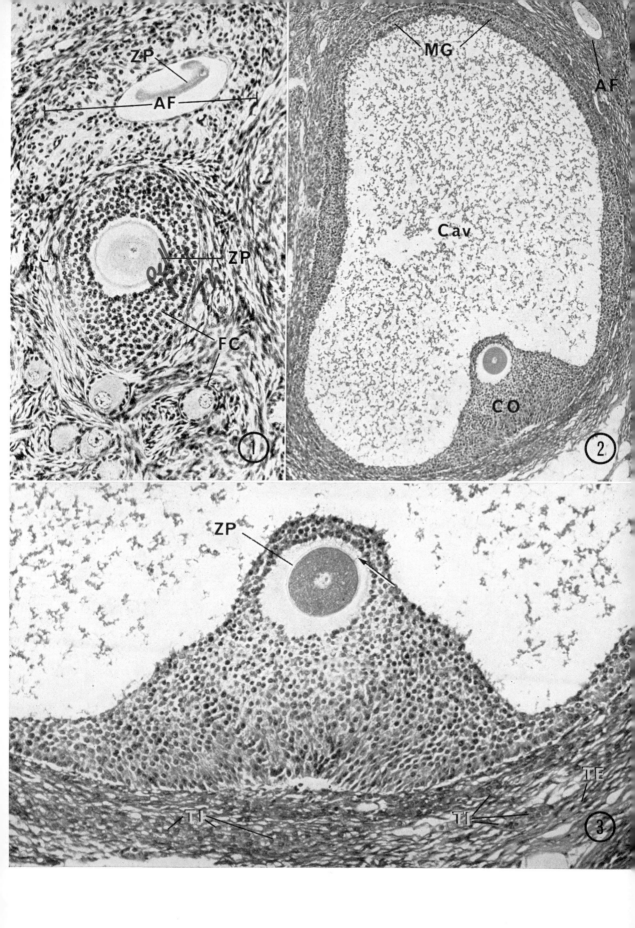

Plate 73. CORPUS LUTEUM

After the oocyte and some surrounding cumulus cells break out of the mature ovarian follicle (ovulation), the remaining follicle cells (stratum granulosum) and the adjacent connective tissue (theca interna) undergo certain changes that result in the formation of a new functional unit, the *corpus luteum.*

The cells that previously constituted the membrana granulosum of the follicle undergo considerable enlargement and are now called *granulosa lutein cells* (**GLC**). They form an extremely thick and folded layer that surrounds the remains of the former follicular cavity (**Cav**) (Fig. 1). The cavity appears stellate because of the folded nature of the thick layer of granulosa lutein cells. This cavity usually contains serous material and variable amounts of fibrin. Immediately after the rupture of the follicle, however, it may also contain some blood. Subsequently, the cavity is invaded by connective tissue. Some connective tissue (**CT**) can already be seen at the periphery of the cavity.

At about the same time, the theca interna also undergoes changes. The cells of this layer become enlarged and fill in the outer depressions (**arrows**) that are formed by the folded layer of granulosa lutein cells. These epithelioid cells that develop from the theca interna are now called *theca lutein cells* (**TLC**) and are an integral part of the corpus luteum (Fig. 2). Blood vessels (**BV**) accompany the theca lutein cells into the outer folds of the granulosa lutein cells.

It should be noted that, on the basis of location, one can readily identify and distinguish between theca lutein cells (**TLC**) and granulosa lutein (**GLC**) cells. The granulosa lutein cells are in relation predominantly to the stellate-shaped former cavity, whereas the theca lutein cells are related predominantly to the outer connective tissue (**CT**) that surrounds the total structure.

When examined more closely (Fig. 3), the granulosa lutein cells (**GLC**) can be seen to contain a large spherical nucleus and a large amount of cytoplasm. The cytoplasm contains lipid and pigment, therefore the name, corpus luteum. However, neither pigment nor lipid

KEY

BV, blood vessels
Cav, former follicular cavity
CT, connective tissue
GLC, granulosa lutein cells
TLC, theca lutein cells
arrows (Fig. 1) theca lutein cells
arrows (Fig. 3), nuclei of connective tissue and vascular cells

Fig. 1 (human), x 16; Fig. 2 (human), x 65; Fig. 3 (human), x 160.

are evident in routine H & E sections because they are lost during tissue preparation. Theca lutein cells (**TLC**) also possess spherical nuclei, but they are smaller than those of the granulosa lutein cells. Because of the difference in cell size, the nuclei of theca lutein cells are closer to each other than nuclei of granulosa lutein cells. Moreover, because of the smaller size, the theca lutein nuclei stain more intensely. As indicated above, the location should be taken into consideration when trying to identify these cells. Connective tissue cells and small blood vessels from the theca externa ultimately come to invade the layer of granulosa lutein cells. The nuclei of the invading connective tissue and vascular cells appear flattened and elongated (**arrows**) in contrast to the round nuclei of the theca and granulosa lutein cells.

The changes whereby the ruptured ovarian follicle is transformed into a corpus luteum occur under the stimulus of a pituitary hormone (luteinizing hormone). The corpus luteum in turn elaborates another hormone, progesterone, which has a profound effect on the estrogen-primed uterus. If pregnancy occurs, the corpus luteum remains functional. However, if the ovum is not fertilized, the corpus luteum regresses after having reached a point of peak development, roughly two weeks after ovulation.

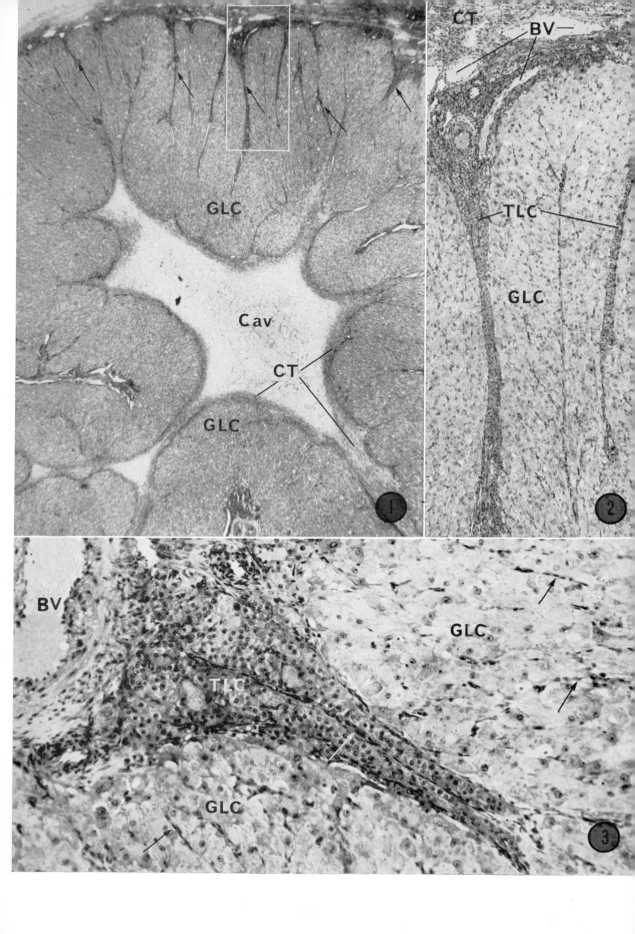

Plate 74. U<small>TERINE</small> T<small>UBE</small>

The *uterine tubes* (*oviducts*) are joined to the uterus and extend to the ovaries where they present an open flared end for entry of the ovum. Fertilization of the ovum usually occurs in the uterine tube, and for the first several days, the developing embryonic cells are contained in the uterine tube as they travel to the uterus. The tube undergoes cyclical changes, but these are not nearly as marked as uterine changes. The tubal changes involve the height of the epithelial cells. These increase in height during the middle of the uterine cycle, just about the time that the ovum will be passing through the tube, but they become reduced during the premenstrual period. Some of the epithelial cells are ciliated, and it has been suggested that the percentage of ciliated cells also changes during the cycle.

The uterine tube varies slightly in size and degree of mucosal folding along its length. Near the uterus, it is narrow and referred to as the *isthmus*. Then for about two thirds of its length it is in an expanded form and is referred to as the *ampulla*. Near the opening it flares outward and is called the *infundibulum*. This has fringed folded edges that are called *fimbria*. The mucosal folds are more numerous near the open end and less numerous near the uterus.

A cross section through the ampulla of the tube is shown in the **inset** (middle of page). Many mucosal folds project into the lumen, and the complicated nature of the folds is evident by the variety of profiles that are seen. The remainder of the wall consists of smooth muscle and connective tissue.

The wall of the uterine tube is shown at higher magnification in Figure 1. It is described as consisting of a *mucosa* (**Muc**), a *muscularis* (**Mus**), and a *serosa* (not shown). The mucosa has a surface of simple columnar epithelium. Two kinds of cells are present (Fig. 2), nonciliated cells and ciliated cells (**Cil**). The ciliated cells have a round nucleus and a relatively clear cytoplasm. The cilia are clearly seen in Figure 2. The aggregation of basal bodies appears as the dense band at the base of the cilia. The nonciliated cells are also called *peg cells*. They have elongated

KEY

BV, blood vessels
CT, connective tissue
Cil, ciliated cells
Muc, mucosa
Mus, muscularis
arrows, isolated peg cells
arrowheads, longitudinally sectioned smooth muscle

Fig. 1 (human), x 160; inset (human), x 16; Fig. 2 (human), x 640.

nuclei and sometimes appear to be squeezed between the ciliated cells (**arrows,** Fig. 1).

The connective tissue (**CT**) contains cells whose nuclei appear in a random manner. They vary in shape, being elongated, oval, or round, and their cytoplasm cannot be distinguished from the intercellular material (Fig. 2). The nature of the connective tissue is essentially the same from the epithelium to the muscularis, and for this reason, no submucosa is described.

The muscularis (**Mus**) consists of smooth muscle which forms a relatively thick layer of circular fibers (Fig. 1) and a thinner outer layer of longitudinal fibers. The layers are not clearly delineated and no sharp boundary separates the two. In comparing the two, attention should be given to the following points: the connective tissue is immediately under the epithelial surface and contains nuclei that are not oriented; the smooth muscle is not immediately under the epithelium and contains nuclei that are oriented. When cut longitudinally the nuclei of muscle cells appear elongated, about the same size and roughly parallel (**arrowheads**). When cut in cross section the nuclei appear spherical. Some blood vessels (**BV**) are seen in the muscularis.

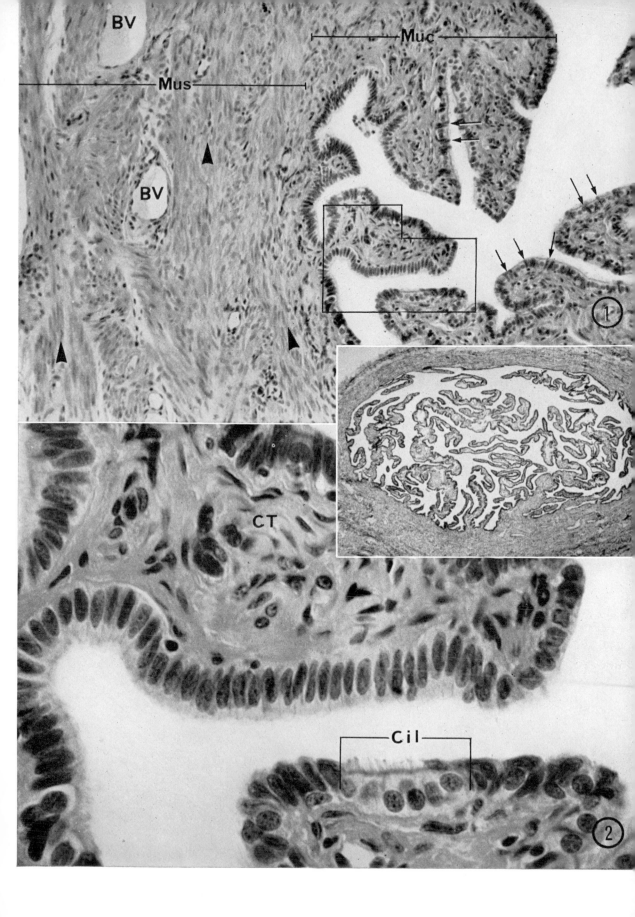

BV

Muc

Mus

BV

1

CT

Cil

2

Plate 75. UTERUS

The mucous membrane of the uterus is called the *endometrium*. It is comprised of simple columnar epithelium and a supporting, extremely cellular connective tissue. The epithelium may be ciliated. Large numbers of tubular glands extend from the surface epithelium into the underlying connective tissue and the extent of the glands determines the thickness of the endometrium. Deep to the endometrium is a thick layer of smooth muscle called the *myometrium*. The muscle cells are organized as interlacing bundles which are separated by connective tissue. External to the myometrium is either connective tissue or, over much of the uterine surface, a serosal cover, namely, visceral peritoneum.

The uterus undergoes cyclical changes, during part of which implantation is possible. If implantation does not occur, the state of readiness is not maintained and much of the endometrium is sloughed off, constituting the menstrual flow. The part of the endometrium that is lost is referred to as the *decidua functionalis*. The part that is retained is called the *decidua basalis*. The decidua basalis is the deepest part, and is close to the myometrium.

After the decidua functionalis is sloughed off, resurfacing of the raw tissue occurs. The epithelium (**Ep**) for this comes from the glands (**Gl**) that are left in the decidua basalis (**DB**). Figure 1 shows the endometrium as it appears when resurfacing is almost complete. The endometrium is relatively thin at this time and over half of it consists of the decidua basalis. Below the endometrium is the myometrium (**M**) in which are a large number of blood vessels (**BV**).

Under the influence of estrogen, the various components of the endometrium proliferate (*proliferative stage*) so that the total thickness of the endometrium is increased (Fig. 2). The glands (**Gl**) are rather long and fairly straight, with only a slight amount of waviness. The connection of some glands to the surface epithelium (**Ep**) is shown (**arrows**). The decidua basalis (**DB**) remains essentially unaffected by the estrogen and appears much the same as in Figure 1. The decidua functionalis (**DF**), on the other hand, increases in thickness

KEY

BV, blood vessels
CT, connective tissue
DB, decidua basalis
DF, decidua functionalis
Ep, epithelium
Gl, glands
M, myometrium
arrows, junction of gland and surface epithelium

Fig. 1 (human), x 40; Fig. 2 (monkey), x 16; Fig. 3 (human), x 65; Fig. 4 (human), x 160.

and constitutes about 4/5 of the endometrial thickness.

After estrogen acts on the endometrium to bring about the above changes, progesterone brings about additional changes. The endometrial thickness increases further and again the changes are conspicuous in the decidua functionalis; the glands become extremely wavy (Fig. 3) and the cells accumulate glycogen. At this time (*secretory stage*) the endometrium is ready for implantation. Note, however, that the basal layer again is relatively unaffected by these changes.

The epithelium and supporting connective tissue stroma (**CT**) of the glands are shown at higher magnification in Figure 4. Note the columnar epithelium (**Ep**) and the highly cellular connective tissue. The surface epithelium (not shown) is also columnar, except that in some patches it may be ciliated. The stromal cells become enlarged during pregnancy and are referred to as *decidual cells*. These are associated with the process of implantation.

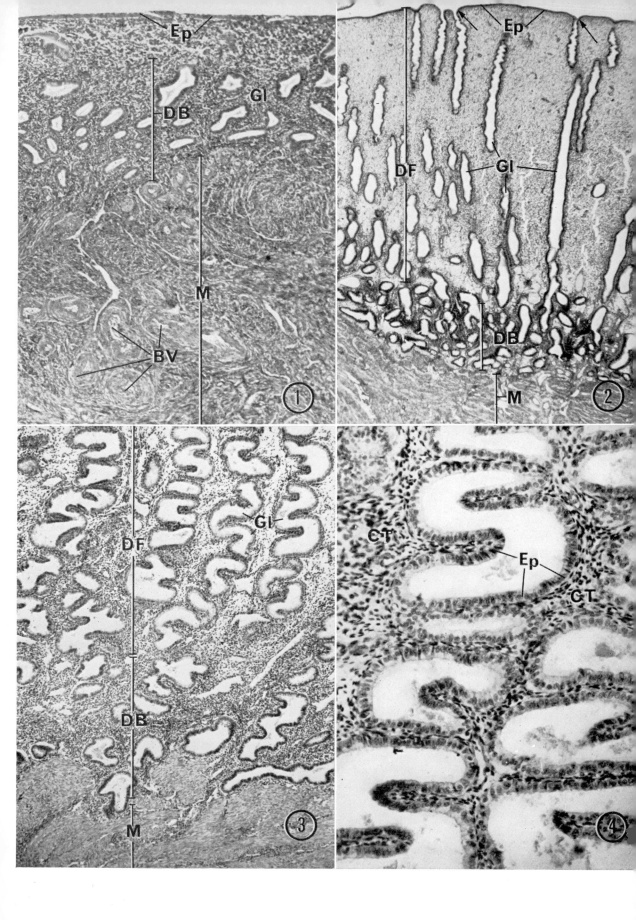

Plate 76. MAMMARY GLAND, INACTIVE

The *mammary glands* are branched tubuloalveolar glands which develop from the epidermis and come to lie in the subcutaneous tissue (superficial fascia). They begin to develop at puberty in the female, but do not reach a full functional state until after pregnancy. The glands also develop more or less slightly in the male at puberty. However, the development is limited and the glands usually remain in a stabilized state.

Figure 1 is a section through an inactive gland. The parenchyma is sparse and consists mainly of duct elements. Four longitudinally cut ducts (**D**) are shown in the center of the field. A small lumen can be seen in each. A resting lobule is to the right of the ducts and is shown at higher magnification in Figure 2.

The epithelial elements of the *resting mammary gland* are contained in a loose, cellular connective tissue [**CT(L)**] which is readily distinguished from the more dense connective tissue [**CT(D)**] beyond the area of the lobule. Note the more numerous nuclei in the loose connective tissue in contrast to the fewer nuclei in the dense connective tissue. Note also that the connective tissue fibers are thicker in the dense connective tissue than in the loose connective tissue. The loose irregular connective tissue also surrounds the duct elements, but it is not as clearly delineated from the dense connective tissue as it is in the lobules. Variable amounts of adipose tissue (**AT**) are found in the dense connective tissue.

The epithelial cells (**EP**) within the resting lobule are regarded as being chiefly duct elements. In the resting state, the epithelium is typically two cells deep rather than a single layer. "Alveoli" are not present as structures with lumens, but rather are represented as cellular thickenings of the duct wall.

During pregnancy the glands begin to proliferate. This can be thought of as a dual process in which ducts proliferate and alveoli spring from the ducts. Figure 3 shows a lobule and its ducts in an early state of proliferation. The *proliferating gland* shows many epithelial sprouts from the enlarged duct (**arrows**).

KEY

AT, adipose tissue
CT(D), dense connective tissue
CT(L), loose connective tissue
D, duct
Ep, epithelium
arrows, epithelial sprouts

Fig. 1 (human), x 65; Fig. 2 (human) x 160; Fig. 3 (human), x 65.

In contrast, the resting duct (Fig. 1) shows smooth contours without any conspicuous branching or evidence of proliferation. In the proliferating gland, the demarcation between the loose connective tissue and the epithelial elements is no longer distinct.

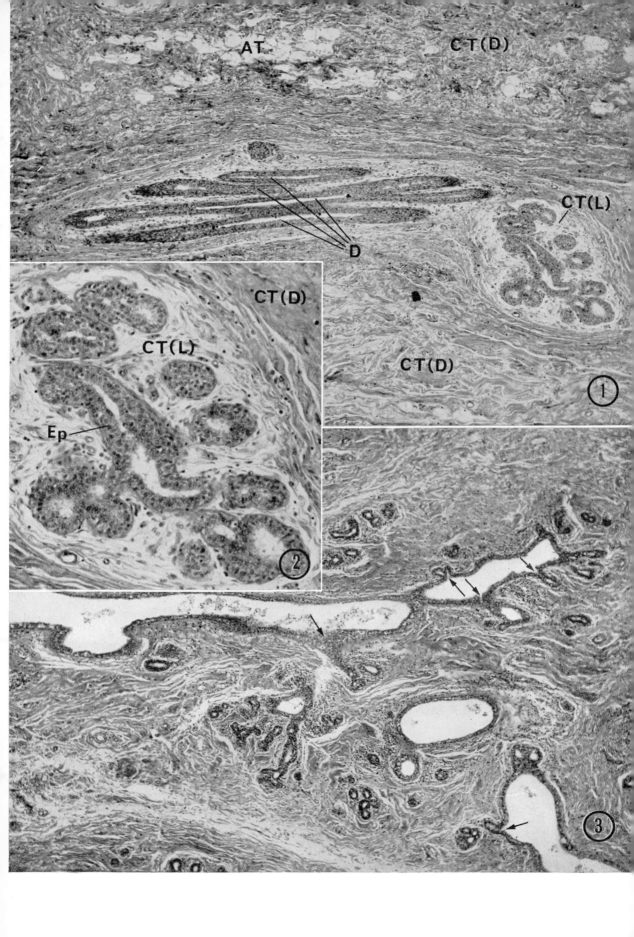

Plate 77. MAMMARY GLAND, PROLIFERATIVE

Whereas the proliferation of the duct elements is well marked during early stages of proliferation, the development of the alveolar elements becomes conspicuous at a later time. Figure 1 shows several lobules (**L**) at a later stage of proliferation than is shown in the preceding plate. Distinct alveoli (**A**) can now be recognized. These are all joined to a duct (**D**), although the connections may not be seen in a two-dimensional section. Lobules are separated by dense connective tissue septa (**S**), and some ducts can be recognized as being in an interlobular location. Some elements are still in a relatively early stage of proliferation. The **inset** (Fig. 1) shows where epithelial sprouting has occurred along the length of a duct (**arrowheads**).

A closer look at one of the proliferating lobules is provided in Figure 2. Numerous alveoli (**A**) are evident. The alveoli consist of a single layer of cuboidal epithelium. A small amount of precipitate is located in the lumen of some of the alveoli. This represents the early secretory activity of the cells.

The large duct (**D**) through which the alveoli will discharge their product is shown on the left, almost like a stalk. It can be recognized because of its location and its elongated profile. Some of the flattened nuclei that are closely applied to the duct belong to *myoepithelial cells.*

The connective tissue (**CT**) surrounding the alveoli is loose, and contains delicate collagenous fibers and large numbers of round cells (**arrows**). The identity of these cells is difficult to establish at this magnification, though most are probably lymphocytes.

KEY

A, alveoli
CT, connective tissue
D, duct
L, lobule
S, septa
arrows, round connective tissue cells
arrowheads, epithelial sprouts

Fig. 1 (human), x 65, (inset), x 160; Fig. 2 (human), x 160.

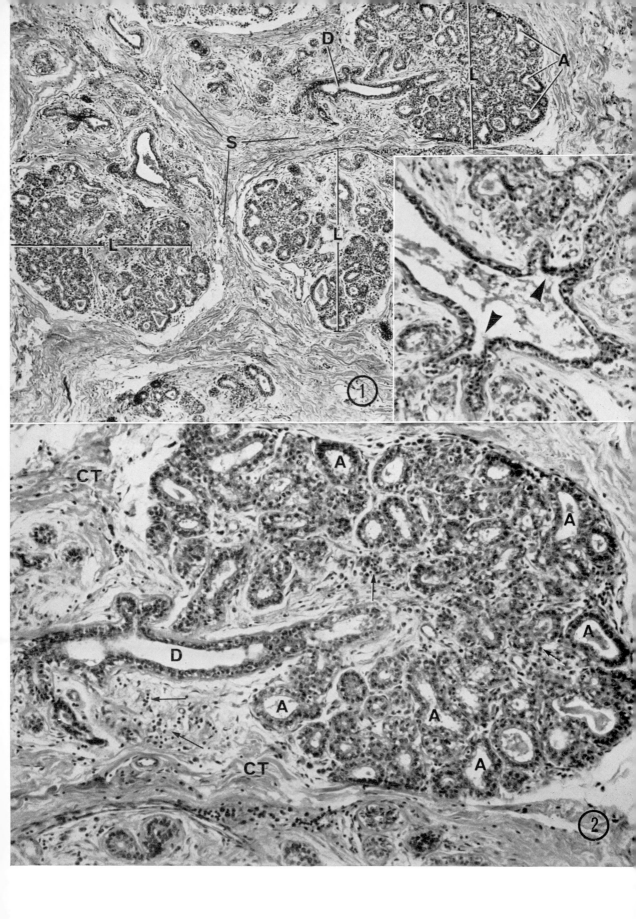

Plate 78. Mammary Gland, Lactating

The *lactating mammary gland* is characterized by the presence of large numbers of alveoli (Fig. 1). Many of these appear as oval or spherical profiles and in this respect, on cursory examination, the gland is easy to confuse with the thyroid gland. However, all of the alveoli in the mammary gland are joined to a duct and often the place where several alveoli open into a central channel can be seen. These connections represent branchings of a terminal duct system. The presence of connected alveoli (**asterisks**) enables one to identify the lactating mammary gland and distinguish it from thyroid tissue, even if the duct elements are not conspicuous. Sections of mammary glands usually include duct elements, but the small ducts are difficult to identify since they resemble the alveoli. A large duct (**D**), easily recognized by its size, is in the upper left of the figure. A number of connective tissue septa (**S**) separate the alveoli of neighboring lobules. Large blood vessels (**BV**) are within the connective tissue septa.

The alveoli of lactating mammary glands are made up of cuboidal epithelium. Frequently, some precipitated product can be seen within the lumen of the alveolus. Several alveoli are shown in Figures 2 and 3. Only a small amount of connective tissue separates the cuboidal cells of neighboring alveoli. Capillaries (**Cap**) can be seen in this connective tissue. Figure 2 is a typical H & E section and the resemblance of mammary alveoli to thyroid follicles is especially evident. Figure 3 is a special preparation showing some of the lipid that is present in the mammary secretion. The lipid appears as the black spheres of various size. It can also be seen in some of the cells. This lipid first appears as small droplets within the cells. These droplets become larger and ultimately they are discharged into the alveolus.

The lymphatic vessels of the mammary glands, which are so important clinically, are not usually evident in histological sections.

KEY

BV, blood vessels
Cap, capillaries
D, duct
S, septa
asterisks, branchings of terminal duct system
Fig. 1 (human), x 160; Figs. 2 and 3 (human), x 640.

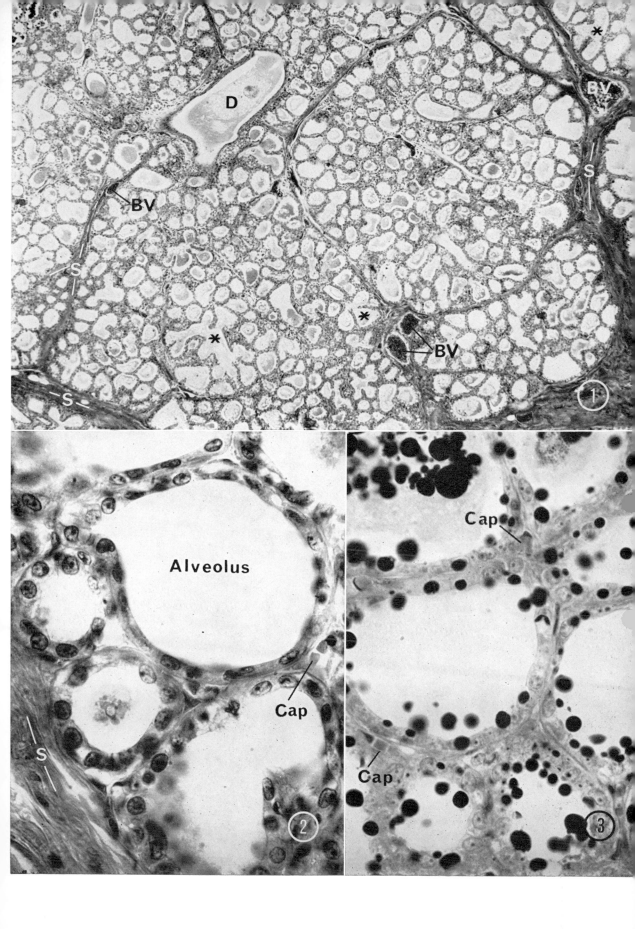

ENDOCRINE SYSTEM

THE ENDOCRINE SYSTEM consists of the following glands: the *thyroid, parathyroids, pituitary, adrenals,* and *parts of the testes* (Plate 67), *ovaries* (Plates 72 and 73) and *pancreas* (Plate 56). The *pineal gland* is included with the endocrine system although its function is not understood.

Whereas exocrine glands secrete their products onto a surface either directly or via a duct, the products of endocrine glands, the *hormones,* pass into neighboring blood vessels and by means of the blood vessels the hormones reach their site of action. Endocrine glands are also called *ductless glands* or *glands of internal secretion.* Although hormones are also produced by the placenta and the gastrointestinal mucosa, these structures are not thought of as endocrine glands.

The various endocrine glands differ in their manner of development and in the nature of their product. They display a variety of structural forms which makes it difficult to generalize about them. For example, the parathyroid, adenohypophysis (part of the pituitary gland), adrenal glands, and the islets of Langerhans (in the pancreas) are arranged as cords of cells that are richly supplied with blood vessels. The thyroid gland is also richly supplied with blood vessels, but it has an additional provision, in the form of follicles, for storing its product. The ovaries have a distinctive feature: transient endocrine-producing structures appear during different parts of the ovarian cycle. The hormone-producing cells of the testes are arranged as small, isolated islands of cells. The neurohypophysis (part of the pituitary gland) bears some resemblance to nerve tissue.

The structural feature which is most common to the endocrine glands is that the cells have an epithelial arrangement, but they do not possess a free surface. Rather they are closely opposed to blood vessels. But even here, the neurohypophysis is an exception to the generalization in that it does not develop the characteristics of epithelial tissue.

ENDOCRINE SYSTEM

Plate 79. THYROID GLAND

The *thyroid gland* is located in the neck in close relation to the upper part of the trachea and the lower part of the larynx. It consists of two lateral lobes that are joined by a narrow isthmus. The functional unit of the thyroid gland is the *follicle,* which consists of a single layer of cuboidal or low columnar epithelium surrounding a colloid-filled space. A rich capillary network is present in the connective tissue that separates the follicles. The posterior aspect of the thyroid gland is in relation to the parathyroid glands, which are frequently imbedded in the thyroid tissue.

A histological section of the thyroid gland is shown in Figure 1. The follicles (**F**) vary somewhat in size and shape, and they appear closely packed. The homogeneous mass in the center of each follicle is the *colloid* (**C**). The thyroid cells appear to form a ring around the colloid. Although the individual cells are difficult to distinguish at this magnification, the nuclei of the cells serve as an indication of their location and arrangement.

Large groups of cells (**X**) are present between some of the follicles. Where the nuclei are of the same size and staining characteristics, one can conclude that the section went through the wall of the follicle in a tangential manner without including the lumen. In other places, connective tissue (**CT**) and small blood vessels can be recognized between the follicles. At the bottom of the field is a portion of a parathyroid (**P**) gland which was removed with the thyroid specimen.

Thyroid follicles are shown at higher magnification in Figure 2. In this specimen, the thyroid cells are cuboidal, but they may be more flattened (when they are in a less active state) or columnar (when they are in a more active state). In some follicles, there are vacuolar spaces at the periphery of the colloid (**arrowheads**). These spaces, from which colloid was lost, are regarded as artefacts; however, they reflect differences in the state of the colloid. Examination of Figure 2 (and Fig. 1) reveals that adjacent follicles are extremely close and separated by a small amount of connective tissue (**CT**). A rich capillary network is present in this connective tissue. The

KEY

C, colloid
CT, connective tissue
F, follicles
P, parathyroid gland
X, tangential section of follicular epithelium
arrows, connective tissue or vascular nuclei
arrowheads, vacuolar spaces in colloid
Fig. 1, (monkey), x 190; Fig. 2 (monkey), x 480.

elongated nuclei (**arrows**) between the follicles belong to connective tissue cells or to the capillary endothelium. The blood capillaries are not conspicuous in this specimen.

188

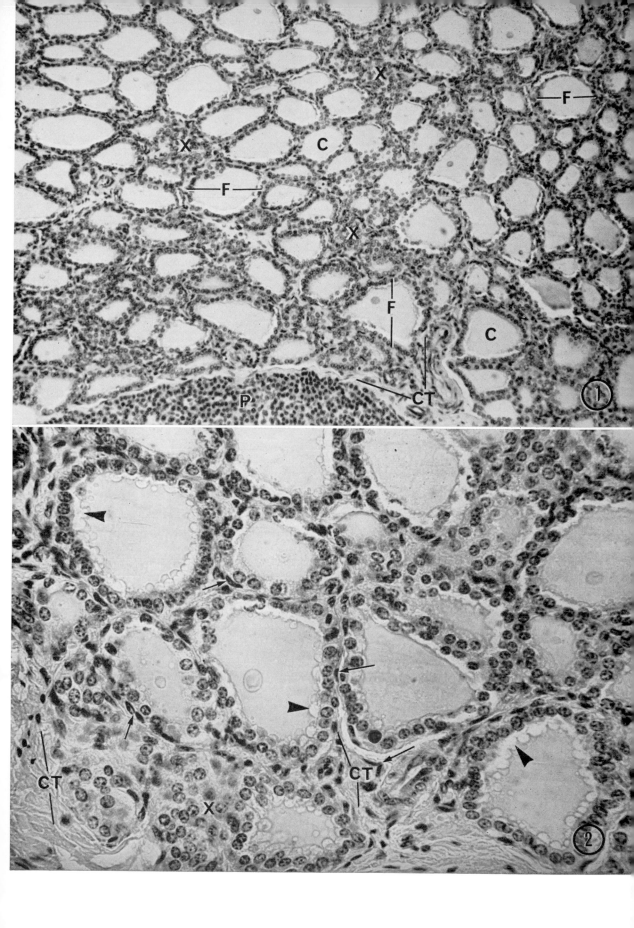

Plate 80. PARATHYROID GLAND

The *parathyroid glands* develop from the third and fourth pharyngeal pouches and come to lie in or in close contact to the posterior aspect of the thyroid gland. Usually four parathyroid glands are present.

A connective tissue capsule (**Cap**) surrounds each parathyroid gland and separates it from adjacent thyroid tissue. Connective tissue trabeculae extend from the capsule into the substance of the gland, and associated with these trabeculae are the larger blood vessels (**BV**) and occasionally fat cells (**FC**). The parenchyma of the parathyroid glands appears as cords or sheets of cells, separated by capillaries and delicate connective tissue septa. In a low-power view (Fig. 1) of the parathyroid gland there is no suggestion of any special organization of the parenchymal elements.

Two parenchymal cell types can be distinguished in routine H & E sections: *chief cells (principal cells)* and *oxyphil cells* (**rectangle,** Fig. 1). These are shown at higher magnification in Figure 2. The **curved broken line** indicates the boundary between the oxyphil cells (**OC**) and the chief cells (**CC**). The chief cells are more numerous. They contain a spherical nucleus that is surrounded by a small amount of cytoplasm. The boundaries between the cells are evident in some places. Oxyphil cells are not found in some species. In man they are said to appear during the first decade of life and increase somewhat in number in older individuals. Oxyphil cells are larger than chief cells, but have a slightly smaller and more intensely staining nucleus. The cytoplasm of oxyphil cells stains with eosin. The boundaries between these cells are well marked. Oxyphil cells are arranged in small or large groups that are scattered about in a much larger field of chief cells. Even with low magnification it is often possible to identify clusters of oxyphil cells (Fig. 1).

The delicate connective tissue septa in the parathyroids are not conspicuous in H & E preparation. However, the elongated nuclei (**arrows**) (Fig. 2) that can be seen between the parenchymal cells belong either to connective tissue cells (fibrocytes) or capillary endothelium.

KEY

BV, blood vessels
Cap, capsule
CC, chief cells
FC, fat cells
OC, oxyphil cells
arrows, nuclei of fibrocytes or endothelial cells
Fig. 1 (human), x 160; Fig. 2 (human), x 640.

Several other types of cells have been described in the parathyroids. For example, some chief cells are described as having a darker cytoplasm (*dark cells*), while others are described as having a lighter cytoplasm (*light cells*). If the cytoplasm of the light cells is clear, they are called *clear cells.* Some appear transitional between chief and oxyphil cells. They are called *transitional cells.* The significance of the foregoing is not clear. However, the interpretation that at least two functionally distinct types of cells exist appears reasonable.

The parathyroid glands elaborate a hormone that influences calcium and bone metabolism. Injection of parathyroid hormone into laboratory animals results in bone resorption by osteoclastic activity.

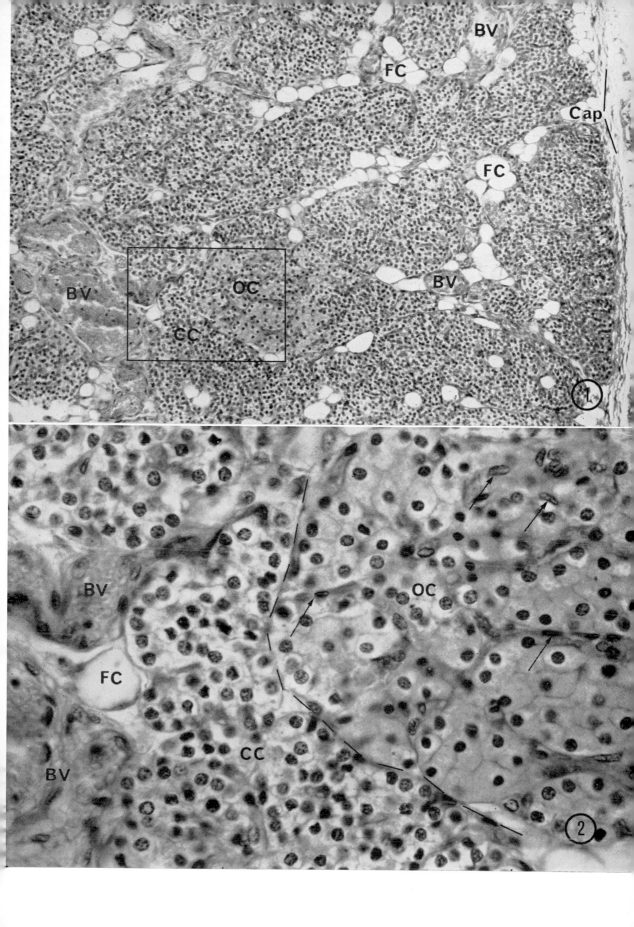

Plate 81. PITUITARY GLAND I

The *pituitary gland,* or *hypophysis cerebri,* is located in a small bony fossa in the floor of the cranial cavity. It is connected by a stalk to the base of the brain. Although it is joined to the brain, only part of the pituitary gland develops from neural ectoderm; this is referred to as the *neurohypophysis.* The larger part of the pituitary gland develops from the oral ectoderm; this part is called the *adenohypophysis.* The adenohypophysis develops as a diverticulum of the buccal epithelium, called *Rathke's pouch.* In the fully developed gland, the lumen of Rathke's pouch may be retained as a vestigial cleft.

Both the adenohypophysis and neurohypophysis are further subdivided as follows:

Adenohypophysis
    a) pars distalis (anterior lobe)
    b) pars tuberalis
    c) pars intermedia

Neurohypophysis   (posterior lobe)
    a) pars nervosa
    b) infundibulum (infundibular stem and median eminence of tuber cinereum).

These parts are shown in a sagittal section of the pituitary gland. The neurohypophysis is marked by the **broken lines.** The pars nervosa is the expanded portion which is continuous with the infundibulum (**I**). The pars tuberalis (**PT**) is located around the infundibular stem. The pars intermedia (**PI**) is between the pars distalis and the pars nervosa. It borders a small cleft (**C**) which constitutes the remains of the lumen of Rathke's pouch. The pars distalis is the largest part of the pituitary gland. It contains a variety of cell types, some of which are more numerous in one region, some in another. This accounts for the difference in staining (light and dark areas) that is to be seen throughout the pars distalis.

In a low-power view of a sagittal section of the pituitary gland, the parts are identified largely on the basis of their location and relation to each other. For example, the pars nervosa can be identified readily if it is continuous with a stem or stalk of essentially the same kind of material. The pars intermedia

KEY

C, vestigial cleft of Rathke's pouch
I, infundibulum
PI, pars intermedia
PT, pars tuberalis
Fig. (monkey), x 40.

is in an intermediate location, and in relation to the cleft; however, the cleft may not be evident and the pars intermedia may be more extensive (in this specimen it continues along the surface of the gland).

Upon considering the cell types at higher magnification (next plate), one comes to realize that these serve as a major indication as to the part of the gland that is being examined.

The blood supply to the pars distalis of the pituitary gland is unique and requires special mention. It is supplied by two sets of vessels. While one group of arteries passes directly into the sinusoidal capillaries of the pars distalis, the sinusoids of the pars distalis also receive blood via a hypophyseal portal system. The latter originates as capillaries in the infundibulum. These capillaries drain into a venous network which follows the pars tuberalis to the pars distalis where they empty into the capillary sinusoids. This system appears to serve as a route whereby neurohumoral substances from the base of the brain can pass to the pars distalis and exert an influence on its function.

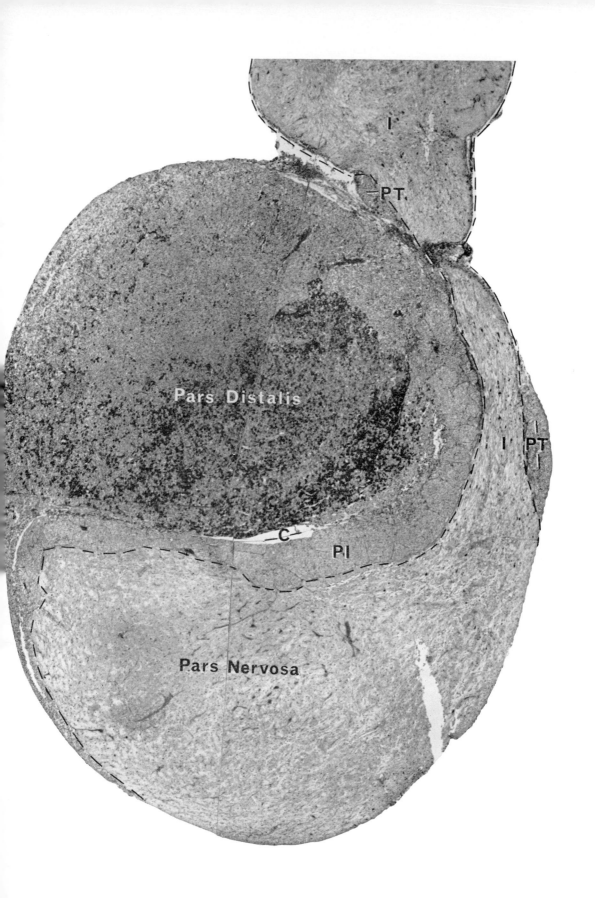

Plate 82. PITUITARY GLAND II

The parenchyma of the *pars distalis* consists of two main cell types, *chromophobes* and *chromophils*. Chromophobes stain poorly; chromophils stain well with a variety of dyes. The chromophils are further subdivided into *acidophils* or *basophils,* according to whether the cytoplasm stains with hematoxylin (basophil) or with eosin (acidophil).

A region of the pars distalis which shows a large number of basophils is illustrated in Figure 1. The field also includes acidophils, chromophobes, and stromal elements. The basophils (**B**) can be distinguished from acidophils (**A**) because they are slightly larger than the acidophils, and the cytoplasm stains with hematoxylin, whereas the cytoplasm of the acidophils stains with eosin. Both of these cell types can be distinguished from the chromophobes (**C**), which contain only a small amount of poorly staining cytoplasm. The parenchymal components of the pars distalis are arranged as cords of cells. These are separated by a delicate connective tissue stroma which contains sinusoids. The elongated nuclei (**arrows**) belong to either cells of the connective tissue stroma or to the sinusoidal capillary cells. The lining cells of the sinusoids are phagocytic.

A region of the pars distalis which shows predominantly acidophils is illustrated in Figure 2. A definite amount of eosinophilic cytoplasm can be seen in each cell. In contrast, the nuclei of chromophobes (**C**) are surrounded by a small amount of poorly staining cytoplasm. The elongated nuclei of stromal and vascular cells are readily distinguished from the spherical nuclei of the parenchymal cells. Acidophils are considered to produce growth hormone; basophils, on the other hand, are associated with the production of gonadotrophin and thyrotrophin.

The *pars tuberalis* (Fig. 3) surrounds the infundibular stem. It consists of small acidophil and basophil cells. Frequently, these are arranged as small vesicles (**V**) that contain colloid. The pars tuberalis is highly vascular. Its function is not known.

The *pars intermedia* (**PI**) varies in size in different mammals (Fig. 4). It is relatively

KEY

A, acidophils
B, basophils
BV, blood vessel
C, chromophobes
HB, Herring bodies
PI, pars intermedia
PN, pars nervosa
V, vesicles
arrows, nuclei of stromal or vascular cells
Figs. 1 and 2 (cat), x 640; Figs. 3–5 (cat), x 400.

small in the human. It consists of cords of cells which resemble basophils, except that they are smaller. They sometimes form colloid-filled vesicles. Cells from the pars intermedia are occasionally seen in the pars nervosa (**PN**). The function of the pars intermedia in man is not clear. Studies with frogs indicate that a hormone from this lobe, called intermedin, plays a regulatory role in pigmentation.

The *neurohypophysis* (Fig. 5) consists of cells called *pituicytes.* The nuclei of the cells are round or oval; the cytoplasm extends from the nuclear region of the cell as long processes. In addition, the neurohypophysis contains nonmyelinated nerve fibers from the supraoptic and paraventricular nuclei of the hypothalamus. In H & E preparations, the cytoplasm of the pituicytes cannot be distinguished from the nonmyelinated nerve fibers. The hormones of the neurohypophysis, oxytocin and vasopressin, are formed in the hypothalmic nuclei, pass via the fibers of the *hypothalamo-hypophyseal* tract to the neurohypophysis where they are stored in the expanded terminal portions of the nerve fibers. In histological sections, the stored neurosecretory material appears as the *Herring bodies* (**HB**).

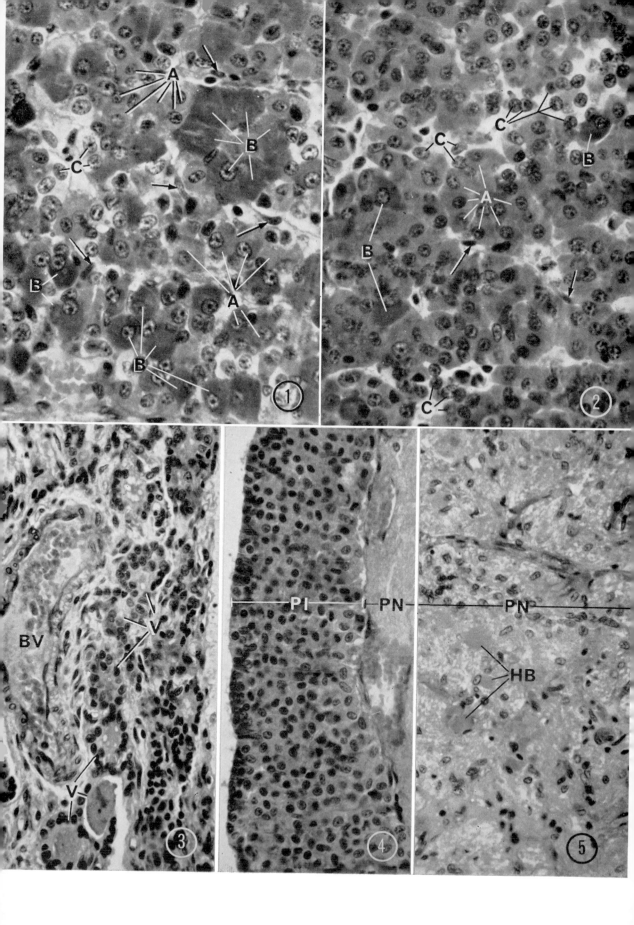

Plate 83. ADRENAL GLAND I

There are two adrenal glands, one situated at the upper pole of each kidney. An adrenal gland is a composite of two distinct structural and functional components, the cortex and the medulla. The cortex develops from mesoderm, the medulla from ectoderm.

A section through the entire thickness of an adrenal gland is shown in Figure 1. Several histological features are readily evident in low-power views. The outer part of the gland, the *cortex,* has a distinctly different appearance from the inner portion, the *medulla.* Several large blood vessels (**BV**) are in the medulla. These are veins which drain the entire gland. A capsule (**Cap**) surrounds the gland and from the capsule delicate trabeculae extend into the substance of the gland.

The cortex is divided into three parts according to the type and arrangement of cells. These are designated as the *zona glomerulosa* (**ZG**), the *zona fasciculata* (**ZF**), and the *zona reticularis* (**ZR**). The zona glomerulosa is located at the outer part of the cortex, immediately under the capsule (Figs. 1 and 2). The parenchyma of this zone consists of small cells which are arranged as arching cords or as oval groups. The nuclei of the parenchymal cells are spherical, and the cells possess a small amount of lightly staining cytoplasm. Because of the small amount of cytoplasm, the nuclei in this zone appear crowded. Between the cords of cells are elongated nuclei (**arrows**) which belong either to cells of the delicate connective tissue stroma or to the vascular wall. The vessels have traditionally been described as sinusoids. The zona fasciculata can be divided into two parts, an outer and an inner, based on the appearance of the cells in routine H & E preparations. The outer part of the zona fasciculata (**ZF**) is shown in Figure 3 and in the lower part of Figure 2. The nuclei of these cells are about the same size as those of the zona glomerulosa; however, there is more cytoplasm and the nuclei appear to be more separated than those of the zona glomerulosa. Occasionally, binucleate cells (**asterisks**) are seen in the zona fasciculata. These may be difficult to recognize because the cell boundaries are not always conspicu-

KEY

BV, blood vessels
Cap, capsule
ZF, zona fasciculata
ZG, zona glomerulosa
ZR, zona reticularis
arrows, nuclei of sinusoidal lining cells, or of connective tissue cells
asterisks, binucleate cells

Fig. 1 (monkey), x 30; Figs. 2 and 3 (monkey), x 400.

ous. The cells of the outer part of the zona fasciculata contain a considerably greater amount of lipid than the cells in the other parts of the cortex. During the preparation of routine H & E specimens, the lipid is lost, and as a consequence, the cytoplasm has a noticeably empty or spongy appearance. The part of the zona fasciculata which contains these cells, i.e., the outer part, is sometimes referred to as the spongy part. This region constitutes the largest part of the zona fasciculata.

The cords are radially oriented, that is, at right angles to the capsule and usually two cells in width.

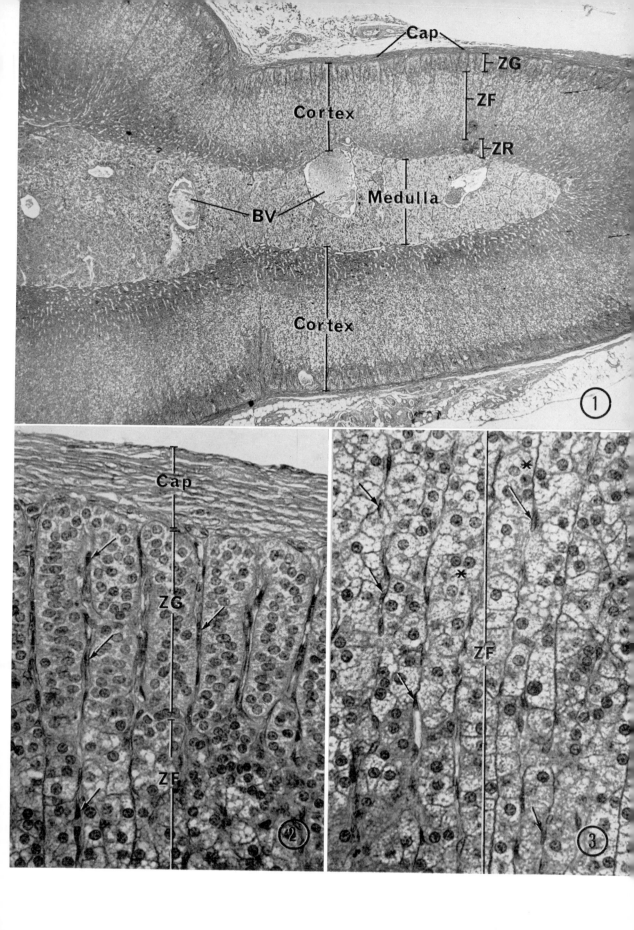

Plate 84. ADRENAL GLAND II

The outer part of the zona fasciculata, as described in the previous plate, consists of cells whose cytoplasm has a spongy appearance [**ZF(S)**]. This constitutes the bulk of the fascicular zone. The inner part of the zona fasciculata consists of smaller cells [**ZF(C)**]. The cytoplasm of these cells appears more compact than that of the cells in the outer part. The junction between these two parts of the zona fasciculata is shown in Figure 1. As mentioned before (page 196), the spongy appearance of the outer part is due to the loss of lipid that occurs during the preparation of the tissue. Throughout the entire zona fasciculata the cells are arranged as cords and between the cords one can see the elongated nuclei (**arrows**) that belong either to cells of the delicate connective tissue stroma, or to the endothelial cells that line the sinusoids.

The zona reticularis (**ZR**) is shown in Figure 2. This is the deepest part of the cortex, immediately adjacent to the medulla. It consists of interconnecting, irregular cords of small cells. The cords are narrower than those of the other parts of the cortex; in many places they are only one cell wide. (In contrast, they appear to be two or more cells wide in the zona fasciculata.) Between the cords of cells are the sinusoids which in this zone are regularly dilated. As in the other parts of the gland, the spherical nuclei belong to the parenchymal cells, the elongated nuclei (**arrows**) belong to the lining cells of the sinusoids or to cells of the connective tissue stroma.

The adrenal cortex produces a large number of steroid hormones. These have a profound effect on connective tissue, metabolism, electrolyte balance, and some have androgen activity.

In mammals, the adrenal *medulla* (**M**) is in the center of the gland, surrounded by the cortex. It consists of large cells (Fig. 3) which are organized in ovoid groups or as short, interconnecting cords. The cytoplasm of neighboring cells may stain with different intensity. These cells color when treated with chromate reagents and for this reason they are sometimes called *chromaffin cells*. Elongated nuclei

KEY

M, adrenal medulla
ZF(C), zona fasciculata, compact cells
ZF(S), zona fasciculata, spongy cells
ZR, zona reticularis
arrows, nuclei of sinusoidal lining cells, or of connective tissue cells
Figs. 1–3 (monkey), x 400.

(**arrows**) of vascular or connective tissue cells can be seen in the delicate stroma which separates the groups of parenchymal cells. *Ganglion cells* are occasionally seen in sections of the adrenal medulla.

The cells of the adrenal medulla develop from the same source as the postganglionic cells of the sympathetic nervous system. They are directly innervated by preganglionic cells of the sympathetic system and may be regarded as modified postglanglionic cells that are specialized to secrete. These cells produce epinephrine and norepinephrine.

The adrenal medulla receives its blood supply via two routes. It is supplied by arterioles which pass through the cortex, and it is supplied by capillaries that continue from the cortex. This means that some of the blood reaching the medulla contains cortical secretion.

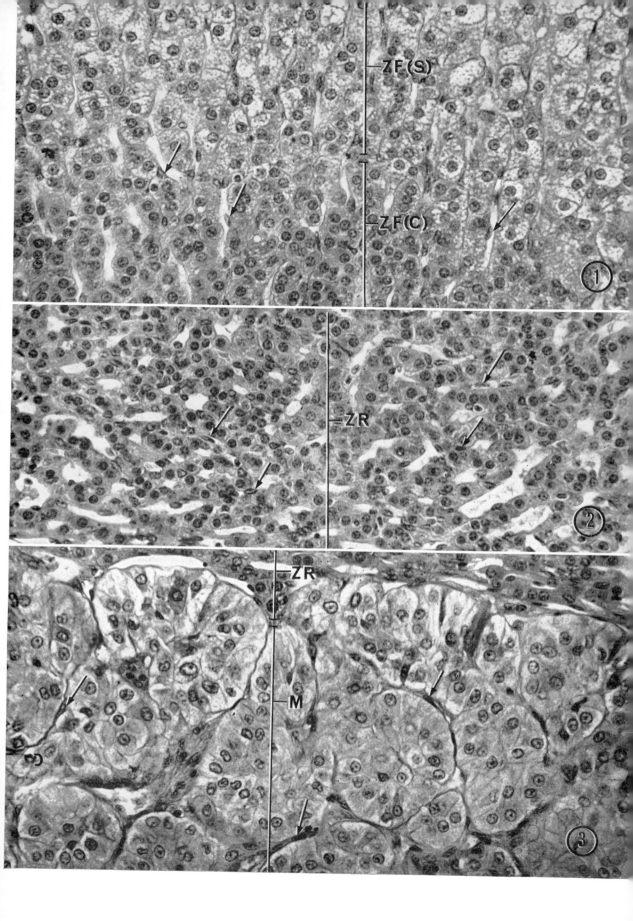

Plate 85. Pineal Body

The *pineal body (pineal gland, epiphysis cerebri)* is located in the brain above the superior colliculi. Although two cell types have been described in the pineal body, *parenchymal cells* and *glial cells,* the function of these cells or of the pineal body itself is not understood.

The pineal gland is surrounded by a capsule (**Cap**) except at its stalk. The capsule is formed by the *pia mater.* Trabeculae extend from the capsule into the substance of the gland and divide it into lobules (Fig. 1). The lobules (**L**) appear as the indistinct groups of cells surrounded by connective tissue (**CT**). The adult pineal body contains calcareous deposits (**BS**) which are regularly found in histological sections. They are called *brain sand* or *corpora amylacea.* When viewed with higher magnification they can be seen to possess a lamellated structure.

Two cell types have been described within the pineal gland: parenchymal cells and glial cells. The full extent of these cells cannot be appreciated without the application of special methods. These would show that the glial cells and the parenchymal cells have processes and that the processes of the parenchymal cells are expanded at their periphery. The parenchymal cells are more numerous. In an H & E section the nuclei of the parenchymal cells are described as being pale staining and somewhat vesicular. The nuclei of the glial cells on the other hand are described as being smaller and as staining more intensely. In Figure 2, two nuclear types can be seen. The more numerous nuclei are the larger ones; they stain less intensely and are somewhat vesiculated; they belong to parenchymal cells (**PC**). The less numerous nuclei are the smaller ones; they stain more intensely; they belong to glial cells (**GC**).

KEY

BS, brain sand
Cap, capsule
CT, connective tissue
GC, nuclei of glial cells
L, lobules
PC, nuclei of parenchymal cells
Fig. 1 (human), x 80; Fig. 2 (human), x 185.

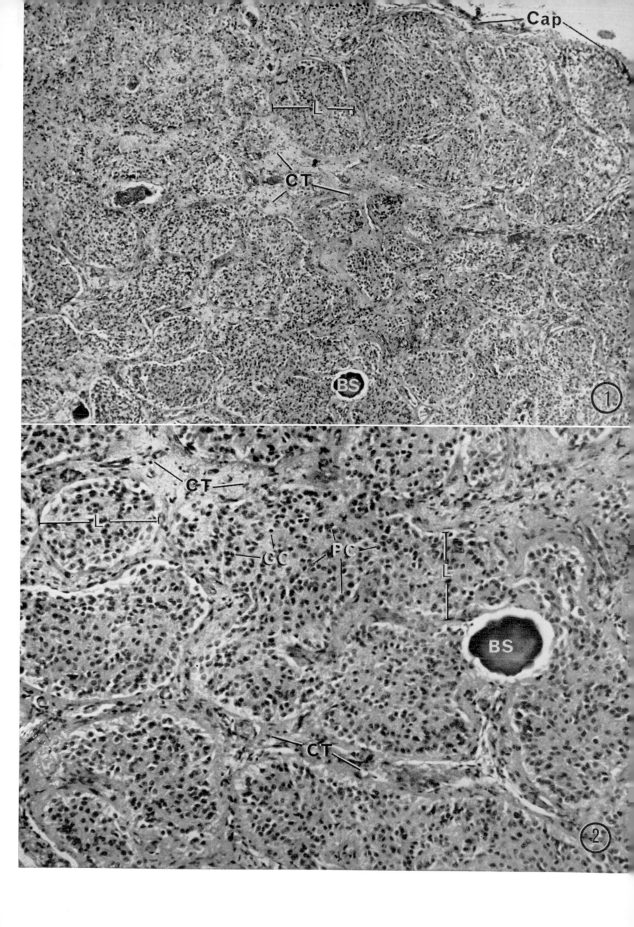

INDEX

Absorptive cells, 6
Acini, mucous, salivary, 100, 102
  serous, salivary, 100, 102
Adipose tissue, 13
Adrenal gland, 196-199
  medulla, 198
Alimentary canal, organization, 92
Alveolar duct, 142
Alveolar sac, 142
Alveoli, lung, 135, 142
  serous, pancreas, 132
Ameloblasts, 104
Aorta, 68
  nerva vasorum, 68
  tunica adventitia, 68
  tunica intima, 68
  tunica media, 68
  vasa vasorum, 68
Appendix, 122
Argentaffine cells, large intestine, 122
  small intestine, 120
  stomach, 110
Arrector pili muscle, 88
Arterioles, 72
Artery (ies), elastic, 20
  hepatic, 126, 128
  internal elastic membrane, 70
  muscular, 70
  tunica adventitia, 70
  tunica, intima, 70
  tunica media, 70
Atretic follicles, ovary, 170, 172
Auerbach's plexus, 120

Basal bodies, ciliated epithelium, 6, 138, 140
Basal cells, 6
Basement membrane, 6
  relationship to epithelium, 2
  trachea, 138
Betz cells, cerebrum, 58
Bile canaliculi, 128
Billroth's cords, 80, 82
Binucleate cells, liver, 128
  transitional epithelium, 8
  urinary bladder, 154
Bladder, urinary, 154
Bone, 23, 36, 38
  canaliculi, 23, 32
  cancellous, 23, 28
  compact, 23, 32
  decalcified sections, 23

Bone (continued)
  epiphyseal plate (disc), 28, 34, 36
  formation, endochondral, 34, 36
    intramembranous, 38
  ground sections, 23, 32
  Haversian canal, 32
  Haversian systems, 23, 32
  lacunae, 23, 28, 32
  lamellae, 32
  marrow, 28, 36
  marrow cells, 36
  matrix, 36
  medullary cavity, 34
  osteoblasts, 34, 36, 38
  osteoclasts, 38
  osteocytes, 28, 36, 38
  osteoid, 36, 38
  osteons, 23, 32
  perichondral, 34
  periosteal, 34
  remodeling of, 34, 38
  resorption, 38
  spicules, 28, 36, 38
  spongy, 28
  trabeculae, 28
  Volkmanns canals, 32
Bowman's capsule, 145, 148
Bowman's glands, 136
Brain sand, 200
Bridges, intercellular, 90, 96
Bronchiole, 140
  respiratory, 140, 142
  terminal, 140
Bronchus, 138, 140
Brunner's glands, 116
Brush border, 3, 148

Calyx, renal, 150
Canal, portal, 126
Canaliculi, bile, 128
Capillaries, peritubular, 148
  sinusoidal, liver, 126
Capsule, Bowman's, 148
Cardiac muscle (see *Muscle*)
Cardiovascular system, 64-73
  arterioles, 64, 72
  elastic tissue, 64, 68
  endothelium, 64-72
  organization of, 64
  valves, 64, 65

Cartilage, 23-30, 34, 36
  appositional growth, 24
  articular, 28
  calcified, 34, 36
  cells, 23, 24, 28, 30, 36
  elastic, 28
  erosion of, 34
  fibrocartilage, 30
  ground substance, 24
  hyaline, 24, 26, 28
  hypertrophic, 34, 36
  interstitial growth, 24
  lacunae, 23, 24, 28, 30, 36
  matrix, 23, 24, 26, 30, 36
    extraterritorial, 24
    territorial, 24
  proliferating, 36
  reserve, 36
  resorption of, 36
  spicules, 36
Cavity, joint, 26
Cell(s), absorptive, 6
  alpha (A), pancreas, 132
  argentaffine, large intestine, 122
    small intestine, 120
    stomach, 110
  basal, 6
  basket, 60
  beta (B), pancreas, 132
  Betz, 58
  binucleate (see *Binucleate cells*)
  centro-acinar, 132
  chief, stomach, 108, 110
  connective tissue, 16
  D, pancreas, 132
  endothelium, 4
  epithelial, 2-8
  epithelioid, 8
    testis, 160
    thymus, 84
  ganglion, 52, 54
  goblet, 6
  Golgi type II, 60
  granule, 58, 60
  granulosa lutein, 174
  hepatic, 126
  interstitial, of Leydig, 160
  Kupffer, 128
  of Leydig, 157, 160
  of Martinotti, 58
  mast, 12, 13
  mucous, salivary, 100
  mucous neck, stomach, 110
  myoepithelial, 40, 90
  neuroglial, 58, 62
  Paneth, 120, 122

Cells (*continued*)
  parietal, stomach, 110
  plasma, 13, 118
  primordial spermatogenic, 160
  Purkinje, 60
  pyramidal, 58
  replacement of, 4
  reticular, 75, 78
  serous, salivary, 100
  Sertoli, 158
  sustentacular, testis, 158
  theca lutein, 174
Cerebellum, basket cells, 60
  cortex, 60
  Golgi type II cells, 60
  granular layer, 60
  granule cells, 60
  molecular layer, 60
  plexiform layer, 60
  Purkinje cells, 60
Cerebrum, Betz cells, 58
  cells of Martinotti, 58
  cortex, 58
  granule cells, 58
  layers, 58
  neuroglial cells, 58
  neuropil, 58
  pyramidal cells, 58
Chondrocytes, 24
Cilia, 6
  bronchiole, 140
  efferent ductules, 162
  respiratory system, 138, 140
  uterine tube, 176
Cohnheim's fields, 44
Collagen, 11, 13
Collagenous fibers, 11, 13, 14
Collecting tubules, 145, 148, 150
Colloid, thyroid gland, 188
Colon, 122
Connective tissue, 11-21
  cell types, 12, 13, 16
  classification, 11
  dense, 14, 16
  elastic, 13
  embryonic, 20
  fibers, 14
  loose, 14
  mucous, 13, 20
  organization, 11
    loose and dense, 14
  regular, 13, 18
  staining, fibers, 12
Convoluted tubules, renal, 145, 146, 148, 150
Corpora amylacea, 200

Corpuscle(s), Hassall's, 84
  Malpighian (see *renal*)
  Meissner's, 88, 90
  pacinian, 90
  renal (Malpighian), 145, 146, 148
Corpus luteum, 174
Cross striations, 40
Crypts, of Lieberkühn, 114, 116, 122, 124
  tonsilar, 76
Cumulus oophorus, 172

Decidua basalis, 178
Decidua functionalis, 178
Demilunes, 100, 102
Dental lamina, 104
Dental papilla, 104
Dental sac, 104
Dental tubule, 104
Dentin, 104
Dentino-enamel junction, 104
Dermis, 87, 88, 90
Digestive system, 92-133
  glands, 92, 93
Disse's space, 128
Duct, alveolar, 142
  hepatic, 126, 128
  mammary gland, 180-184
  pancreatic, 132
  salivary, 100, 102
Ductless glands, 187-201
Ductus deferens, 164
Duodenum, 114, 116

Efferent ductules, 162
Elastic artery, 20
Elastic cartilage, 28
Elastic fibers, 11, 20
Elastic tissue, 13
Enamel, 104
Enamel organ, 104
  inner enamel epithelium, 104
  outer enamel epithelium, 104
  stellate reticulum, 104
  stratum intermedium, 104
Endocardium, 66
Endocrine glands, 187-201
Endometrium, 178
Endomysium, 44
Endoneurium, 56
Endothelium, 2, 4, 64-72
  replacement of, 4
Epicardium, 66
Epidermis, 87, 88, 90
Epididymis, 162
  stereocilia, 162

Epineurium, 56
Epiphyseal plate (disc), 28, 34, 36
Epithelioid cells, 8
  testis, 160
  thymus, 84
Epithelium, 2-9
  classification of, 2
  columnar, 6
  cuboidal, 6
  general description, 2
  glandular, 8
  pseudostratified columnar, 6
    ciliated, 6
  replacement of, 4
  simple squamous, 4
  stratified squamous, 4
  surface modifications, 3
  transitional, 8, 154
Esophagus, 106-109
Estrogen, 169

Fat cells, 12, 13
Fenestrated membranes, 20
Fiber(s), collagenous, 11, 12, 13, 14
  connective tissue, 11
  elastic, 11, 12, 20
    cartilage, 28
  muscle, 40
  nerve, 52, 54, 56
  Purkinje, heart, 48
  reticular, 11, 12, 13
    lymph nodes, 78
    spleen, 82
Fibroblast, 11-13
Fibrocartilage, 30
Fibrocyte, 11-13
Filiform papillae, 94
Follicle(s), atretic, 172
  Graafian, 172
  primary, ovarian, 170
  thyroid gland, 188
Formation, endochondrial bone, 36
Fungiform papillae, 94

Gall bladder, 130
Ganglion, capsule cell, 54
  cell, 52, 54
    lung, 140
    pancreas, 132
    small intestine, 120
  dorsal root, 54
  satellite cell, 54
  supporting cells, 54
  sympathetic, 52
Gastric pits, 108, 110, 112

Germinal centers, lymph node, 76, 78
  spleen, 80
  tonsil, 76
Germinal epithelium, ovary, 170
Glands, adrenal, 196, 198
  Bowman's, 136
  Brunner's, 116
  development of, 2
  ductless, 187
  endocrine, 187-201
  exocrine, 187
  holocrine, 90
  of internal secretion, 187
  mucous, soft palate, 98
  parathyroid, 190
  parotid, 102
  pineal, 200
  pituitary, 192-194
  prostate, 166
  salivary, 100, 102
  sebaceous, 88, 90
  sero-mucous, soft palate, 98
  serous, tongue, 96
  sublingual, 102
  submandibular, 100
  sweat, 88, 90
  thymus, 84
  thyroid, 188
  von Ebner's, 96
Goblet cells, 6
Graafian follicle, 172
Granule(s), keratohyaline, 88
  secretory, 102
  zymogen, 102
Granulosa lutein cells, 174
Ground substance, 13, 14
  cartilage, 24
  connective tissue, 11
  staining, 11

Hair follicle, 88, 90
Hassall's corpuscles, 84
Haversian canal, 32
Haversian systems, 23, 32
Heart, endocardium, 66
  epicardium, 66
  myocardium, 66
  Purkinje fibers, 66
  subendocardial layer, 66
  subendothelial layer, 66
Henle's loop, 150
Herring bodies, 194
Histiocytes, 12
Howship's lacuna, 38
Hypophysis cerebri (see *Pituitary gland*)

Ileum, 114
Integument (see *Skin*)
Intercellular bridges, 90, 96
Internal elastic membrane, 70, 72
Interstitial cells of Leydig, 157, 160
Intestine, large, 122, 124
  small, 114
Islets of Langerhans, 132

Jejunum, 114
Joint, developing, 26
Joint cavity, 26

Keratin, 88
Keratohyaline granules, 88
Kidney, 145-151
  calyx, 150
  collecting tubules, 148, 150
  convoluted tubules, 146, 148, 150
  cortex, 146
  cortical labyrinth, 146, 148
  Henle's loop, 150
  medulla, 146
  medullary rays, 146
  peritubular capillaries, 148
  pyramid(s), 146, 150
  renal (Malpighian) corpuscles, 146
  sinus, 150
Kupffer cells, 128

Lacteal, 118, 120
Lacunae (see *Bone; Cartilage*)
Lamina propria, 13
  appendix, 122
  duodenum, 116
  esophagus, 106, 108
  large intestine, 124
  stomach, 108, 110, 112
  trachea, 138
Leydig cells, 157, 160
Ligament(s), 18
  developing, 26
Lipofuchsin, 52
Liver, 126-129
  bile canaliculi, 128
  central veins, 126
  hepatic cells, 126, 128
  hepatic ducts, 128
  Kupffer cells, 128
  lobules, 126
  sinusoids, 126, 128
Lobule, liver, 126
Lungs, 135, 138, 140
Lymph node(s), 76, 78
  capsule, 76
  cortex, 76, 78

Lymph node(s) (*continued*)
  cortical sinus, 76. 78
  germinal center, 76. 78
  hilus, 76
  medulla, 76, 78
  medullary cords, 76
  medullary sinuses, 76
  reticular cells, 78
  stroma, 78
  trabeculum, 78
Lymph nodule(s), 75
  lymph node, 76, 78
  small intestine, 114
  stomach, 108
  tonsil, 76
Lymphatic organs, 75
Lymphatic tissue, 75-85
  dense, 75
  diffuse, 75
  distribution, 75
Lymphatic vessels, 72
Lymphocytes, large, 78
  medium-sized, 78
  small, 78

Macrophage, 13
Macula densa. 148
Malpighian corpuscles, kidney, 145
  spleen, 80
Mammary gland, 180-185
  inactive, 180
  lactating, 184
  proliferative, 182
Mast cells, 12, 13
Matrix (see *Bone; Cartilage*)
Meckel's cartilage, 38
Medullary cavity, 34
Meissner's corpuscles, 88, 90
Meissner's plexus, 120
Membrana granulosum, 174
Membrane, fenestrated elastic, 20
  synovial, 26
Mesenchyme, 13, 20
Mesentery. 114
Mesothelium, 2, 4
  replacement of, 4
  small intestine, 120
Mucosa, appendix, 122
  duodenum, 116
  esophagus, 106, 108
  gall bladder, 130
  large intestine, 122
  nasal, 98
  olfactory, 136

Mucosa (*continued*)
  oral, 98
  small intestine, 114
  stomach, 108, 110, 112
  tongue, 94
  trachea, 138
  ureter, 152
  urinary bladder, 154
Muscle, 40-49
  arrector pili, 88
  cardiac, 41, 46, 48, 66
    cross striations, 46
    fibers, 46
    intercalated discs, 41, 46
    myofibrils, 46
  cross striations, 40, 41
  fibers, 40, 44, 46
  myofibrils, 40, 41
  myofilaments, 40, 41
  sarcolemma, 40
  skeletal, 41
  smooth, 40, 42
    distribution, 40 (see also *Muscularis;*
      Muscularis externa; Muscularis mucosae)
    organization, 42
  striated, 40, 41, 44
    Cohnheim's fields, 44
    cross striations, 44
    developing, 20
    endomysium, 44
    fibers, 44
    myofibrils, 44
    sarcostyles, 44
  visceral, 40
Muscularis, gall bladder, 130
  ureter. 152
  urinary bladder, 154
Muscularis externa, appendix, 122
  duodenum, 116
  esophagus, 106
  large intestine, 122
  small intestine, 114, 120
  stomach, 110, 112
Muscularis mucosae, appendix, 122
  duodenum, 116
  esophagus, 106
  large intestine, 124
  stomach, 110, 112
Myelin, 50, 54, 56
Myocardium, 66
Myoepithelial cells, 40, 90
Myofibrils, 40, 41, 44, 46
  Purkinje fibers, heart, 48
Myofilaments, 40, 41
Myometrium, 178

Nerva vasorum, aorta, 68
Nerve(s), 56
  endoneurium, 56
  epineurium, 56
  fiber, 50-56
  neurilemma, 56
  perineurium, 56
  sheath of Schwann (see *Neurilemma*)
Nervous system, 50-63
  cells of, 50
  divisions, 50
  myelin, 50
  nerve fibers, 50
  neurilemma, 50
  neuroglia, 50
  neuron, 50
  node of Ranvier, 51
  organization, 50
  Schwann cell, 50 (see also *Neurilemma*)
Neurilemma, 50, 51, 54, 56
Neuron, 50
  cell bodies, 52, 54
  lipofuchsin, 52
  multipolar, 52
  Nissl bodies, 62
  pseudo-unipolar, 54
  unipolar, 54
Neuropil, 58, 62
Nissl bodies, 62
Nodules [see *Lymph nodule(s)*]

Odontoblasts, 104
Olfactory mucosa, 136
  basal cells, 136
  glands, 136
  lymphatic vessels, 136
  receptor cells, 136
  sustentacular cells, 136
Oocyte, 170
Osteoblasts, 34, 36, 38
Osteoclasts, 38
Osteocytes, 28, 36, 38
Osteoid, 36, 38
Osteons, 23, 32
Ovary, 170-173
  atretic follicles, 170, 172
  corpus luteum, 174
  cortex, 170
  cumulus oophorus, 172
  follicle cells, 170
  germinal epithelium, 170
  granulosa lutein cells, 174
  medulla, 170
  oocyte, 170
  primary follicles, 170
  theca lutein cells, 174

Ovary (*continued*)
  tunica albuginea, 170
  zona pellucida, 172
Oviduct, 176

Pacinian corpuscles, 90
Palatine tonsils, 78
Pancreas, 132
Paneth cells, 120, 122
Papillae, dermal, 88
  tongue, 94, 96
Parathyroid gland, 190
  chief cells, 190
  oxyphil cells, 190
Parietal cells, 110
Parotid gland, 102
Perichondrium, 24, 26, 28
Perineurium, 56
Periosteum, 34
Peyers patches, 114
Pia mater, cerebellum, 60
  spinal cord, 62
Pituitary gland, 192-195
  blood supply, 192
  cell types, 194
  divisions, 192
Plasma cells, 13, 118
Plexus, Auerbach's, 120
  Meissner's, 120
Plicae circulares, 114
Polysaccharides, 11
  sulfated, 23
Portal canal, 126
Portal system, 128
Portal triad, 128
Portal vein, 126, 128
Predentin, 104
Progesterone, 169
Prostate gland, 166
Prostatic concretions, 166
Purkinje cells, 60
Purkinje fibers, 48, 66
Pyramidal cells, 58
Pyramids, renal, 146, 150

Renal corpuscles (Malpighian), 146, 148
Renal sinus, 150
Reproductive system, female, 169-185
  male, 157-167
Respiratory system, 135-143
Rete testes, 160
Reticular cells, lymph nodes, 78
Reticular fibers, 11, 12, 13
  lymph nodes, 78
  spleen, 82
Reticular tissue, 13

Sac, alveolar, 142
Salivary glands, 100-103
    ducts, 100, 102
        excretory, 100, 102
        intercalary, 100, 102
        striated, 100, 102
Sarcolemma, 40
Sarcostyles, 44
Sebaceous glands, 88, 90
Seminal vesicle, 164
Seminiferous tubules, 157, 158
Serosa, appendix, 122
    large intestine, 122
    small intestine, 114, 120
    stomach, 110
    urinary bladder, 154
Serous glands, tongue, 96
Sertoli cells, 158
Sheath of Schwann, 56
Sinus, renal, 150
    venous, spleen, 82
Sinusoids, liver, 128
Skeletal muscle, 41
Skeleton, fetal, 26
Skin, 87-91
    glands, 87, 90
    organization of, 87
    receptors, 87, 90
    stratum corneum, 88
    stratum germinativum, 88
    stratum granulosum, 88
    stratum lucidum, 88
Smooth muscle (see *Muscle*)
Soft palate, 98
Space of Disse, 128
Spermatids, 158
Spermatocytes, primary, 158
    secondary, 158
Spermatogenesis, 158
Spermatogonia, 158
Spermatozoa, 158
Spinal cord, anterior horn cells, 62
    neuroglial cells, 62
    neuropil, 62
    pia mater, 62
Spleen, 80-83
    Billroth's cords, 80, 82
    capsule, 80, 82
    central artery, 80, 82
    circulation, 82
    germinal centers, 80
    red pulp, 80, 82
    reticular stroma, 82
    trabeculum, 80, 82
    venous sinuses, 80, 82
    white pulp, 80, 82

Splenic nodules, 80
Spongy bone, 28
Stereocilia, 6
    ductus deferens, 164
    epididymis, 162
Stomach, 108, 110-113
    cardiac glands, 108, 112
    fundic glands, 108, 110, 112
    glands, 108, 110, 112
    mamillated areas, 110
    pyloric glands, 108, 112
    pyloric region, 112
Straight tubules, 160
Stratum corneum, 88
Stratum germinativum, 88
Stratum granulosum, 88
Stratum lucidum, 88
Striated border, 6
    gall bladder, 130
    large intestine, 124
    osteoclasts, 38
    small intestine, 118
Striated muscle (see *Muscle*)
Striations, cross, 40
Sublingual glands, 102
Submandibular glands, 100
Submucosa, appendix, 122
    duodenum, 116
    esophagus, 106
    large intestine, 122
    small intestine, 114
    stomach, 110, 112
    trachea, 138
Supporting tissue, 23-39
Sustentacular cells, testis, 158
Sweat glands, 88, 90

Taste buds, 94, 96
Tendon, 18
Terminal bars, 6
Testis, 158-161
    interstitial cells, 160
    Leydig cells, 157, 160
    rete testis, 160
    seminiferous tubules, 158
    straight tubules, 160
    testosterone, 160
    undescended, 160
Theca externa, 172
Theca interna, 172
Theca lutein cells, 174
Thymocytes, 84
Thymus, epithelioid cells, 84
    gland, 84
        cortex, 84

Thymus, gland *(continued)*
   involution, 84
   lobes, 84
   medulla, 84
Thyroid gland, 188
  colloid, 188
  follicles, 188
Tongue, 94-97
  filiform papillae, 94
  fungiform papillae, 94
  vallate papillae, 94
Tonsil, 76
  crypts, 76
  epithelium, 76
  germinal center, 76
  lymph nodules, 76
  palatine, 76
Tooth, developing, 104
Tooth germ, 104
Trachea, 138
  basement membrane, 138
  glands, 138
  hyaline cartilage, 138
Tube, uterine, 176
Tubules, convoluted, 146, 148, 150
  seminiferous, 158
Tunica adventitia, 70
  aorta, 68
Tunica albuginea, ovary, 170
  testis, 158
Tunica intima, 70
  aorta, 68
Tunica media, 70
  aorta, 68

Umbilical cord, 20
Ureter(s), 152
  transitional epithelium, 152
Urinary bladder, 154
  transitional epithelium, 154
Urinary system, 145-155

Uterine tube, 176
  peg cells, 176
Uterus, 178
  decidua basalis, 178
  decidua functionalis, 178
  decidual cells, 178
  endometrium, 178
  myometrium, 178

Vallate papillae, tongue, 94
Valves of Kerckring, 114
Valvulae conniventes, 114
Vasa vasorum, aorta, 68
Vein(s), 70
  central, liver, 126
  hepatic, 126, 128
  portal, 126, 128
Venous sinuses, spleen, 80
Vesicle, seminal, 164
Villi, 118, 120
  absorptive cells, 118
  basement membrane, 118
  endothelial cells, 118
  goblet cells, 118
  lacteal, 118
  lamina propria, 118
  lymphocytes, 118
  smooth muscle cells, 118
  striated border, 118
Volkmanns canals, 32
Von Ebner's glands, 96

White matter, cerebrum, 58
  spinal cord, 62

Zona fasciculata, adrenal gland, 196-198
Zona glomerulosa, adrenal gland, 196
Zona pellucida, 172
Zona reticularis, adrenal gland, 198